A Handbook of Interactive Management

SECOND EDITION

A Handbook of Interactive Management

SECOND EDITION

by

John N. Warfield and A. Roxana Cárdenas

IOWA STATE UNIVERSITY PRESS / AMES

John N. Warfield is University Professor in The Institute of Public Policy (TIPP), and Director of the Institute for Advanced Study in the Integrative Sciences at George Mason University, Fairfax, Virginia. He received B.A., B.S., and M.S. degrees from the University of Missouri, Columbia, and the Ph.D. from Purdue University, West Lafayette, Indiana, where his major was electrical engineering with a specialty in communications engineering.

Alda Roxana Cárdenas Esparza is Associate Professor in the Department of Systems Engineering in the School of Engineering and Architecture at the Instituto Tecnológico y de Estudios Superiores de Monterrey (ITESM), in Monterrey, México. She received the B.S. in Industrial and Systems Engineering and the M.S. in Information Systems from ITESM and the Diplôme d'Etudes Approffondies (D.E.A.) in Economic Systems Engineering from the Université d'Aix-Marseille III, in Aix-en-Provence, France.

♾ Printed on acid-free paper

First Edition, 1993
Second Edition, 1994

Library of Congress Cataloging-in-Publication Data

Warfield, John N.
    A handbook of interactive management/John N. Warfield and A. Roxana Cárdenas.—2nd ed.
        p.   cm.
    Includes bibliographical references and index.
    ISBN 0-8138-2407-9
    1. Systems analysis. 2. Systems design. 3. Interactive management. I. Cárdenas, A. Roxana. II. Title.
T57.6.W37   1994
    658.4—dc20   94-30917

CONTENTS

List of Figures

List of Tables

PREFACE

This **HANDBOOK OF INTERACTIVE MANAGEMENT** is intended to put in one place and in modular form much of the material that practitioners need to know about Interactive Management (IM). It is intended to help bridge an acknowledged gap between the material in the senior author's 1990 book **A SCIENCE OF GENERIC DESIGN: MANAGING COMPLEXITY THROUGH SYSTEMS DESIGN** and the needs of the practitioner or potential practitioner to translate the science into action in organizations. The practitioner may find parts of this **HANDBOOK** useful in marketing IM to clients or for training others.

The reader who is unfamiliar with the history of IM will need to know that a large array of backup literature is available. Of special importance are two books. The first book titled **SOCIETAL SYSTEMS: PLANNING, POLICY, AND COMPLEXITY,** was published by Warfield in 1976. It had a very broad systems engineering orientation, and it introduced the process called Interpretive Structural Modeling (ISM), presenting the theory, methods, and some initial applications. The 1976 book was reprinted and part of it will be required reading for anyone wishing to study the nature and processes of IM. The second book, mentioned in the preceding paragraph, also requires recourse to the 1976 book for detailed material relating to the ISM process. This second book provides the scientific basis for IM. These two books merely cap the literature. An extensive set of publications providing backup detail and applications reporting appears in <u>The IASIS File: A Bibliography of Books and Papers Relevant to Complexity.</u> This book is located in the Library of Congress and various university libraries. The documents are accessible in the Library of the Defense Systems Management College in Fort Belvoir, Virginia and at ITESM, Monterrey, Mexico.

The text begins by responding to the question "What is Interactive Management?" It continues by giving the primary set of outcomes from its use, the several levels of success from which users can choose, the phases through which IM passes, and the roles that are important in applying IM. Then typical types of products that are produced by using IM are described, and the processes that are used to produce these products are discussed. The kind of facility that is very helpful in carrying out IM is described. Next several versions of IM Software are discussed, the software being essential to carrying out the IM processes. The three phases of IM activity are then discussed in detail.

Evaluation criteria are given which can be applied to assess the quality of the work being done in applications, and to assess the performance of various roles, with the aim of helping actors to improve their capabilities to work with IM. In view of the applications of IM to system design and implementation, it is appropriate to compare IM with other approaches to system design and implementation. Among the approaches currently being used routinely or experimentally are methods usually associated with Japan. These include Quality Function Deployment and the so-called "7-QC-Tools and 7-M-Tools". A thorough comparison of IM with these methods is presented, along with recommendations for a superior process.

Appendix 1 gives an executive overview of IM for orientation of a busy executive who will not have time to get into many important details. Appendix 2 gives a detailed user guide for using one of the several versions of the IM software, namely the GMU ISM Software, operating on IBM compatible PC equipment.

Appendix 3 presents a discussion of group facilitation, with emphasis on activity involving complex issues. Appendix 4 gives a case study showing how to interpret certain products of IM activity.

Appendix 5 lists qualified practitioners who have varying degrees of experience in applying IM, and who are capable of planning and conducting IM work. Appendix 6 gives details of how to develop an IM Workshop Plan.

Most of the text for this work was written by the senior author. The junior author made major changes in the organization of the material, and added key comments in various places, based on her own significant experience in setting up an IM center and applying IM at ITESM (her home institution in Monterrey, Mexico). She has introduced IM on many ITESM branch campuses, where it is being applied in strategic planning.

This book benefited from research support provided by the Defense Systems Management College, Fort Belvoir, Virginia, and from the Ford Research Laboratory of the Ford Motor Company. The authors appreciate the support, and acknowledge the cooperation of Professor Henry Alberts at the Defense Systems Management College and of Dr. Scott Staley, P. E., at the Ford Research Laboratory of the Ford Motor Company. George Mason University (GMU) has been the home organization where most of the work reported in this **HANDBOOK** has been accomplished. The computer equipment made available has greatly facilitated the writing of this book. Professor Benjamin Broome of the GMU Communication Department has been a colleague of both authors for several years and his help, which has come in a variety of ways, is much appreciated. He has been practicing IM with several Native American tribes in cooperation with the Americans for Indian Opportunity (AIO) as a colleague of LaDonna Harris, President of AIO, and through this collaboration is becoming well known as a major actor in helping the Native American community become more capable in self-governance.

In lieu of any other institutional support, Rosamond Warfield has been donating her services as office manager and librarian of the Institute for Advanced Study in the Integrative Sciences at George Mason University for over four years, and this has helped greatly to make this work possible.

The senior author is a member of the faculty of The Institute of Public Policy (TIPP) at George Mason University. Dr. Kingsley Haynes and Dr. Roger Stough of TIPP have given moral support to this work and to the overall goals that this work reflects, which is greatly appreciated.

CHAPTER 1

WHAT IS INTERACTIVE MANAGEMENT ?

Interactive Management (IM) is a system of management invented explicitly to apply to the management of complexity. It is intended to be applied intermittently in organizations to enable those organizations to cope with *issues or situations whose scope is beyond that of the normal type of problem that organizations can readily solve.*

The development of IM is based on the recognition that for coping with complex situations there is a need for a group of people, knowledgable of the situation, to tackle together the main aspects of concern, to develop a deep understanding of the situation under analysis and to elaborate the basis for effective action; all these founded in a spirit of collaboration, commitment and within the framework of a serious and organized effort.

1.1 CONNECTION TO SCIENCE.

IM is related to a new science called the "Science of Generic Design", which provides a scientific basis for the practice of IM.

1.2 NEED FOR SPECIAL TRAINING.

Since IM is intended to serve when normal methods fail, it is natural that the practitioners of IM will require special training in order to know how to practice it. The people who provide this special training will benefit if they understand the Science of Generic Design and know how it relates to IM.

1.3 APPLICATIONS TESTING.

The concept of IM was developed at the University of Virginia in 1980. Since that time the concept has been enlarged somewhat, the practice of IM has spread to many places, and many applications of IM have been carried out. Before IM was conceived as a system, numerous other applications of predecessor component parts were carried out, starting in 1974 and continuing until 1980.

The two principal predecessors to IM were nominally referred to as Unified Program Planning (UPP) and Interpretive Structural Modeling (ISM). The former was developed at Battelle

Memorial Institute in 1971, and the latter was also developed there in 1972-73. Most of the applications in the period 1974-1980 were of ISM, but UPP came into use in India at Tata Consultancy Services Hyderabad location, where it has been applied to significant projects.

1.4 DOCUMENTATION.

IM is one of the most heavily documented systems ever invented. At present, many of the publications relating to this subject and to generic design science are located in the IASIS file of the David Acker Library at the Defense Systems Management College, Fort Belvoir, Virginia and at ITESM, Monterrey, Mexico. Annotated bibliographies are available. Two books are available that deal with the theory. Several books are available that deal with applications. The file is indexed for computer retrieval.

1.5 TYPICAL APPLICATION.

In a typical application, some organization has been trying to deal with a complex issue for some time and has had little success. It then brings this application to a center where IM is practiced. The staff of this center work with the client to plan the approach to the definition of the issue and to the design of alternatives for resolving the issue. Some clients will carry the work further to choice and implementation of a preferred alternative.

1.6 THREE PHASES.

IM involves three closely-linked IM phases: the Planning Phase, the Workshop Phase, and the Followup Phase. The Planning Phase identifies the people, information, and facility requirements for the other two phases. The Workshop Phase involves bringing together a selected group of participants who have knowledge about the issue or situation. This group works together in a specially-designed situation room, under the guidance of a skilled IM facilitator, and with the help of a trained staff. The Followup Phase may involve iteration, implementation, or both.

1.7 PROCESSES.

The IM processes that are carried out involve substantial communication among the group members, and typically lead to significant learning about the issue or situation, as the participants learn from each other during the facilitated processes. All work is carefully documented.

1.8 DISTINCTIVE FEATURES.

IM is sometimes confused with work done involving groups at other organizations who are not practicing IM. There are quite a few locations where special facilities have been set up for working with groups. Also some software has been written for use in these organizations. Typically these organizations deal with issues that are considerably smaller in scope than those for which IM was constructed.

Such organizations may even use some of the methodology that is used in IM. However they typically place much less emphasis on constructing and rationalizing the logical relationships among aspects of the problem, and much more on rapid achievement of numerical results.

When asked to identify the scientific basis for what they are doing, they usually cannot offer any good answer.

The emphasis they place on the use of a highly-trained facilitator is usually much less than is done in IM, and some of those organizations actually see the computer as the group facilitator. In contrast, in IM the computer is seen as a significant aide to the IM facilitator.

Such organizations typically are hardware-driven and software-addictive, as opposed to being driven by humanistic concerns and behavioral research results. As evidence of the hardware drive, most of these organizations require that each participant use a computer most of the time, and that all participants use computers simultaneously. Since computer manufacturers have been the primary sponsors of such work, it is clear that this practice is consistent with the desire for manufacturers to sell machines. In the practice of IM, it is common that only one computer will be used, and a terminal will be used for recording purposes. Participants are not asked to operate computers, but instead are asked to concentrate on thinking and rendering their best thoughts verbally as they engage in joint learning with their co-participants.

As part of the documentation of IM and its underpinning Science of Generic Design, the connection of this work to the main flow of scientific thought has been a constant goal. The foundations of the Science of Generic Design can largely be traced to specific research, some of which started as early as 400 B.C., and some of which has been carried out during the development of the design science. Hardly any of the other organizations engaged in group work are able to connect much of what they do to the corpus of scientific knowledge.

1.9 PRINCIPAL PRODUCTS.

The principal tangible IM products are typically logical structures, which may also be called "maps" or "patterns", and which reveal significant aspects of the issue or the alternatives that are invented for its resolution.

It is in the part of this work in which the participants design alternatives that the benefits of the Science of Generic Design, as applied in IM, may be most distinctive from other kinds of activity in which groups engage.

On the other hand, the learning that takes place among the participants during an IM session can also be regarded as one of its primary products; it is within the context of sharing together the various points of view and information that the different participants bring to the table, that the final results are shaped, and the people reach the required shared understanding of the situation for developing serious commitment to the issue in hand.

1.10 INTELLIGENCE, DESIGN, AND CHOICE.

As originally conceived, IM involves the managerial functions of Intelligence, Design, and Choice, as set forth by H. A. Simon around 1960. These functions are modularized separately in the group process work, but each is emphasized as a key aspect of the work, and the modules are strongly connected from a logical point of view. Each of these functions will be found in each of the three phases of IM, but the relative emphasis will shift from one phase to another.

1.11 COOPERATION BREEDS SUCCESS.

Typically IM works best when there is close cooperation and interaction between the staff of the center that practices IM and the client organization. Such interaction must take place in all three phases for best results.

1.12 INSTALLATION OF IM.

This Handbook primarily discusses the situation where a professional organization provides IM services to a client organization. This is the typical situation in which IM will be introduced to an organization not accustomed to its application. Nonetheless the ultimate aim is that those organizations that can anticipate an ongoing need for its application will "install" IM within their organization. This will involve education and training of any

4

existing staff of the client organization who will become part of the service unit that provides IM services within that organization. It is also possible that some staff of the IM organization that provided initial services to the client organization will migrate to the client organization. Such migration is likely to prove a healthy development to ensure continuity of IM practice, and to help develop and maintain standards of quality in its practice within the receiving organization.

1.13 SOME APPLICATIONS OF IM.

Hundreds of applications of IM have been carried out in many locations. Table 1.1 lists some of these as a way to help the reader see the variety available in using IM. These are listed in approximate reverse chronological order, the most recent having the lower numbers. (When organizations appear more than once in the last column, full identification is given only in the initial listing.)

TABLE 1.1
SOME APPLICATIONS OF INTERACTIVE MANAGEMENT

No.	Type of Application	Managing Actor(s) or Organization(s) or Both
	Some Applications in 1994	
1	Strategic Planning with the Taruhamari Indian Tribe in northwest Mexico	Benjamin Broome, Carmen Moreno, Cristina Salas-Porras
2	First Mexico Interloquium, World and Mexico Future in the Year 2,010--Planning for the 21st Century	Governor of Guanajuato and Dr. Carlos Flores, ITESM, Campus Leon
3	Strategic Planning for the Food and Drug Administration	Dr. Alexander Christakis, CWA
4	Product Information Management at Ford	Dr. Scott Staley, Ford Motor Company Research Laboratory, Dearborn, MI
	Some Applications in 1993	
5	Rapid Response Manufacturing Joint Application Development	Dr. Scott Staley, Ford
6	Americans for Indian Opportunity, Ambassador Program	Dr. Benjamin Broome, GMU and Ms. LaDonna Harris, AIO
7	Systemwide Planning for Analytical Powertrain (1992-93)	Dr. Scott Staley, Ford

Some Applications in 1992		
8	Design of Strategic, Managerial, and Operational Plans--National Oceanic and Atmospheric Administration (NOAA) Coastwatch Program's Inter-Agency Satellite Ocean Color Project	Dr. Alexander Christakis; (CWA), Berwyn, PA
9	Definition of Stakeholder Issues to be Considered in the Development of a Comprehensive Fishery Management Plan for Pacific Coastal Pelagic Fisheries	David J. Mackett, Southwest Fisheries Science Center (SWFSC), La Jolla, California
10	Designing an Action Plan in Anticipation of Bringing a Pharmaceutical Product to the Market With Speed and Prudence	Dr. Alexander Christakis and Mr. Robert J. Whitehouse (CWA), Berwyn, PA, and Schering-Plough, Inc.
11	Policy Directives for a Telecommunications Holding Company	Dr. James Wright, University of São Paulo (USP), Brasil, Prof. Bruce Johnson, Fundação Instituto de Administração (FIA)-USP; TELEBRAS
12	Intervention in a Building Services Co-Partnership	Prof. Derek Hitchins, Royal Military College of Science, (RMCS), Shrivenham, England
13	Community-Based Design for the Future of the Pawnee (Oklahoma) Tribe: Problem Definition, Vision Statement, and Integrated Plan	Iola Hayden, Oklahomans for Indian Opportunity (OIO), Normal, Oklahoma & Benjamin J. Broome, George Mason University (GMU)
14	Community-Based Design for the Future of the Apache (Oklahoma) Tribe: Problem Definition, Vision Statement, and Integrated Plan	Iola Hayden (OIO) and Benjamin J. Broome (GMU)
15	Planning a Hospital's Growth to the Year 2000	Dr. James Wright, USP and HCRP
16	Impact of Information Technology on Organisation Structures and Processes (1991-1992)	Mr. S. K. Batra, Tata Consultancy Services (TCS), as part of doctoral program
Some Applications in 1991		
17	Designing a Strategic Plan for Privatizing Three Companies in Greece	Dr. Alexander Christakis (CWA), and Spyros Megápanos of EUROTRANSFORM, Athens, Greece

18	Designing Improvements for the Human Performance Enhancement Systems of Niagara-Mohawk Power Company	Dr. Alexander Christakis (CWA), Berwyn, PA and Paul Wilde, Niagara-Mohawk Power Company, Syracuse, NY
19	Social and Economic Development in the Area of the New Bridge Between the U. S. A. and Mexico	Carmen Moreno, Roxana Cárdenas, (ITESM), Monterrey, N. L., Mexico-- FIDENOR
20	Planning for a Total Quality Program at Química del Rey, S. A.	Carmen Moreno, Carlos Villanueva, ITESM-- Química del Rey
21	Development of Objectives and Intent Structures for an Urban Police Force	Prof. Derek Hitchins, RMCS, Shrivenham, England
22	North American Defense Industrial Base Critical Technologies Workshop	Prof. Henry Alberts, Defense Systems Management College (DSMC), Fort Belvoir, VA
23	Concurrent Engineering Workshop	Professor Henry Alberts, DSMC
24	Contractor Integrated Technical Information Service (CITIS) Workshop	Professor Henry Alberts, DSMC
25	Defense Industrial Base Workshop	Professor Henry Alberts, DSMC
26	Klamath River Basin Fisheries Task Force: Design of a Watershed-based Task Force Management System for Carrying out the Klamath River Basin Fishery Restoration Program	David J. Mackett, SWFSC, La Jolla, CA
27	Klamath River Basin Fisheries Task Force: Definition of Priorities for Implementing Policies of the "Long-range Restoration Plan"	David J. Mackett, SWFSC, La Jolla, CA
28	Design of an Inter-Agency Cooperative System for Planning and Execution of Tuna Research and Management in Response to Changes in the Magnuson Fisheries Conservation and Management Act	David J. Mackett, SWFSC, La Jolla, CA
29	Design of an Improved Planning and Budgeting System for the National Marine Fisheries Service	David J. Mackett, SWFSC, La Jolla, CA
30	Department of Defense Fuze Industry Workshop	Dr. Alexander Christakis (CWA) and Mr. David Dierolf, Institute for Defense Analyses (IDA)

31	Planning for the Department of Systems Science at City University (London, England)	Ross Janes, Ken Hammer, Interactive Management Unit (IMU), City University (London, England)
32	Objectives for the Electric Utility R&D Center	Dr. James Wright, USP, Prof. Bruce Johnson, FIA-USP; CEPEL
33	Community-Based Design for the Future of the Cheyenne/Arapaho (Oklahoma) Tribe: Problem Definition, Vision Statement, and Integrated Plan	Iola Hayden, OIO & Benjamin J. Broome, GMU
34	Promoting Greater Participation in Comanche Tribal Governance	Ladonna Harris, Americans for Indian Opportnity (AIO) and Benjamin J. Broome, GMU
35	Design of a Tribal Issues Management System	Ladonna Harris, AIO, Iola Hayden, OIO, and Benjamin J. Broome, GMU
36	Proposal for the Restructuring of the Port of Santos	Dr. James Wright, USP, Prof. Bruce Johnson, FIA-USP; Longshoremens' Union
Some Applications in 1990		
37	Implications of Vocational Training for Advanced Technology in India (1990-1991)	S. K. Batra of TCS; International Labor Organisation/Asian and Pacific Skills Development Programme
38	Impact of Telecommunication and Data Services on Software Services (1990-1991)	S. K. Batra of TCS; Atwater Institute, Montreal, Canada
39	Development of Integrated Cooperative Development Project for Two Districts of a State of India (1990-1991)	S. K. Batra, TCS; and Department of Cooperatives of the Government of Himachal Pradesh, India
40	Developing Systems Education at the ITESM System (1990-1991)	Carmen Moreno, Roxana Cárdenas, ITESM
41	Redesigning the Defense Acquisition System (1990-94)	Prof. Henry Alberts, (DSMC) and Dr. Alexander Christakis, CWA, Berwyn, PA
42	Operational Planning at the International Division of BANORTE	Ma. Carmen Temblador, Carlos Villanueva, Roxana Cárdenas, ITESM--BANORTE

43	Strategy Setting for a Telecommunications Equipment Manufacturer	Dr. James Wright, USP, Prof. Bruce Johnson, FIA-USP, NEC do Brasil
44	Establishing an Industrial Policy for the Electric Utilities Sector	Dr. James Wright, USP, Prof. Bruce Johnson, FIA-USP; ELETROBRAS
45	Directives for Restructuring a Medical School Curriculum	Dr. James Wright, USP; FMRP-USP
46	Characteristics and Identity of the Organization Development Group of a Professional Management Consultancy	Ross Janes, Keith Ellis, Ken Hammer, IMU, City University
47	Investigation of Nuclear Unit 2 Design Issues	Dr. Alexander Christakis (CWA), Berwyn, PA, and Jack Benson, Niagara-Mohawk Power Corporation, Syracuse
48	Klamath Fishery Management Council: Strategic Plan for the Management of the Harvest of Anadromous Fish Populations of the Klamath River Basin	David J. Mackett, SWFSC, La Jolla, CA
49	Smart Munitions Acquisition Management	Dr. Alexander Christakis, Center for Interactive Management (CIM), George Mason University (GMU)
50	Objectives and Priorities for a Quality Program in a Regional Bank in the United Kingdom	Richard Jeffery, PA Consulting Group, London, England
51	Problem Definition and Goal Setting for the Economic Future of the Menominee Tribe	Ladonna Harris, AIO, and Benjamin J. Broome, GMU
52	Problem Definition and Resolution for Comanche Tribe	Ladonna Harris, AIO; Kenneth Saupity, Comanche Tribe; and Benjamin J. Broome, GMU

Some Applications in 1989		
53	Diagnostic Study on the Energy Sector of Ghana	S. K. Batra, TCS, and the Technology Transfer Centre, Council of Scientific and Industrial Research, Ghana
54	Designing a University Centre for Enterprise Management	Ross Janes, Prof. Derek Hitchins, Richard Jeffery, Ken Hammer, IMU, City University

55	Issues, Objectives, and Priorities for a University Department of Civil Engineering	Ross Janes, Ken Hammer, Richard Jeffery, IMU, City University
56	Solutions and Priorities for a Community-Based Speech Therapy Service in a Health Authority	Richard Jeffery, Ross Janes, Ken Hammer, IMU, City University
57	Strategic Plan for Research Needed to Meet the Goals of the Convention for the Conservation of Antarctic Marine Living Resources by the Year 2000	David J. Mackett, SWFSC, La Jolla, CA
58	Design of a United States Agency for International Development Program for Developing and Maintaining Viable Fisheries in Developing Countries Utilizing Fish Aggregating Devices (FADs)	David J. Mackett, SWFSC, La Jolla, CA
59	Design of an Administrative Information Management System for the Southwest Fisheries Science Center	David J. Mackett, SWFSC, La Jolla, CA
60	Research Initiatives in the Photonics Field	Dr. David Keever, CIM, GMU
Some Applications in 1988		
61	Forum on the Future of Pediatric Nursing: Looking Toward the 21st Century	Dr. Alexander Christakis, CIM, GMU, and Professor Veronica Feeg, Dept. of Nursing, GMU
62	Planning for the Short Course Unit of City University	Richard Jeffery, Ross Janes, IMU, City University
63	Setting Requirements and Priorities for a Speech Therapy Service in a District Health Authority	Richard Jeffery, Ross Janes, IMU, City University
64	Long-Range Planning Guidebook for the Communication Department, George Mason University	Dr. Benjamin J. Broome, and Dr. Don Boileau, Communication Dept., GMU
65	Developing a Design Culture in Higher Education	Dr. Alexander Christakis, CIM, GMU, and Dr. Ioanna Tsivakou, Univ. of the Aegean
66	Shared Governance in Selected Pennsylvania School Districts	Dr. Alexander Christakis, CIM, GMU
67	Human Service Needs: Setting Priorities for Fairfax/Falls Church United Way	Dr. Alexander Christakis, CIM, GMU
68	National Atmospheric Administration/National Marine Fisheries Service Program Development Plan for California Current and Pacific Oceanic Regional Marine Ecosystems	David J. Mackett, SWFSC, La Jolla, CA

69	Design of the SWFSC's Eastern Tropical Pacific Dolphin Survey	David J. Mackett, SWFSC, La Jolla, CA
70	Operational Plan for National Marine Fisheries Service Research on the Demersal Fishery Resources of the California Current Ecosystem	David J. Mackett, SWFSC, La Jolla, CA
71	Joint US/Canada Strategic Plan for Research on the International Squid Drift-Gillnet Fishery and Protected Species Entanglement Problem in the North Pacific	David J. Mackett, SWFSC, La Jolla, CA
Some Applications in 1987		
72	Business Planning Workshop for the Regional Managers of an Industrial Training Board	Ross Janes, Keith Ellis, Department of Systems Sciences (DSS), City University (London)
73	Priority Setting for a County's Highway Scheme	Ross Janes, DSS, City University (London)
74	Department Chain Objectives	Dr. James Wright, USP, Prof. Bruce Johnson, FIA-USP, SUSA Group
75	Operational Plan for SWFSC Research on Tunas and Large Pelagics	David J. Mackett, SWFSC, La Jolla, CA
76	Strategic Plan for a Joint State of California/National Marine Fisheries Service Program for Marine Recreational Fisheries	David J. Mackett, SWFSC, La Jolla, CA
77	Operational Plan for Improving Availability to the Scientific Community of the Historical Ichthyoplankton Data Base of the California Cooperative Oceanic Fisheries Investigation	David J. Mackett, SWFSC, La Jolla, CA
78	American Public Power Association Fuel Cell Market Workshop	Dr. Alexander Christakis, CIM, GMU
79	Building a Consensus on a Winnebago Self-Sufficiency Plan	Ladonna Harris, AIO; Reuben Snake, Chairman, Winnebago Tribe; and Dr. Alexander Christakis, CIM, GMU
80	Designing a Computer Science Curriculum for the 21st Century	Dr. John N. Warfield, Dr. Alexander Christakis, and Dr. David Keever, CIM, GMU
Some Applications in 1986		
81	Planning for the Department of Systems Science at City University	Ross Janes, DSS, City University (London)

82	Strategic Planning for the National Marine Fisheries Service's Research Program on Tuna Resources	David J. Mackett, SWFSC, La Jolla, CA
83	Strategic Objectives for the São Paulo State Bank - BANESPA	Dr. James Wright, USP, Prof. Bruce Johnson, FIA-USP; BANESPA
84	Operational Planning for the Analysis of Tuna Vessel Observer Data for Porpoise Stock Assessment	David J. Mackett, SWFSC, La Jolla, CA
85	Investigation of Forces of Change in the Hawaiian Aku (Skipjack Tuna) Fishery	David J. Mackett, SWFSC, La Jolla, CA
86	Moving Toward a Consensus for Nursing in Virginia	Dr. Alexander Christakis, CIM, GMU
87	Redesigning the National Marine Fisheries Service for the 1990's	Dr. Alexander Christakis, CIM, GMU
88	Identifying and Mapping Tribal Governance Issues	Ladonna Harris, AIO and Dr. Alexander Christakis, CIM, GMU
89	Southwest Fisheries Science Center's Affirmative Action Plan	David J. Mackett, SWFSC, La Jolla, CA
Some Applications in 1985		
90	Planning for an Industrial Training Board Development Team	Ross Janes, DSS, City University (London)
91	Setting and Structuring Objectives for an Industrial Training Board Fellowship Program	Ross Janes, Prof. Philip M'Pherson, DSS, City University (London)
92	Factors Affecting the Expansion of a Military Reserve Force	Ross Janes, Brian McCormack, DSS, City University (London)
93	Planning for the Management Support Department of a City Police Force (1985)	Ross Janes, Prof. Philip M'Pherson, DSS, City University (London)
94	Tuna Fisheries Forum (1985)	Dr. Alexander Christakis, CIM, and Mr. David Mackett, SWFSC, La Jolla, CA
95	Agricultural Research Service Management Retreat (1985)	Dr. Alexander Christakis, Interactive Management Corporation

96	Operational Plan for the Southwest Fisheries Science Center's Pacific Coast Groundfish Research Program at Tiburon and La Jolla, CA (1985)	David J. Mackett, SWFSC, La Jolla, CA
97	Strategic and Operational Planning for a Joint State of California/National Marine Fisheries Service Program for Research and Management of Coastal Marine Mammals (1985)	David J. Mackett, SWFSC, La Jolla, CA
98	Strategic and Operational Plan for a Research Program on the Fisher Resources of Pacific Seamounts (1985)	David J. Mackett, SWFSC, La Jolla, CA
99	Strategic Plan for Fisheries Habitat Research and Conservation in Hawaii (1985)	David J. Mackett, SWFSC, La Jolla, CA

Some Applications in 1984

100	Planning for a Technical Advisory Committee of a Professional Engineering Institution	Ross Janes, Prof. Philip M'Pherson, DSS, City University (London)
101	Strategic Planning for the National Fisheries Service's Pacific Coast Groundfish Research and Management Program	David J. Mackett, SWFSC, La Jolla, CA
102	Plan for Research Program for the Recovery of the Endangered Hawaiian Monk Seal	David J. Mackett, SWFSC, La Jolla, CA
103	Strategic Planning for the New Management Regime for the Tuna/Porpoise Fishery	David J. Mackett, SWFSC, La Jolla, CA

Some Applications in the Period 1974-1983

104	Non-Industrial Private Forest Lands Forum-Issues, Options and Responsibilities, U. S. Forest Service (1983)	Dr. Alexander Christakis, CIM, UVA, and Mr. Robert McDonald, U. S. Forest Service
105	Sugar Cane Harvest Extension--Bottlenecks and Critical Issues (1983)	Dr. James Wright, USP, Prof. Bruce Johnson, FIA-USP; IAA-MIC
106	Definition of the Mission of the Southwest Fisheries Science Center and the Development of the Strategy for Carrying it Out (1982)	Dr. Alexander Christakis, CIM, University of Virginia and David J. Mackett, SWFSC
107	Business School Curriculum: Course Precedence Requirements (1982)	Dr. James Wright, USP
108	Impacts of Brazil's Fuel Alcohol Program (1981)	Dr. James Wright, USP
109	Long-Range Planning Workshop for Saudi Arabian National Center for Science and Technology (SANCST) (1980)	J. N. Warfield, R. J. Waller, K. Kawamura, and Hashim Yemani of SANCST

110	Making Decisions on Reducing Public Expenditures: Kent City Council (1979)	Dr. Carl Moore, Kent State University, Kent, OH
111	Structure of Technology Assessment (1975)	Dr. Alexander Christakis and Sherry Arnstein, Academy for Contemporary Problems, Columbus, OH
112	Management of the Learning Disabled (1975)	Dr. Robert J. Waller, Univ. of No. Iowa, Cedar Falls, IA
113	Climax Agriculture in the Sahel Region of Africa (1975)	Professors Zamierowski, Hornbach, and Fitz, Univ. of Dayton, Dayton, OH
114	Priority-Setting in Urban Systems Management (1974)	Dr. Robert J. Waller, Univ. of No. Iowa, Cedar Falls, IA
115	Transportation Planning for Dayton, Ohio (1974)	Brother Raym ond Fitz, Kettering Foundation, Dayton, OH

STUDY QUESTIONS
CHAPTER 1. WHAT IS INTERACTIVE MANAGEMENT?

1. What is Interactive Management?

2. When is IM intended to be used?

3. What is the main reason for the development of IM?

4. What provides the scientific basis for IM?

5. What do practitioners of IM need?

6. Over what period of time has testing of IM or components of IM occurred?

7. What were the two principal predecessors of IM?

8. Where is the most complete information base on IM located?

9. What is typical about situations where IM might be used?

10. How can IM be distinguished from other kinds of management practices?

11. What are the principal products (tangible and intangible) of IM?

12. What three primary managerial functions are supported by IM?

13. What is meant by "installation of IM"?

14. In what countries or states of the USA has IM been used?

CHAPTER 2

IM OUTCOMES

For convenience in understanding IM and in organizing for its use, the outcomes of IM work have been placed in three major categories. These are (a) *Definition,* which refers to constructing a thorough definition of the situation that is the focus for the work; (b) Alternative Designs, which refers to constructing in a prescribed format two or more alternative designs aimed at correcting the undesired conditions in the defined situation, or otherwise to determine the new possibilities that might be open in that particular situation; and (c) Choice of a Design, which refers to the studied selection of one of the alternative designs as the basis for implementing the desired corrective measures.

In each particular case, the possible outcomes of IM are carefully defined in order to suit the special requirements of the situation, but keeping in mind that in most cases these outcomes follow the general sequence that has been established for the management process: Intelligence (definition), Design (alternative designs), and Choice (choice of a design).

2.1 DEFINITION.

Interactive Management (IM) can be used to define a complex issue, problem, or situation. When used in this way, IM is intended to support the following:

* Description of Context. The description of the context within which the issue is to be explored
* Identification of Components. Identification of components involved in the definition
* Construction of Patterns. Construction of patterns that show how the components are related
* Interpretation of Patterns. Interpretation of the patterns that are produced, to gain a good understanding of the definition, and to get insight into the requirements for designing alternatives to resolve the issue
* Mapping on Patterns. Mapping of information onto patterns to help illuminate aspects of the patterns

The most common products that arise from using IM to develop a definition are *sets and structural patterns.* The *sets* are usually the following:

* Sets of component problems
* A set of component problem types

The *most common structural patterns* produced are:

- A problematique (a pattern that shows how the problems are related to each other)
- A problem field (a pattern that shows how the problems subdivide into problem types)

Other possible sets could include:

- A set of objectives
- A set of organizations

Another possible structural pattern that could be produced is an intent structure (showing how the objectives are related)

The most common types of *mapping onto patterns* produced with IM are the following:

- Organizations mapped onto either problematiques or problem fields
- Problem types mapped onto problematiques

Occasionally it will prove beneficial to assess the *intensity of relationships.* When this is appropriate, another type of mapping can take place: Intensity numbers mapped onto problematiques or intent structures

The interpretation of the products of IM, as applied in definition work, requires a careful study of those products and especially the relationships portrayed therein. If the products contain cycles, as is very frequently the case, methods of cycle resolution may be considered. These include the method of simplifying structures by the use of thresholds and the method of geodetic cycles[1] .

Focus is provided by the creation of the following:

- A context statement, which guides all the work
- One or more triggering questions[2] , which guide the production of sets
- One or more generic questions[3] , which guide the production of structural patterns

These items are jointly developed by (a) the person who will plan (and often conduct) the IM work activity, i.e., the Group Activity Planner, and (b) the IM Broker.

The group activity typically consists of a small number of action modules carried out in a planned sequence. Each action module will be drawn from the IM Processes (Chap. 7), and each will produce a particular product of the kind discussed previously in this section. For example, the Nominal Group Technique (NGT) module will always be used to produce a set;

and the set will often be component problems or objectives.

The specific action modules used, and the sequence in which they will be used, will be determined in the light of the particular situation that is to be the focus of the work.

2.2 ALTERNATIVE DESIGNS.

Interactive Management (IM) is used to construct alternative designs for resolving some complex situation or issue, or to conceive a way of creating some artifact or system.

Before engaging in a process to construct alternative designs, it is expected that IM will have been used to define the situation. In the process of definition, participants will have introduced their concepts about the situation being explored. Through dialog, the collective best ideas of participants will have emerged as part of the definition, and the incorrect or fuzzy ideas that participants held at the outset will have been recognized as incorrect or sharpened to make them useful. Participants will have become aware of critical relationships among factors, and can take these into account as they design alternatives.

The design of alternatives begins with the generation of options in response to a triggering question. These options will typically be small in scale with respect to the large issue or situation being dealt with. (A design will involve a collection of compatible options.) Production of between 40 and 120 options is a likely result of using the Nominal Group Technique. The Nominal Group Technique (NGT) will be used to facilitate the generation and clarification of options.

Once the options are all clarified, a preliminary vote can be taken to see which are deemed the most important. This vote will split the set of options into two parts: those receiving at least one vote from at least one participant (Subset A) and those receiving no votes from any participant (Subset B).

The members of Subset A will be divided into categories which may emerge as design dimensions. This work is described as "constructing an Options Field" (e.g., see page 296). The process used for this purpose is Interpretive Structural Modeling (ISM).

Once the categories are identified and named, the question is raised as to whether each category is essential to the definition of an alternative. If so, it becomes a design dimension. If not it is removed from the Options Field.

Design dimensions are then examined to see whether they are dependent or not, using ISM. Two dimensions are dependent if and only if the choice of some option in one of them rules out the choice of some option in the other. A set of dependent dimensions is called a "cluster". All clusters are identified. Dimensions that fall in a cluster are grouped.

The set of clusters is then placed in a sequence, using ISM. The first cluster in the sequence is the one from which options will be chosen first in constructing a design alternative. The second cluster is the one from which options will be chosen next, and so on.

Once a sequence is determined for the clusters, a sequence of the dimensions in each cluster is selected. Since clusters are usually small, the sequencing of dimensions in a cluster can probably be done without using ISM.

After all the foregoing structuring has been done, the product is a "triply-structured quad"[4].

It is then appropriate to consider whether it is desirable to repeat this process for one or more of the options. If the means of implementing an option is sufficiently unclear that it requires elaboration, the result could be to construct a new triply-structured quad that would overlap the first one produced. The top member of the new quad would be the unclear option. This would yield a "tapestry" formed from two quads. Additional quads might be added to the tapestry as needed.

Once the entire structure is finished, attention is turned to the choice of options. One or more options will be chosen from each dimension, following the choice sequence established earlier. As each option is chosen, the choosing is documented by drawing the selection line from the bullet in front of the option down to the Tie Line. In this way, a graphic image unfolds before the group, showing which option(s) have been chosen in each dimension. After the options have been chosen in every dimension, the result becomes an "Options Profile", which is a graphical representation of one design alternative.

It is reasonable to write an explanation of this particular alternative to accompany the graphic.

Other design alternatives may be developed in the same way, perhaps by other groups. It may be, for example, that the group that did the definitional work can be split into two or more groups, and each smaller group can construct and describe one or more Option Profiles.

At the conclusion of this work, a report can be prepared that contains the definitional work, a description of the design alternatives that have been invented, and a writeup of the graphic that explains the choices that were made.

2.3 CHOICE OF A DESIGN.

Action to choose a particular design begins with the availability of two or more design alternatives. The documentation that describes these alternatives will include the results of prior work to define the situation and prior work to create the design alternatives. The methodology used to make an initial design choice is the Tradeoff Analysis Methodology (TAM)[5]. This methodology leads to bar charts which compare all pairs of available design alternatives. The comparisons show total scores for each alternative, derived from the scores on each of the criteria used to make the comparisons.

Sometimes the choice made using the TAM will be the one selected for implementation. More likely the choice will be the basis for a more detailed study, using appropriate analytical tools, to verify the reasoning behind the initial choice.

The selection of criteria must be done before the choice is explored. Idea generation methods, e.g., the Nominal Group Technique, may be used to arrive at a set of criteria. Criteria may be quantitative or qualitative, depending on the nature of the attribute that is being scored.

2.4 OTHER RELEVANT OUTCOMES.

Besides the specific categories of outcomes that has just been mentioned, it is worth noting that no matter in which category of the above the IM work may be concentrated, other important aspects of the outcomes that are obtained with IM are the following :

- *The learning that takes place among the participants.* Since the group of participants is engaged in a focused and structured dialogue, IM provides the framework for a real and deep understanding of the situation that is under consideration; the people engaged in an IM activity are exposed to a real sharing of ideas and information, and thus are actively learning about the issue at hand.

- *Commitment to the decisions taken.* Because of the fact that the definition of the situation and the design and choice of alternatives are made participatively, the decisions taken by the group are their own decisions; only through this kind of approach can a genuine commitment be achieved. In turn this commitment leads to a better basis for the implementation of the decision within the organization.

- *Documentation.* During the IM process the information generated by the participants and the decisions taken are being recorded and organized. The documentation obtained provides the basis for a larger diffusion of the outcomes and also for keeping a good "memory" of the rationales and main issues considered during the IM activity.

NOTES

1. See: John N. Warfield, <u>Societal Systems: Planning, Policy, and Complexity,</u> (SSPPC) Salinas, CA: Intersystems, 1989.

2. See: John N. Warfield, <u>A Science of Generic Design: Managing Complexity Through Systems Design,</u> (ASOGD), First Edition, Salinas, CA: Intersystems, 1990; Second Edition, Ames, Iowa: Iowa State University Press, 1994.

3. See: ASOGD, page 517.

4. See: ASOGD, pages 90 and 172.

5. See: ASOGD, page 240.

STUDY QUESTIONS
CHAPTER 2. IM OUTCOMES

1. What are the three major categories of outcomes of the use of IM?

2. What five functions is IM intended to support in arriving at definitions of complex situations?

3. What are typical sets that are produced when using IM to develop a definition?

4. What are typical structural patterns produced when using IM to develop a definition?

5. What provides focus to IM work?

6. Who develops the "focus providers" for IM work?

7. What should occur before IM is used to produce alternative designs?

8. How does the design of an alternative begin?

9. What process is used to generate and clarify the set of options?

10. What process is used to split the set of options into two parts?

11. What is meant by "construction of an Options Field"?

12. What process is used to construct an Options Field?

13. What is meant by a "design dimension"?

14. How is interdependency of design dimensions defined?

15. What name is given to a set of dependent dimensions?

16. What is a "triply-structured quad"? What are the three structuring concepts?

17. What should occur before starting the process of choosing a design?

18. What process is used to make an initial design choice?

19. What must be done before exploring a choice?

CHAPTER 3

IM SUCCESS LEVELS

Planning for success is inherent in the application of Interactive Management.

3.1 LEVELS OF SUCCESS.

Success in anything relates to how the term "success" is defined with respect to the particular situation. Experience shows that success in using IM can be defined legitimately in at least five ways, largely because of the nature of complex issues and the wide variation in the status of such issues at the time the application of IM to them is considered.

By virtue of their nature, complex issues are never well understood at the beginning of their consideration. Normally one cannot initially predict which level of success will be attained. Ability to predict may improve significantly after each pass through the three Phases of IM .

The following distinguishable levels of success are listed in the order of progressively more in-depth consequences of working with the issue using IM:

Level 1: Learning more about what is involved in approaching the issue (the lowest level of success)
Level 2: Learning more about the issue itself
Level 3: Achieving a good definition of the issue
Level 4: Finding good alternative designs for resolving the issue
Level 5: Arriving at a good action choice to resolve the issue

It is good practice to be conservative in predicting which level can be attained, because unnecessarily raised (and then unmet) expectations may lead to negative reactions that are unwarranted by the situation.

3.2   LEARNING MORE ABOUT WHAT IS INVOLVED IN APPROACHING AN ISSUE.

IM has been used with groups that had a reason to be interested in "concurrent engineering" as a way to improve efficiency, effectiveness, and competitiveness. The primary driving force seemed to be an awareness that competitors were gaining advantage by using concurrent engineering. While the participants chosen for the work, were positioned where they could possibly have a wide impact on the use of concurrent engineering, they were generally not well informed and seemingly did not know how to approach the subject. As a result of applying IM in workshops with these groups, it became clear that most of the participants had begun with some relevant knowledge. By sharing the knowledge through discussion, as well as by structuring the knowledge that was collectively held, the participants got a much better feeling for what is involved in approaching the subject of concurrent engineering. This included insights into what kind of organizational changes would be needed, what new roles would be required, and what kind of interactions among organizations would be called for. Insights were gained into needed changes in laws or regulations. However one couldn't feel confident that the level of success had gone beyond the first level.

The primary benefit of this kind of success is to help assure that the next time the subject is approached a higher level of success is likely to result, assuming that what was learned in the first instance is fully understood and applied in designing the next iteration.

3.3 LEARNING MORE ABOUT THE ISSUE.

In one situation, a governmental interagency task force had been working intermittently for six months to create a joint recommendation concerning a complex physical system design for a cabinet officer, but had no luck. With only two weeks remaining, the group decided to test the IM system to try to construct an appropriate recommendation.

The participant group included individuals with significant expertise in candidate subsystems for the system that was to be proposed. The primary weakness was in dealing with such matters as how various combinations of modular subsystems to create a system would compare, and which of the competing modular subsystems should be selected to carry out a particular function.

At the conclusion of this work, significant insights had been gained into which modular subsystems should be chosen and why. Also insights had been gained into the mode of operation of systems comprised of selected subsystems.

The products were deemed adequate for submission to the cabinet officer. On the other hand, they did not reach the depth of specific system design, because there remained various questions of quantitative choice and various design tradeoffs.

Nevertheless the group felt that the work had been very successful in the light of comparisons with what had been attained to date, and with what they had hoped to be able to present as a preliminary approach to a complex system design.

3.4   DEFINING THE ISSUE.

A sizeable federal service agency had developed a history of problems with their prescribed constituency. Citizens were writing to the federal government complaining about the indifference and relative isolation of parts of the agency. In addition, competitive and legal problems were buffeting the agency and threatening its ability to fulfill its legislative mandate.

The agency elected to consider its difficulties collectively as a basis for redesigning the agency, using IM as the basis for the work.

As a consequence, the participants were able to develop a thorough definition and classification of the problems facing the agency. With these results in hand, the participants had attained the level of success described as "defining the issue".

3.5   FINDING ALTERNATIVE DESIGNS.

The same agency mentioned in 3.4 was able to take the definitional material and produce a set of alternative agency designs, with the thought that one of these designs might be the basis for an agency reorganization that could carry the agency through several years or perhaps a decade.

In the process of producing the designs, numerous observers from the agency could hear the participant discussions and become much better informed on the agency's mission, subdivisions, interactions among subdivisions, challenges facing the agency, approaches to meeting those challenges, and the roles of individuals (including themselves) in the proposed organizational revision.

3.6   ARRIVING AT A GOOD ACTION CHOICE.

A midwestern manufacturing firm combined IM with some quantitative information to revise a process for manufacturing an expensive pump, with the aim of increasing significantly the acceptance rate of pumps at the end of the manufacturing test operation.

As a result, the organization was able to raise the acceptance rate from around 50% to 87%.

3.7   A BAD EXPERIENCE.

One may learn from a bad experience. An individual who had been quite successful in applying IM to define problem situations relating to certain military systems, and to construct designs for improving significantly those systems, was encouraged to move into a new situation. In this new situation, this individual allowed a high-level federal official to believe that the highest level of success mentioned above could be attained through less than 3 days of work.

The federal official decided to appear at 2 PM on the third day of group work, and expected to learn at that time what was required to resolve a very complex issue, only to learn (in our present language) that the level of success achieved was the fourth level, not the fifth. Moreover the time consumed by this official's appearance ensured that the fifth level could not be attained on that day. As a result the federal official put the convening individual through a rough period.

Ultimately the participants reconvened for a fourth day of work, which produced the kinds of recommendations the high-level official had been expecting. To a considerable extent this produced a recovery from the bad situation that had transpired.

However all of the abuse or agony could have been prevented by a more conservative or better informed handling of the situation.

This experience is one of many that motivated the development of this Handbook of Interactive Management.

STUDY QUESTIONS
CHAPTER 3. IM SUCCESS LEVELS

1. What five success levels have been defined for IM? Under what conditions should each be chosen?

2. Why is it desirable to select a specific success level to provide a basis for future work before moving ahead?

CHAPTER 4

IM PHASES

IM is designed to support a three-phase activity sequence through one or more passes. If the initial pass through the three-phase sequence proves productive, a second and more involved pass will often be seen as justifiable and necessary. The three Phases are: (a) *Planning,* in which the basis is laid and the plan developed for the following two Phases; (b) *Workshop,* in which the selected participants work together with the aid of a highly-skilled IM Facilitator ("Pilotos", to distinguish this Role from the normal role of "facilitator"); and (c) *Follow- up,* in which the results are implemented or another iteration is done through the Phases.

4.1   PHASE 1 (THE PLANNING PHASE).

In the Planning Phase, the first critical concept is the "situation".

The Situation. Normally a situation involves at least one organization and often several. One intends to characterize the situation as a "single-organization situation" or a "multiple-organization situation". The distinction is made as follows: the situation includes what will be called an "issue", but people will use synonyms such as "problem", or "mess". The issue will involve a "scope". As the scope of the issue becomes clear, it can be envisaged that in implementing any proposed resolution of the issue a certain set of "implementing actors" will be involved. If the members of this set of implementing actors are all affiliates of a single organization, the situation can be described as a single-organization situation; and the issue can be described as "internal". If the set of implementing actors involves people from more than one organization, then the situation is a multiple-organizational situation. The issue can be described as "polymorphic."

The Issue. Under present conditions, Interactive Management will almost never be applied to work with an issue until other ways have been tried and have failed. If a situation is encountered where an issue has been recognized for some time and numerous ways have been tried without success to resolve it, this is an indicator that IM is needed in that situation.

Initial Meeting Goals. In order to bring IM to bear on the issue, there will normally be an initial contact between two people. One of them will be a prominent member of the set of implementing actors. The other one will be a person who is very knowledgeable about IM. At this first meeting, the goals of the meeting will include:

A. Scope and Context Statement Writing. Assessing the scope of the issue, and writing a Scope Statement. Once the scope is described, a Context Statement is written to focus the

Workshop. The context is usually narrower than the scope. The latter deals with all aspects of the issue, while the former extracts the aspects directly relevant to the Workshop.

B. Actor Identification. Arriving at a preliminary identification of a subset of the implementing actors, to include: the Client, the Sponsor, and the IM Broker.

C. State of Definition Assessment. Assessing the state of definition of the issue.

D. White Paper Investigation. Determining whether a "white paper" can be produced (for distribution to participants before the Workshop Phase) that will contain essentially all the known key information about the issue. The White Paper normally will contain only well-accepted terminology, and only well-accepted data and interpretations. It provides a platform from which the Workshop can be launched, to expand what appears in the White Paper.

Clarification of these goals will include consideration of the following:
The Client is the individual who is perceived to be in the highest position of authority with respect to the issue. The Client will typically be in a position both to suppress the results of any work that is done (i.e., to prevent implementation and possibly even punish individuals for working on the issue) and to set in motion the implementation of the results.

The Sponsor is the individual who will provide the funds to pay for the IM activity. Many times the Client and the Sponsor will be the same person. At other times, the Sponsor may be government or a foundation, while the Client will lack the resources to pay for the work.

The IM Broker is an individual who is a member of the set of implementation actors. This person has certain special knowledge and responsibility, as described in Chapter 5 of this Handbook. Broker selection is a vital part of the work to be done in the Preparatory Phase.

The Context Statement will inform the Workshop Phase, by focusing the discussion. The state of definition will reveal questions that need to be answered during the Workshop.

The white paper, if prepared and distributed ahead of time, will help assure commonality of knowledge and language among the participants; and it will add further insight into the kinds of questions that need to be answered during the Workshop. (It may also be part of a final report that would be produced after all the IM work has been completed.) Normally the white paper would be produced by an exceptionally well-informed, long-time employee of the organization(s) involved with the issue.

Second Meeting Goals. The second meeting in the Planning Phase will normally be a meeting between the chosen IM Broker (who represents the Client) and the IM Workshop Planner (who represents the IM organization). The second meeting will be strongly informed by the

Scope and Context Statements prepared in the first meeting. The goals of this second meeting are:

A. Role Familiarization. To familiarize the Broker with the IM Broker's role. (After the Broker becomes aware of this role, the Broker should either agree to meet the conditions of the role or to take steps to get another person named as IM Broker.)

B. Phase Familiarization. To familiarize the IM Broker with the three phases of IM and to describe what must be developed in the Planning Phase in order to move on to the Workshop Phase.

C. Major Outcome Planning. To familiarize the IM Broker with the three major outcomes of IM, and to arrive at agreement on Issue Definition as the first major outcome to be sought in a Workshop. Further an initial agreement should be made on the conditions under which the second and third outcomes will be sought in workshops following the first one to arrive at a Definition.

D. Detailed Planning for Issue Definition. To prepare a detailed plan jointly by the IM Broker and the IM Workshop Planner for the conduct of the Issue Definition Workshop. This detailed plan will include:

- Application Structural Types to be sought
- Methodologies to be used
- Triggering Questions to be used
- Generic Questions to be used
- Types of participants needed
- Plans for observers, if any
- Role of the Client and the Sponsor
- Budget
- Time of Workshop
- Location of Workshop
- Duration of Workshop
- Workshop staff plan
- White paper availability, if any, and a white paper distribution plan, if such will be prepared.

Communications. Once the plan has been completed the IM Broker will proceed to identify appropriate workshop participants. The IM Broker will inform them of all prior conditions and will ensure that no participant arrives at the Workshop who will not be willing to work in the IM system. The Broker will also inform the Client and Sponsor, and will make sure that they are not confused about their own roles.

The IM Workshop Planner will meet with the anticipated staff of the Workshop and make sure that all Workshop roles are understood. A schedule will be worked out in detail and responsibilities will be assigned. All materials needed for the meeting, such as flip charts and other information displays will be prepared in advance. The facility will be inspected for suitability before a final decision is made to use that facility for the Workshop. (If a dedicated facility is available, much of the work will be avoided, because much of what is needed will be available from the preceding workshop.) Meal plans will be worked out. Transportation of participants (e.g., from motel to workshop site) will be arranged, if this has not been done before, and communicated to the IM Broker. (See Appendix 6 for details.)

All inter-organizational communications will be between the IM Broker and the IM Workshop Planner.

A final check to ensure that all arrangements are satisfactory will be made between the IM Broker and the IM Workshop Planner as the last step to complete the Planning Phase.

4.2   PHASE 2 (THE WORKSHOP PHASE).

In the Workshop Phase, participants will come together to work as a group. Their work will be governed by the IM Facilitator, based on the Workshop Plan. Three key concepts related to the issue are Context, Content, and Process. The ***Context*** will be set by the Scope Statement arrived at in the Planning Phase. The ***Content*** will be provided by the Participants, who will be informed by the White Paper previously studied, if any. The ***Process*** will be provided by the IM Facilitator. The IM Facilitator will advise the participants of the respective role responsibilities of the Participants, the IM Facilitator, and the IM Broker, to make sure that there is no role confusion.

The conduct of the Workshop Phase will be explored thoroughly in Chapter 11 of this Handbook.

4.3   PHASE 3 (THE FOLLOWUP PHASE).

The Followup Phase might finally be described in one of the following ways:

• The Phase in which nothing was done to implement anything discovered during the Workshop (This could be a legitimate Followup, provided the Workshop Success Level [See Chapter 3] turned out to be primarily Level 1, i.e., learning more about how to approach the issue; or if the definition of the issue revealed that the issue had been misperceived and, in effect, can be dissolved as an issue)

32

- The Phase in which the outcome of an Issue Definition Workshop was used to enter a new Planning Phase to plan for a new Workshop Phase, aimed at the Design of Alternatives
- The Phase in which the outcome of a Design of Alternatives Workshop was used to enter a new Planning Phase to plan for a new Workshop Phase, aimed at the Choice of an Alternative
- The Phase in which the Choice of an Alternative is taken as the basis for implementation; and the Followup Phase is used, either to enter a new Planning Phase to plan for a Workshop that will produce the plan for implementation of the chosen alternative or, alternatively, if it is clear how to implement the chosen alternative, implementation proceeds

Additional detail concerning the Followup Phase will be provided in Chapter 12.

STUDY QUESTIONS
CHAPTER 4. IM PHASES

1. What are the three Phases of IM work?

2. What is the critical concept to focus on in the Planning Phase?

3. What is the initial characterization of the situation?

4. What indicator suggests a need for using IM?

5. What are the goals of the initial meeting to consider the use of IM?

6. How can the initial meeting be described?

7. What are the goals of the second meeting to consider the use of IM?

8. What occurs at the second meeting to consider the use of IM?

9. What is the nature of the IM Broker?

10. What is the nature of the IM Workshop Planner?

11. What three issue-related factors must be considered in planning an IM Workshop?

12. What is the nature of the IM Followup Phase ?

CHAPTER 5

IM ROLES

In looking at organizations, Sir Geoffrey Vickers commented: "I find it convenient to regard institutions as structures of mutual expectation, attached to roles which define what each of its members shall expect from others and from himself."[1]

This comment is particularly relevant to applications of Interactive Management, where various roles are interacting for a few days to try to unravel a complex issue. One can compare the activity to a dramatic production, where a set of actors called the Cast interacts in a highly cooperative and mutually supporting way. The involved roles make up the Cast; which, together with the interactions among the roles, make up the social system. Members of the Cast create the "script" as they utter the lines. What is required to set a proper stage?

A set of roles is most effective when the environment is supportive. A social system expecting good results from its designers will strive to make the environment supportive of effective design activity. In Chapter 8, the nature of the supportive environment will be discussed.

Roles in the Cast are *designed*, chosen on the basis of the findings of the Generic Design Science. The roles are placed in three categories. The *External Roles* involve individuals from a client organization. The *Internal Professional Roles* and the *Internal Support Roles* both involve individuals from the Interactive Management services organization.

The **External Roles** are the following:

- *Client (Top Manager, Followup Executive),* a person who is able to authorize the provision of the services of people to fill the other External Roles and also can offer the leadership ability to implement the results (or to prevent implementation)
- *Sponsor,* a person who controls the financial resources required to carry out the work (and who often will also be the Client)
- *IM Broker,* a person who is intimately acquainted with the Design Situation, and who selects the Participant group; and who also makes available the financial resources to carry out the design work; but who normally acquires these resources from the Sponsor.
- *IM Participant (Designer, Stakeholder, Implementer),* a member of a design team who holds content knowledge relevant to the design task and is motivated to contribute to the design
- *Observer (Stakeholder, Implementer),* a person who is closely related with the Design Situation because somehow he is affected by it, or maybe is in a position to influence

that situation, but for some important reason may not be able to be a part of the design team. The Observer will observe the work of the design team and, if necessary in an emergency, may substitute for a participant.

The **Internal Professional Roles** are the following:

- *IM Workshop Planner,* a person who formulates the process sequences to carry out the work in a given Design Situation, in collaboration with the IM Broker and the IM Facilitator, and who may also fill the IM Facilitator Role
- *IM Facilitator (Pilotos),* a person who is intimately acquainted with Generic Design Science, and is able to manage the interaction among the members of the Participant group and the supporting actors and facilities, including the displays and the computer. The IM Facilitator will be supported by various technologies that are part of the IM process. (In addition to Chapter 5, see Appendix 3 for a discussion of facilitation.)
- *Pattern Interpreter,* a person who is skilled in interpreting and explaining the patterns that are developed in the Workshop activity
- *Report Manager,* a person who manages the documentation of all the work and integrates it into a report

The **Internal Support Roles** are the following:

- *Facilities Preparation Manager*
- *Computer Operator*
- *Scribe*
- *Display Arranger*
- *Video Tape Operator*

These roles will be described in Section 5.3.

While it is normal that one individual will fill just one role, it is also possible that in some situations an individual may play several roles. It is part of the general philosophy, however, that the actor who takes the role of Facilitator will not also take the role of Participant in a given Design Situation. The credibility and effectiveness of the role of Facilitator depends on adhering to this requirement.

Role descriptions for IM stem primarily from two sources: the science of generic design, which incorporates significant components from social science research; and experience stemming from numerous IM projects. The science and the experience reinforce each other and collectively lead to the following descriptions of roles. The descriptions reflect the knowledge and wisdom gained from past mistakes as well as past successes.

Not all roles are required in all phases of IM. The role descriptions are broken out for each appropriate phase for all roles. Sometimes a single actor will play several roles. When this occurs, the actor will do well to keep in mind which role is being played at which time; and will work hard to avoid both internal and external role conflicts.

5.1   EXTERNAL ROLES.

5.1.1   Client (and Followup Executive). The IM Client is the individual in a position of authority in an organization. This person typically has experienced failure over a period of months or years with a particular issue. Having tried several approaches to resolving it, with no luck, this individual may be skeptical that IM can provide any resolution.

Phase 1. In the Planning Phase of IM, the Client has these responsibilities: (a) make a determination as to whether IM will be used or not, (b) get acquainted with the IM Workshop Planner and learn enough about IM to know how the Client role connects to it; (c) learn how success is measured and be prepared to deal with the uncertainty involved; (d) learn about the Client role in the other two phases; (e) approve or disapprove of the Workshop Plan; (f) learn about the IM Broker role and select an individual to fill that role on behalf of the Client; and (g) learn about the required interaction between Client, Broker, and Interpreter in Phase 3, and be prepared to take part in this interaction.

Phase 2. The Client's role in Phase 2, the Workshop Phase, is almost always limited to staying informed about what is going on through interaction with the IM Broker. The normal Client will have no part in the Workshop.

Rare exceptions to the foregoing have been noted. In these exceptions, the Client is a very mature individual who is inclined to stimulate others to perform independently. In these exceptional cases, the Client arrives before the Workshop begins and socializes with the persons involved. The Client gives a short introduction explaining his interest in the work, introduces the IM Broker, and explains that the Broker is his representative and will remain in that role throughout the Workshop. The Client remains outside of the formal IM activity throughout the Workshop, and serves as a resource person during breaks in the formal action. At the conclusion of the Workshop, the Client thanks the participants.

Phase 3. In the Followup phases, the actions of the Client will often be pivotal in determing the ultimate consequences of the IM activity. If the issue dealt with was so poorly understood at the beginning that success had to be measured simply through participants learning more about the issue, neither the Client nor the IM staff can do much to follow up directly on the Workshop outcomes. In this instance, the key decision to be made by the Client is whether to proceed to a second Workshop that will build on the learning from the first one. In any case, the Client is the Followup Executive in Phase 3.

At the other extreme, if enough IM activity has been done to produce a chosen design to resolve the issue, the Client, Broker, and IM Interpreter should collectively work to understand how best to implement that design. In this collaborative activity, the IM Interpreter's primary responsibility is to ensure that both the Broker and the Client understand thoroughly how to interpret the Workshop products. If the IM Broker understands the products, the Client can get suggestions for implementation from the IM Broker.

The Client ultimately must decide whether the IM results are sufficiently high in quality to warrant implementation, or whether the chosen design is still inadequate. The Client must decide on the next step, and hopefully will do so in a state of enlightenment achieved through sufficient interaction with the IM Interpreter and IM Broker. Because Clients are often pressed for time, the greatest hazard is that the Client will act without adequate understanding of the products of the IM activity and bring sadness to all those who worked hard to arrive at a high-quality result, further undermining the potential resolution of the issue.

It is the responsibility of the IM Broker and the IM Interpreter to make sure that the Client has adequate advance information concerning the role situation just described.

It is also possible that the IM Interpreter will not understand the importance of careful work to explain the products and will mistakenly assume that the IM Broker and the Client can and will acquire this understanding, even though the situation may entail their first exposure to products of IM activity.

5.1.2 Sponsor. The Sponsor furnishes the financial resources for the conduct of the IM activity. Many times the Sponsor will also be the Client. If so, knowledge of the Client role is sufficient.

In other instances, the Client may have considerable authority but no financial resources, as occurs with underprivileged social groups. In these instances, the Sponsor typically lies outside the group that is involved with the issue. In such instances, the Sponsor should be made aware by the IM Planner of the importance of finding key roles in the client organization, and the Sponsor should be sensitized to the need to play a supportive but not dominating role. The ideal Sponsor will provide the resources and observe what happens, without interfering in any of the phases.

Phase 1. The Sponsor must furnish resources during Phase 1 to allow the Workshop to proceed (and sometimes may be asked to do so even before Phase 1 begins, in order to facilitate Client interaction with the IM Workshop Planner).

Phase 2. In Phase 2, the Sponsor should maintain continuous cognizance of what is going on, in order to be in a position to play an informed role in Phase 3.

Phase 3. It is appropriate to expect a Sponsor to "gamble" on the first Workshop, if the issue is important and of interest to the Sponsor. It is not appropriate to expect a Sponsor to continue to furnish resources for followup IM activity, unless the Sponsor is as well-informed as the Client on the results and interpretations from the first Workshop. Therefore the Sponsor should monitor the Phase 3 discussions.

It is important to keep in mind that IM is designed to work with complex issues. It is not reasonable to believe that casual or remote oversight will enable a Sponsor to learn well what has been accomplished, and make good decisions about whether to support followup activity. A good Sponsor will have the insight to understand the special requirements that accompany work with complex issues that lie beyond the scope of normal activity.

5.1.3 IM Broker. The IM Broker has an important role to play in all three phases. A primary responsibility is to maintain continuity throughout the three phases, and to be aware of what goes on in all of the phases. The broker role is a highly interactive role, and can best be understood in terms of who the IM Broker interacts with and the nature of that interaction, in each of the three phases. Because the IM Broker is chosen early in Phase 1, it is important to know the qualifications for this position.

Interactive Management and Client Organizations. Interactive Management is made possible by a trained staff who specialize in this work. Clients may come from many different fields of endeavor. Successful use of IM means that a tight, well-thought-out connection must be made between the IM staff and the Client Organization. IM staff will seldom be knowledgeable of the Client Organization, its personnel, its problems, or its goals. *The IM Broker has the responsibility to instruct the IM staff concerning the Client Organization.* The IM Broker will be a person who is intimately familiar with the Client Organization by virtue of being an employee (or possible a recently-retired former employee) of that organization. *This intimate knowledge of the Client Organization coupled with a good ability to communicate reliably about it is one of the two key requirements to qualify someone to serve as an IM Broker.*

A Fast Learner. The other key requirement of the IM Broker is *a willingness to take some instruction in the success factors required for application of Interactive Management, and to reflect that instruction in working with the Client Organization.*

Phase 1. In interacting with the Client Organization, the IM Broker must operate in both a proactive mode to make certain things happen and in a protective position to prevent certain things from happening. The ability of the IM Broker to do both will be critical to success of the IM Broker in the role, as well as to success of the Workshop and to the implementation of workshop results in the Client Organization.

What the IM Broker does proactively in the Client Organization before the workshop occurs cannot, by itself, guarantee the success of the workshop. What the IM Broker fails to do protectively in the Client Organization before the workshop occurs can, by itself, largely guarantee the failure of the workshop.

Upon being appointed as IM Broker in Phase 1, the Broker will quickly learn the essence of IM and the nature of the Client Role. The Broker will then interact with the Client to make sure that the Client can play an appropriate role. If so, the Broker will then communicate an understanding of the Client organization to the IM staff.

The IM Broker will then work with the IM Workshop Planner to develop the detailed plan for the Workshop. As part of this activity, the IM Broker will select appropriate participants for the Workshop and from this tentative listing will work individually to arrive at a final slate of participants. As part of this work, the IM Broker will clarify to each participant the nature of IM, the nature of the participant role, what is sought from the Workshop, and other important details.

Planning for Success: Quality Control. Any individual or organization who has been producing a certain kind of product for many years will have in mind the necessary conditions for success. In order to create and sustain these conditions, the individual or organization may set certain standards for quality control. Both of these statements just made apply to Interactive Management. The necessary conditions for success are known, and the requirements for control of quality are likewise known.

The IM Broker and the Client. It is essential that the IM Broker become aware of planning for success and quality control, as exercised in conducting Interactive Management workshops. The IM Broker must have the intestinal fortitude to honor these ideas and, if necessary, to make these matters known to the executive in the Client Organization. It is almost always true that the IM Broker is *not* the executive who is seeking value from the application of Interactive Management. The IM Broker must be aware of the high probability that the executive does not understand IM and is not interested in understanding IM. Because of this the IM Broker must not place the executive at risk by allowing the executive to impose mindless constraints on the IM activity (that might be imposed because the executive is accustomed to attending meetings run by people who do not know how to manage group activity and who do not impose quality standards on the planning and conduct of group work). *The likely outcome of inappropriate constraints by the Client on the IM workshop is failure of the workshop caused by the Client's imposition of the constraints.*

The IM staff are acutely conscious of the fact that executive judgments of success are often based on incorrect expectations. *The IM Broker must control very carefully the expectations that the executive develops during the period prior to the conduct of an IM workshop.*
It is the goal of the IM staff that the executive and the IM staff will both find the workshop to be successful. Moreover it is the goal of the IM staff that whatever accrues from the workshop will be implemented in the Client Organization. This requires that the executive understand the judgment of the IM staff concerning the amount of time required to assure a high-quality product. This judgment cannot be reliably made before the workshop begins, because it depends on factors that no one can control. The only way to assure success under these conditions is to allow a flexible duration to the project. This may require that the initial workshop be followed by additional workshops until the final result is achieved. If the executive cannot accept this fact of life, the workshop should not be conducted.

It is the responsibility of the IM Broker to make sure that the executive understands this. *High-quality work cannot be forced, but it can be assured if patience is seen as a virtue.*

Proactive Duties of the IM Broker. The IM Broker must carry out these proactive duties in the Client Organization:

* Develop a clear statement of the workshop goals
* Develop a clear statement of the context within which the work is to be carried out
* Develop the working agreement between the Client Organization and the IM staff
* Develop the budget for the work and get agreement on the budget from the Client Organization and the IM staff
* Select the candidate participants for the workshop, based on the criteria mutually developed by the IM Broker and the IM Workshop Planner
* Inform the candidate participants about the workshop, determine their willingness to participate in a workshop of the type planned, and coordinate the paperwork and schedules in the Client Organization
* Inform IM staff of the names, titles, and responsibilities of workshop participants
* Advise the participants of the IM Broker's role in the workshop and of the IM Facilitator's role in the workshop
* Brief the Client on the plan and the quality control, and make sure that the Client's expectations align with what can realistically be anticipated

Protective Duties of the IM Broker. The IM Broker must protect the IM staff from the following:

* Imposition of constraints that are not consistent with the success plan and IM quality control
* Invasion of the IM process by the Client Organization

• Development of unrealistic expectations within the Client Organization

Collaborative Duties of the IM Broker. The IM Broker must collaborate with the IM Planner in determining the following:

• The scope and context of the workshop
• The goals of the workshop
• The process sequence plan for the workshop
• The product plan for the workshop (what will be delivered at its conclusion)
• The triggering questions planned for the workshop
• The generic questions planned for the workshop
• The workshop location
• The workshop duration
• Participant living accommodations
• Participant local transportation accommodations
• Workshop budget
• Meal schedules and plans
• Special problems
• Contingency plans
• Workshop followup activity

Phase 2. The two most demanding roles in carrying out Interactive Management Workshops are the IM Broker and the IM Facilitator. Success in group work involving complex issues is heavily dependent on these two roles. While each role has certain responsibilities that must be borne individually, some of the responsibilities for success require close collaboration and cooperative interrelationships between the IM Broker and the IM Facilitator.

The IM Facilitator is responsible for all of the activity carried out in an IM Workshop. However the IM Facilitator must begin the workshop with the prior conditions that have been set by the IM Broker, acting cooperatively with the IM Workshop Planner. The IM Facilitator bases his plan for the workshop on the expectation that the IM Broker has carried out both the proactive and protective responsibilities successfully. Based on these expectations, the IM Planner has prepared a workshop plan that has been agreed to by the IM Facilitator and the IM Broker--not the other way around.

The IM Facilitator ***controls the process*** of the IM Workshop completely. If, during Phase 2, any change is suggested in the workshop plan or process, the change will be determined by the IM Facilitator. In making this decision, the IM Facilitator expects to draw on the knowledge and good will of the IM Broker. For this to be possible, *the IM Broker must be present throughout the Workshop as an observer.*

The IM Facilitator conducts various IM processes with a group of participants selected by the IM Broker, using certain criteria that have been mutually agreed to before the workshop begins. This agreement is based on (a) the prolonged experience in conducting IM workshops with many organizations on many complex issues and (b) the IM Broker's intimate knowledge of the Client Organization and of the candidate participants. The combined knowledge of IM Broker and IM Planner enables them collectively to make wise decisions concerning the participant group, helping to assure that the group reflects concerns sufficiently broad to match the goals of the Workshop, and that there are few, if any, built in conflicts of interests coming with any individual participant, that might threaten the success of the Workshop.

The IM Planner, in collaboration with the IM Broker, has chosen the process sequence that seems best suited to achieve the Workshop goals. To do this, the IM Facilitator must be made fully aware of the *context* of the workshop, as seen by the Client Organization. Also the IM Facilitator needs to know the *anticipated use of the products* of the workshop. This information must be supplied to the IM Facilitator by the IM Broker and the IM Planner.

Phase 3. The development and testing of a process for dealing with complexity and the documentation of such a process combine to present a formidable task that cannot be completed in a short time. At the time this document is being written, almost all of the documented experience with IM is limited to Phases 1 and 2. The role descriptions for those Phases derives credibility both from the underlying generic design science and from the empirical observations of many IM Workshops, but in most of the cases where IM has been applied, the client organization has held responsibility for the Followup Phase.

In discussing the role of the IM Broker in Phase 3, the Followup Phase, we are limited to informed speculation. Given the role of this individual as described and tested in the earlier phases, it is reasonable to suppose that the IM Broker will play a major role in the Followup Phase.

The IM Broker brings to the Followup Phase a significant overview of what has transpired so far, as well as a detailed knowledge of the results of the Workshop Phase.

Some IM Brokers, who have had significant management experience in implementation, can no doubt take on a leadership role in implementation, under the oversight of the Client.

Other IM Brokers will be more suited to identify another individual with whom the IM Broker will work very closely in implementation.

Still other IM Brokers will find that implementation itself is a complex problem requiring still more group activity, to which these IM Brokers will contribute by iterating on Phases 1 and 2. They may find that the development of an implementation plan will in itself require the definition of a set of roles, and the choice of a set of actors to fill those roles. In this instance the IM Broker may evolve into a new role in the Followup Phase.

Over time, as experience is gathered in numerous Followup Phases, it may be possible to collect observations and to use these to develop a more insightful statement about the IM Broker in Phase 3 than it is now possible to present.

5.1.4 Participants (Designers, Stakeholders, Implementers). The participants are those individuals who produce the substantive content related to the Design Situation or Issue. Moreover they produce the designs of possible solutions, and it is their learning, augmented by the experience of the Workshop, that is required in order to know how to implement the results. Participants will invariably be stakeholders in the Issue, and if the set of participants does not include representatives of key stakeholder groups, implementation may be severely compromised.

Phase 1. The participants are made aware in Phase 1 of what is anticipated, and their concerns and questions are resolved during that Phase. Their duties in Phase 1 are to become aware of the demands of the Workshop activity, and to make or reject the commitment to serve in the Participant Role.

Phase 2. In Phase 2, the Participants furnish the knowledge required to develop the patterns that will comprise the bulk of the products of the Workshop.

Phase 3. In Phase 3, the Participants will have strong responsibilities for communication and quality control of whatever may be done to carry the work further, whether this involves additional workshops or direct implementation of results.

5.1.5 Observers (Stakeholders, Implementers). The observers are those individuals who are related with the situation of concern by being direct or indirect stakeholders or because somehow they would participate in the implementation phase, but at the same time there are important reasons that prevent them from becoming active participants; among these reasons are a lack of direct involvement with the situation, lack of enough commitment to actively participate during the whole Phase 2, or the need to keep the participant group small enough to allow adequate participant discussion. The observer role is in general an optional one during the IM activity, but its importance lies in the fact that there might be many people interested enough in the issues under consideration and for whom it will be helpful to witness and learn from the dialogue that takes place between the participants.

Phase 1. As in the case of the participants, the observers are made aware in Phase 1 of what is anticipated, and their concerns and questions are resolved during that Phase. Their duties in Phase 1 are to become aware of the demands of the Workshop activity for their role, and to make or reject the commitment to serve in the Observer Role.

Phase 2. In Phase 2, the Observers will be listening to the dialogue that takes place between the participants, and may be able to interact with them during the specified points in the agenda.

Phase 3. In Phase 3, the Observers may have different responsibilities depending on their particular position within the context of the situation, but in general they are expected to contribute by communicating the results of Phase 2 to the people of concern that couldn't participate in it. Sometimes the observers may become participants in other IM sessions and thus are required to bring the learning they had gained as observers, and sometimes they may be involved in different aspects of the implementation of results.

5.2   INTERNAL PROFESSIONAL ROLES.

The Internal Professional Roles comprise the IM Workshop Planner, the IM Facilitator, the Pattern Interpreter, and the Report Manager.

5.2.1 IM Workshop Planner. The IM Workshop Planner takes this role only after considerable experience as a facilitator. This role must involve significant insight into IM, and especially into the conduct of Workshops. In a given situation, a single actor may be both the IM Workshop Planner and the IM Facilitator, shifting from one role to the other with ease. If these two roles are played by different actors, they will communicate regularly so that misunderstandings between them have no opportunity to develop.

Phase 1. In Phase 1, the IM Workshop Planner will carry out these tasks:

• Familiarize the IM Broker with IM and with the IM Broker's duties in all three Phases
• Take the lead in developing all aspects of the IM Workshop Plan and coordinate these with the IM Broker and the IM Facilitator
• Meet the Client and Sponsor and make sure that they agree to their roles
• Fulfill the requirements for effective Quality Control of all aspects of the work
• Write the Workshop Plan and deliver it to the IM Broker and the IM Facilitator

Phase 2. In Phase 2 of the work, the IM Workshop Planner maintains awareness of the conduct of the Workshop, and is available if needed as a backup to the IM Facilitator in case that individual is incapacitated or if the facilitation work is to be shared.

Also in Phase 2, the IM Workshop Planner reflects on Phase 3, in the light of what is learned in Phases 1 and 2, and proposes changes in the Phase 3 outlook, if desirable, to the IM Broker and the IM Facilitator.

Phase 3. In Phase 3 of the work, the IM Workshop Planner anticipates the possibility that the IM activity will undergo an iteration, and if so continues to remain cognizant of the work in Phase 3 which may be a prelude to a new Phase 1, wherein the IM Workshop Planner will again be active in developing a plan for the next iteration.

5.2.2 IM Facilitator (Pilotos). The role of IM Facilitator (or Pilotos) is active only in Phase 2. Frequently, however, an individual actor who fills this role may play other roles in any of the Phases. The description that follows deals only with the IM Facilitator role in Phase 2, i.e., in the IM Workshop.

Phase 2. These are the primary responsibilities of the IM Facilitator in Phase 2:

- Work with the IM staff to assure that all preparations for the Workshop are made satisfactorily, in line with the Workshop Plan. This will include some of the details mentioned below.
- Have flip charts available to communicate rapidly with the participants those key aspects of the conduct of the Workshop, including:
  (a) the context statement for the Workshop,
  (b) the products sought from the Workshop,
  (c) brief descriptions of the processes to be used,
  (d) a nominal schedule for the Workshop,
  (e) role distinctions--the IM Broker approved the context statement, the Participants alone are responsible to provide the content needed to deal with the issue in the way that the processes provide, and the IM Facilitator has sole responsibility for the processes.
- If any changes seem warranted during the course of the Workshop, the IM Broker and IM Facilitator will jointly formulate those changes, taking account of any comments made by the Participants.
- Ensure that the staff have provided all necessary supplies, and that the physical facility in which the Workshop is carried out is fully equipped for the purpose.
- Initiate and lead the processes laid out in the plan, to develop the products required by the plan in the sequence appearing in the plan; while constantly being sensitive to the possibility that events will take place that suggest a need to revise the sequence.
- Manage the time, with appropriate breaks.
- Clarify the expectations for Phase 3.
- Avoid getting involved in the content of the situation.

In addition to the foregoing, the IM Facilitator will understand the need to avoid carefully a variety of actions that have a negative impact on willingness of people to work together in groups. This capability must be learned before an actor starts to work with groups in a facilitative role.

5.2.3 Pattern Interpreter. The learning that takes place in IM work can be regarded as a primary product of the work. It is, however, an intangible product. The tangible products of IM work are patterns of relationships.

In the normal life of an actor, the actor encounters patterns in two ways. In the first, the eye sees patterns in the environment; such as autos in motion on streets and in parking areas, people moving in rooms in relation to aisles and walls, children and animals at play, and movements of clouds and precipitation. In the second, information is absorbed via the natural language either in conversation or in media, and the mind is able to construct patterns from such information.

The IM work produces patterns in explicit form, but not in either of the two familiar forms. Instead, these patterns are combined graphical and prose representations that are generally congruent with the philosophical development of Western logic.

In contrast with the extensive education (many years) that actors receive in prose forms of language, they receive little or no training in combined graphical and prose representations stemming from ideas of formal logic. Even more troublesome is the fact that some actors develop a dysfunctional set of ideas coming from years of using low-quality combined graphical and prose representations. **One must anticipate, therefore, the anomaly that a group of Participants in IM work can produce a set of very insightful representations (with computer and IM facilitator assistance), and yet not be capable of instantly extracting from those representations the high and dense information content of them.**

Three actions can be taken to improve this situation. The **first** is to introduce in the educational system the combined graphical and prose language; however this is beyond the capacity of the IM Facilitator to achieve. The **second** is to provide some specialized training for the Participants before the Workshop begins. While this is conceptually feasible, it has almost never been done, and it remains to be seen whether it will be organizationally feasible in the future. The **third** is to provide professional interpretation by means of a special role called the Pattern Interpreter.

The work of this role can be aided if the patterns are grouped into functional types, so that over time the experience gained with these functional types accumulates and can be used as part of the explanatory repertoire. The functional types can be defined to be compatible with the most frequent needs for patterns to deal with complex issues. Chapter 6, IM Products, presents the functional types that appear to be most valuable in working with complexity.

The Pattern Interpreter will gain detailed knowledge of all of these types, and will develop the capability to explain the information content of these types to the Participants and others. The Pattern Interpreter needs time to study the patterns and prepare a presentation of them. Consequently it would be ideal (from a quality perspective) to have this role active at the onset of Phase 3. Regrettably, it is unlikely that this ideal can be achieved. Huge pressures are present to make the interpretation available near the end of Phase 2. The most reasonable compromise seems to be to provide a long break for participants after they have developed all of the patterns, during which time the Pattern Interpreter can prepare interpretations to be reviewed by the participants.

Phase 2. The Pattern Interpreter should gain good knowledge of how the patterns were developed by the Participants in the Workshop, and should receive a copy of all patterns at the conclusion of the Workshop, along with all other information that was developed in the Workshop enroute to the development of the patterns.

Phase 3. The Pattern Interpreter presents a written explanation of the patterns as a minimum and, if possible, presents an oral interpretation to the re-assembled group, with opportunity for questions and responses.

This explanation should be received by all relevant actors before any further action is taken in Phase 3, since it provides the insight needed to determine the state of knowledge about the issue, which will be a key determinant in any other followup.

  5.2.4 Report Manager. The Report Manager bears the responsibility of providing accurate documentation of all of the significant work done in both Phases 1 and 2. The report will provide the essential background for Phase 3. Because graphics play a significant role in organizing and presenting the results of the Workshop, the use of computer assistance to provide excellent graphics is a requirement on the Report Manager. It is also critical that the Report Manager find a good way to integrate the results of the Pattern Interpreter.

Experience shows that some participants will find it difficult to interpret the graphics in the absence of help. For this reason the Report Manager must be sensitive to the need to provide well-written, understandable, interpretations of the patterns produced. In general the Report Manager will not be expert in writing such interpretations, but instead must show responsibility in making sure that such interpretations are reliably produced and well-integrated into the report.

5.3   INTERNAL SUPPORT ROLES.

The Internal Support Roles comprise the Facilities Preparation Manager, the Computer Operator, the Scribe, the Display Arranger, and the Video Tape Operator.

5.3.1 Facility Preparation Manager. Because the working facility entails significant leverage in terms of the quality of the group work in a Workshop, the quality of the facility preparation is significant in its effect on what is produced. Responsibility falls to the Facility Preparation Manager.

5.3.2 Computer Operator. The Computer Operator is required to know the IM software (Chapter 9) and to be responsible for operating this software during the Workshop, under the direction of the IM Facilitator.

5.3.3 Scribe (Recorder). The Scribe is the person in charge of keeping the record of the ideas that are generated by the participants.

5.3.4 Display Arranger. The Display Arranger has the responsibility for constructing large wall displays of patterns that are developed in Workshops. This entails prior preparation to construct such displays, as well as the most careful attention to make sure that the display reflects totally the information content of the patterns produced during the Workshop. This should entail checking against a computer printout of results of the Workshop, in order to maintain fidelity of representations. In the past, some Workshops have not produced hard copy of results leading to patterns, relying instead on ad hoc notations. This practice should never be permitted, because it opens up the possibility of erroneous reporting of group work, and loss of credibility of the practice of Interactive Management.

5.3.5 Video Tape Operator. Experience has shown that the most effective way of conveying an overview of results of IM Workshops in a short time is through the use of edited video tape. In some instances there may be hundreds or even thousands of people who should be given access to such results. Moreover the video taping of Workshops provides opportunities for scholarly research to assess process details, as well as exemplary material for education and training in the processes used in the Workshops. For this reason, the Client should be offered the opportunity to provide a video tape record as well as a shortened, edited version of this record for future use. The Video Tape Operator will play a role in helping to assure that the video tape operations attain the results desired to enhance communications concerning requirements of implementation.

(Video tapes have been made during many IM workshops. Contact one of the authors for information.)

NOTES

1. This quotation is from Sir Geoffrey Vickers, <u>Control, Stability and Choice,</u> Toronto: The University of Toronto Press, 1956, page 12 (the publication is the text of the Ninth Wallberg Lecture, presented at the University of Toronto on October 30, 1956). Vickers has also had much to say about institutions in his other publications, including (1) <u>Responsibility--Its Sources and Limits,</u> Salinas, CA: Intersystems, 1980; (2) <u>Human Systems are Different,</u> London: Harper and Rowe, 1983, and (3) <u>The Art of Judgment: A Study of Policy Making,</u> London: Harper and Rowe, 1965 and 1983.

STUDY QUESTIONS
CHAPTER 5. IM ROLES

1. What is Sir Geoffrey Vickers' definition of "an organization"?

2. What analogy can be drawn between people working together in an IM Workshop and a dramatic production?

3. What kinds of roles are involved in using IM?

4. Who make up the External Roles?

5. Who make up the Internal Professional Roles?

6. Who make up the Internal Support Roles?

7. What are the client responsibilities in IM work?

8. What are the sponsor responsibilities in IM work?

9. What are the responsibilities of the IM Broker?

10. What distinguishes the proactive and protective aspects of the IM Broker role?

11. What are quality control requirements in using IM?

12. How is the Participant role distinguished from IM staff roles?

13. What prior experience is required from an IM Workshop Planner?

14. What is required of an IM Facilitator?

15. How is an IM Facilitator distinguished from a "normal meeting facilitator"?

16. What is required of a Pattern Interpreter?

CHAPTER 6

IM PRODUCTS (Application Structural Types)

The main tangible products of IM activity are *annotated graphics*, also called: patterns, structural graphics, relationship maps, maps, or interpretive structural models.

The IM support system includes the possibility of developing a very large variety of patterns, only a few of which are described in this chapter. Those described here have been developed frequently in response to many user needs over a period extending from 1974 to the present.

The members of the set described here are called Application Structural Types. They arise from the requirements of applications. They are structural graphics. The individual types fulfill specific kinds of needs. The descriptions given here should help the IM Broker understand the nature and usefulness of the tangible products to be derived using IM, and the need to interpret them for individuals inexperienced in reading designed graphics structures.

Examples of each of the types can be found in various literature stemming from applications carried out since 1974 at various locations. The Preface identifies libraries which can assist the reader in locating specific applications literature on particular topics.

Most of these products correspond loosely to graphics that have been used in other contexts. For example, the use of the PERT system and the Critical Path Method for working with activity sequences has been common for decades. The DELTA Chart[1] was proposed to replace PERT about two decades ago, because PERT has some severe deficiencies which the DELTA Chart corrects. The Union of Japanese Scientists and Engineers has recommended the use of the so-called Seven-M-Tools[2] for helping to manage quality in manufacturing and in management. Six of these seven tools can be related directly to the Application Structural Types to be discussed below. The "Relations Diagram" corresponds to the Problematique. The "Tree Diagram" corresponds to the Intent Structure. The "Process Decision Program Chart" and the "Arrow Diagram" both correspond to the DELTA Chart. The "Affinity Diagram" corresponds to the Field Representation. The "Matrix Diagram" corresponds to the Enhancement Structure. The Ford Motor Company and other firms use an approach to quality enhancement system called "Quality Function Deployment" (QFD) or "The House of Quality" which, according to some reports, was developed at the Mitsubishi Shipyards in the early 1970's and imported to the United States about 14 years later. The essence of this system is a set of linked matrices indexed by various important aspects of system design, manufacturing, and customer views. The QFD corresponds to the Unified Program Planning Linked Matrices, developed at the Battelle Memorial Institute in 1970-71 (See Sec. 6.13 and Chapter 14 for detailed comparisons).

For each of the correspondences mentioned, the Application Structural Types described below incorporate improved aspects that the other graphics do not. Moreover, the Application Structural Types have been designed in response to the content of the Science of Generic Design which requires not only that the patterns have certain characteristics, but also that the processes of creating them have certain characteristics.

Sensitization to Graphics Language. Experience with the DELTA chart has shown that people, in general, either were not sensitive or have been desensitized to the importance of each component symbol used on a chart. Among the things that have not been understood is the notion that poorly-conceived graphical symbols have the power to produce cognitive overload. Those in the information industries tend to use a variety of symbols quite freely, using a variety of shapes to represent different ideas. In our view symbols should be given as much respect and attention as vials of explosive fluid. They should not be tampered with. They should be as simple as possible to draw, while making those distinctions that seem essential. They should not be preemptive and thereby foreclose possibilities.

The language of music illustrates very well the requirement that ***whatever symbols are used should be readily translatable into prose equivalents***. The combined use of graphics and prose is readily observed in sheet music. Such a language thereby attains the degree of communications rigor required to allow its readers to replicate the composer's intent, even though the feature of translatability into prose is seldom or never formally used. It is like the sky, present but not operated with; yet we would not know what to do if it were absent. Though there is no incentive to write out in prose the full information content of the sheet music, it is only the fact that such an activity is made feasible by the design of the language that permits the message to be conveyed through the centuries to diverse cultures which do not share even the same natural language.

Notably also, in sheet music, no writer imagines that by substituting a new kind of symbol for a half note a remarkable feat of creativity will be acknowledged. Instead the view is that the symbols from the language are sacrosanct. What is important is the particular combination and sequence of symbols which the composer's work represents.

Nor is it to be supposed that the language of sheet music was developed without regard to cognitive burden or human limitations. On the contrary, this notation reflects a beautiful synergism between the rate at which the human can read and exercise motor skills and the volume of symbolism to be assimilated per unit of time. The Law of Requisite Parsimony, coming from the Science of Generic Design, formalizes the importance of controlling the rate at which information flows to an individual engaged in intellectual activity. The conditions mentioned concerning sheet music illustrate an application of the Law of Requisite Parsimony in a situation where the effects of ignoring this law would produce immediate detection. (Regrettably in many non-musical situations detection does not occur until long after the fact.)

Imagine the sound of "Eine Kleine Nachtmusik" played for the first time by an orchestra whose members are reading the prose version of the sheet music rather than the music as supplied by music publishers. If you can imagine this, you can be sensitive to the critical nature of simple, standardized language, faithfully applied, and tailored to minimize human cognitive burden and maximize human readability.

With this in mind, the specific symbols used to represent the components of the DELTA chart will now be introduced.

6.1 DELTA CHART.

The DELTA Chart, like most of the other Application Structural Types, is a graphical representation of a relationship among a set of elements. The elements of the DELTA Chart may include Activities, Events, and Decisions. The relationship is time precedence, tempered by logic constraints.

Unlike other graphical systems that are intended also to show time relationships, the DELTA Chart incorporates the designation of the actor(s) who are responsible for carrying out the activities shown on the Chart. Also the DELTA Chart symbols have been carefully designed in the light of communication requirements, rather than following a notational system that clearly was generated in an ad hoc way and has persisted ever since.

The following questions make up the outline of this section:

* What is a DELTA Chart?
* What are the advantages of DELTA Charts?
* How is a DELTA Chart produced?
* Why is it important to produce it in that way?
* What does a DELTA Chart look like?
* Why do people have some problems in interpreting a DELTA Chart?
* How can the information in a DELTA Chart be used?

■   *What is a DELTA Chart?* A DELTA Chart is a graphic portrayal of a prescription for action. In this sense it is like a cooking recipe. Unlike a recipe but, perhaps, like actual cooking, a DELTA Chart may include decision points which lead to alternative courses of action. Its general applicability is indicated by an explanation of the acroynm DELTA:

* The *D* stands for *"decision"*
* The *E* stands for *"event"*
* The *L* stands for *"logic element"* (i.e., *AND* or *OR*)

- The *T* stands for *"time"*
- The *A* stands for *"activity"*

The choice of these five elements as the components of a structure intended to portray temporal relationships indicates that they make up a sufficient set both to describe and to prescribe any process adequately, provided assignment of an actor is made to each activity.

These four graphics principles are applied to the extent possible in the DELTA Chart:

- A different graphics symbol should be assigned to each distinct type of entry on a graphic chart, to help the reader make a quick visual discrimination among the different entries
- The symbols should be as easy to draw as possible, preferably using only straight lines
- The number of different symbols should be limited to seven if possible, to facilitate mental association
- Symbols with special significance should be highlighted for easy location (e.g., decisions, milestone events)

■ *What are the advantages of DELTA Charts?* DELTA Charts enable portrayal of sequences that involve a mix of activities, decisions, and events. It is often true that several sequences are possible, depending on which of several intermediate choices is made by the user as a sequence evolves. Also certain events may be expected to occur in the sequence which are worth spelling out to add greater definition. Other flexibilities will become clear as the discussion unfolds. Carrying out the sequences amounts to following the process to its logical conclusion. Thus a DELTA Chart can be viewed as a prescription for action. In this sense, it is like a recipe. But unlike a recipe a DELTA Chart may include decision points where different courses of action are followed at the discretion of the user. Some of the advantages that DELTA Charts provide to users are:

- *Common Language.* Once the user masters the DELTA Chart language and format, the user will be able to read with facility all of the graphical process descriptions, and will not have to learn a new (and probably idiosyncratic) format every time another process is discussed.
- *Compact Description.* Once the user learns a process, the DELTA Chart can serve as a compact reminder and descriptor of the process, which can be hung on a wall or used in a notebook in a flexible way. Also it is a teaching aid.
- *Clarity of Sequencing.* In contrast to a strictly verbal description of a process, wherein long sequences are hard to present and hard to remember (especially when the sequences include options), the DELTA Charts show clearly most or all of the sequencing involved in using the processes, thereby providing a clarity that is hard to attain without a graphical language.
- *Nesting Capability.* Activities, Events, or Decisions can be nested. For example, a single

56

Activity Box can itself be represented by a DELTA Chart that shows a sequence of lesser Activities, Events, and/or Decisions which can describe the single Activity in much greater detail. By using the principle of nesting, (which is like "zooming", as it is called in computer jargon) individual Charts can be created that provide broad overview as well as the most minute detail, with an inclusion structure being used to guide the reader to some desired level of scrutiny.

■ *How is a DELTA Chart Produced?* A DELTA Chart is produced using the IM system. The methods used differ from those for the other Application Structural Types, because the DELTA Chart includes (a) three types of elements (Decisions, Events, and Activities) and (b) Logic Boxes.

The elements can be generated using the NGT process, with a triggering question like this: "What activities, events, or decisions are anticipated in carrying out this program?" The result will be a mixed list of element types. Editing will then be done as follows. Events will stand as developed. Each activity will be replaced with its starting event and its concluding event. Each decision will be replaced with an event indicating that the decision has been made.

A structure can then be developed using the entire set of events, and omitting the activities, decisions, and logic boxes. The generic question can be like this: "In carrying out this program, and assuming that both events in this question will occur, must event A precede event B on a time scale in the first iteration?" This will produce what might be called a Contingency Event Structure.

When this structure has been posted, points where iterations may be required will be identified. These will normally occur following decisions, which will be introduced manually as required. During this work, new decisions that may be required will also be identified and positioned manually into the structure. This allows feedback cycles to be identified.

After this structure is produced, all the events that were chosen to replace activities will then be replaced with the appropriate activities. Finally logic boxes will be introduced manually.

It is desirable to have augmented ISM software dedicated to the production of DELTA Charts. However such software is not known to exist at present. If and when it is written, the above-described procedures can be modified accordingly.

■ *Why is it Important to Produce it in That Way?* It is important for all the patterns to be produced that way. IM is designed to enable people to manage complexity. Typical of complexity is the fact that no one has all the information needed, nor do individuals perceive issues in the same way. Therefore group work is required to gain the information, and focused dialog is required in order for individuals to learn from each other.

■   *What Does a DELTA Chart Look Like?* All of the DELTA Chart symbols can be drawn with only straight lines, and they are intended to be compatible with simple computer-drawn graphics systems. Each symbol type is distinguished in some way from other symbol types.

Activity. An activity is portrayed by a rectangular box divided into an upper and lower cell. The lower cell will always contain a verbal description of the activity. The description will be written so that an *action* word appears first (e.g., *Carry* coals to Newcastle). Normally the upper cell will contain the name or title of an *Actor*, which may be, e.g., a person, an organization, a machine, or a collection of organizations. It is expected that the Actor shown has been or will be responsible for carrying out the activity.

Time Precedence. Time precedence will be indicated by a straight line containing an arrowhead. The arrowhead indicates the flow of time.

Event. An event is an outcome, a result, a consequence, a happening or, in general, something that normally is considered to have occurred or is expected to occur at some particular time. Unlike an activity, which has a beginning at some point in time and an ending at some later point in time, the event is specified at a point in time. An event box portrays the event. It is a rectangle with a single cell. It is distinguished from the activity box, which has two cells. In describing an event, the primary object appears first, followed by an action word (e.g., *Coals reach* Newcastle, or *Newcastle receives* coal).

Initiating and Concluding Events. Normally a DELTA Chart sequence begins with an initiating event. No special symbol is used. However the event box will have no entering lines, and will always appear either at the top or at the left hand side of the Chart. A special symbol is used to indicate that an event is known to be the last in a sequence. That symbol is the same as the one used for an electrical earth or ground symbol, and is appended to the concluding event box. The ground symbol consists of three straight lines drawn horizontally, in a vertical row, the topmost being the longest, the middle one being shorter, and the bottom one being shorter still.

Consequence of a Decision. The possible consequences of a decision can always be construed as a set of events (which may then be followed by relevant activities and other events). In addition to the standardization that this arbitrary requirement entails, rectangular portrayals can be used to show each of the possible consequences in the standard event portrayal.

Milestone Events. Specific significance may be attached to certain events. These "milestone events" are indicated by emphasizing the bottom line on the event box.

Decisions. A decision is a resolution of a question, involving a choice of one option from a set of two or more options. The "decision diamond" used on many flow charts was rejected for use on a DELTA Chart, for several reasons. First of all, the rectangular box is easier to draw and locate on the graphic. Second, the number of possible consequences should not be restricted by the shape of the box, and with a rectangular box the number of consequences is not restricted by the box shape. In the DELTA Chart, making a decision is represented by a rectangular box much like the activity box, in that it contains two parts. In the upper part is shown the entity responsible for making the decision. In the lower part a question appears which defines the decision to be made. There is one line leaving the bottom of the decision box for each anticipated possible consequence (each option) of the decision. In addition, and to distinguish the decision box from the activity box, there are heavy lines on each side of the decision box. These heavy lines make the decision box stand out from other boxes on the DELTA Chart.

Logic Boxes. Two types of logic boxes may be shown on a DELTA Chart. These are "AND" and "OR" boxes. If several lines run into an AND box, this signifies that all boxes encountered in following a time line that precedes the AND box must have been completed before anything can continue from the exit of the AND box. If several lines follow an AND box, the meaning is that all paths must be followed in parallel. If several lines run into an OR box, it means that entry to and passage through the OR box can be had from any of the entering lines.

■ ***Why do people have some problems in interpreting a DELTA Chart?*** People sometimes have problems in interpreting a DELTA Chart. These problems arise from no experience at reading graphics or too much experience at reading graphics. Those with no experience need a small amount of instruction in order to be able to read DELTA Charts. Those who are very familiar with flow charts and PERT charts already have built-in expectations of what they will see on a chart. The DELTA Chart having been invented to correct deficiences in flow charts and PERT charts, the experienced graphics reader must learn what the deficiencies are and why it is important to correct them. This will free the mind of the reader to absorb the content of the DELTA Chart.

DELTA Charts usually have cycles in them. PERT charts do not. Both the novice and the experienced reader will need some instruction in how to interpret cycles. Cycles on DELTA Charts describe iterative subprocesses; i.e., parts of DELTA Charts where the same sequences appear in succession several times. To leave a cycle always requires a decision concerning whether something has been achieved by virtue of the iteration. If what is to be achieved has not been achieved, another iteration follows; but if what was sought from the cycle is achieved, exit from the cycle occurs and the time flow moves on to the next box or to the termination of the DELTA Chart, whichever is indicated on the Chart.

■   *How can the information in a DELTA Chart be used?* The DELTA Chart is intended either to describe how an existing complex process is being carried out, or to anticipate how some new process will be carried out. The Chart contains the answers to questions of the following type:

* What activities lead to what events?
* What events precede what activities?
* What is the overall process flow?
* Who is responsible for each of the actitivities that are carried out?
* What decisions are intermediate in the process?
* What are the possible consequences of the decisions?
* What are the milestone events in this process?
* How many feedback loops (cycles) occur in this process?

In addition to the foregoing, which are graphically portrayed on the DELTA Chart, one may add other information including such things as (a) time duration estimates associated with activities, (b) time of occurrence anticipated for events, (c) expected costs of activities, and (d) identifying numbers for each box, for ready reference.

Work Breakdown Notebooks. It is possible to supplement the DELTA Chart with what might be called a "Work Breakdown Notebook". Such a notebook may have one page for each box on the DELTA Chart, keyed to the Chart by identifying numbers. The notebook can amplify with prose whatever is shown on the DELTA Chart. For example, such a notebook was developed to accompany a DELTA Chart for the Saudi Arabian National Center for Science and Technology, to describe a proposed national planning process.

6.2   PROBLEMATIQUE.

A particular type of structural model (pattern) called a "problematique" has proved to be of great utility in analyzing complex issues and, subsequently, in resolving them. Despite the utility of this pattern type, it has been found empirically that there is considerable confusion associated with the use of this type. To clarify the problematique, the following questions will be treated in this section:

* What is a problematique?
* How is a problematique produced?
* Why is it important to produce it in that way?

- What does a problematique look like?
- What problems have been encountered in interpreting problematiques?
- How can the information in a problematique be used?

■   *What is a problematique?* A problematique is a structural model (graphical portrait, pattern) that shows how a collection (set) of problems interact in a certain way to create a problem situation that is much larger in scope than that produced by any single member of the set acting alone.

The kind of interaction that is portrayed on the problematique is one of showing which individual problems may contribute to making certain other problems worse.

For a relatively simple problematique in which there are only two problems (say A and B), there are only three theoretically possible types of problematique:

(1)   The No-Way Type, i.e., the simple one in which neither problem makes the other problem in the set any more severe. This can be indicated by the two statements:

> A does not aggravate B
> B does not aggravate A

The graphic representation of this type would show the two problems A and B in circles, and no arrow would connect them.

(2)   The One-Way Type, i.e., the 2-element problematique in which just one of the following [(a) or (b)] is true:

> (a)   A aggravates B
>   B does not aggravate A

or

> (b)   A does not aggravate B
>   B aggravates A

The graphic representation of this type would show the two elements A and B in circles, and there would be a single arrow from one to the other. If (a) is true, the arrow would point from A to B, and if (b) is true, the arrow would point from B to A. *The arrow represents the relationship "aggravates".*

(3)   <u>The Two-Way Type</u>, i.e., the 2-element problematique in which:

> A aggravates B
> B aggravates A

For this type, the two elements would appear in circles and there would be two arrows, one running from A to B and the other from B to A. This third type represents a *cycle of mutual aggravation.*

Most problematiques studied contain 10 or more problems and many contain 30 or more. The number of theoretically possible structural types is then dramatically enlarged, which is one of the reasons the interpretation becomes much more challenging than for the simple 2-element problematiques where there are only three types of structure.

Aggravation Propagates. It is important, in interpreting, to recognize that aggravation propagates. If A aggravates B, and if B aggravates C, and if C aggravates D, and if D aggravates E, then the aggravating impact of A may be much greater than might first appear. The aggravation of A propagates all the way down the line, making B, C, D, and E respectively worse than would otherwise be the case. One may then speak of aggravation pathways, and the length of such pathways is a preliminary, superficial measure of the potential influence of a given problem on the subset of problems that it aggravates. If aggravation did not propagate, then the significance of the problematique would be negligible, and no attention would be given to that type of structure. Because aggravation propagates, the resolution of complex situations is often impossible to achieve because people do not understand that the situation will not yield to piecemeal "solutions" that cope only with a small part of the aggravation.

It is especially notable that aggravation cycles are frequently found when problematiques are developed. An aggravation cycle is a subset of problems such that each member aggravates all other members in the cycle. If aggravation cycles are recognized as such, the problems contained in the aggravation cycle will be attacked as a unit, rather than piecemeal.

■   *How is a problematique produced ?* A problematique is produced using the IM system. This means that a group of knowledgeable people is assembled and their interaction is facilitated according to the IM Workshop Plan, with the aid of selected methodologies, a well-chosen working environment, support staff, and support technology. First the participants are asked to generate the set of problems that will be related in the problematique, and to clarify each of them through dialog. If the set is very large, the group may be asked to identify those members believed to be more important than others.

In any case, after clarification is achieved, the set to be structured is placed in a computer file. The computer begins to present questions to the group, one at a time, designed to draw out the interrelationships among the problems. At the conclusion of this work, the computer prints out the information needed to draw the structure. Depending on the software capability, the computer may be able also to cause a printer to draw an initial version of the problematique.

■   *Why is it important to produce it in that way ?*   Individually-produced problematiques are deficient, lacking important component problems, and overlooking or misinterpreting relationships. Groups, engaging in facilitated dialog, will collectively "purify" the information by reinforcing good ideas and gradually eliminating bad ideas, so that the final problematique does not reflect any individual's choice; but rather reflects the best thinking of the members of the group. The voluminous amount of information involved, and the need for focus, both reflect the importance of computer-sequenced questions; and the latter also enable the organized development of the information needed to construct the problematique. Without the computer, human error would frequently invalidate the process. The computer also is able to make major savings in group time because of its efficiency in managing and inferring information.

■   *What does a problematique look like ?*   The simple two-element structures discussed above give way to structures containing numerous problem statements which typically appear in boxes. Arrows join the boxes to portray the aggravation that has been discovered.

Most problematiques studied contain cycles. The size of the cycle is the number of problems it contains. If the size of a cycle is 2, there are just 2 arrows to be shown. The number of arrows grows much faster than the size of the cycle. For example, a cycle of size 10 would have 90 arrows. Clearly it is absurd to draw all these arrows. Instead, all the problems in a cycle are printed in a single enclosure. Each problem statement is preceded with a "bullet". With this graphic convention, you can easily count the number of problems in a cycle by just counting the number of bullets. The bullets also separate clearly one problem from another. If you want to know how many interactions there are in the cycle of size n, you can readily compute it from the formula $n(n-1)$.

In drawing the problematique, the graphic artist takes advantage of the structure printed out by the computer. The computer printout will show each of the cycles with their respective membership. It also shows which problems or cycles aggravate other problems or cycles.

The structure can be laid out one level at a time, and the interconnecting lines can be drawn to produce the problematique. (See Appendix 4 for a case example.)

In a more sophisticated operation, software can lay out and print the structure, using special sub-algorithms (such as the Warfield crossing-minimization routines[3] and the Fujitsu overall layout algorithms[4] developed by three Fujitsu staff members).

The problematique then appears as a multilevel structure, with individual problems or cycles appearing in different levels of what is called a "hybrid" structure. If, however, there are no cycles with 2 or more members, the structure is just a hierarchy.

■ *What problems have been encountered in interpreting problematiques ?* People may have trouble in reading and interpreting problematiques. What must be remembered is that if there is a path along the arrows from one box to another, the originating element for the path aggravates all other members on the path. This is all that is shown.

It is common to hear people say that the problems at the left of a left-to-right problematique are more fundamental than those at the right. Those on the right, they say, are more symptomatic. Also it is now becoming common to hear people say that the problems at the left are "root causes" of the difficulty associated with the situation.

The first of these statements has some validity, in the sense that those members at the left aggravate more members than do those on the right, as a rule. Their impact is, therefore more widely distributed across the situation. The second statement about "root cause" has no validity, in general.

Before statements such as those mentioned can be given credence, additional work would have to be done. For instance, one could (a) look beyond the existing problem set for problems that aggravate those at the left and/or (b) add quantification to the problematique. Both approaches are perfectly possible in many situations.

■ *How can the information in a problematique be used ?* The kinds of questions that are supported when a problematique is available are the following:

- In seeking a course of action in a situation, to what extent is the interaction among problems important in setting action priorities?
- What interactions have been revealed that have not been systematically addressed, and what are the possible implications of overlooking such interactions?
- What problems and interactions do we already know how to deal with?
- What problems or interactions do we *not* know how to deal with, and what should be done to try to get the missing knowledge?
- How can the implications of large cycles in the structure be understood?
- What organization or group of organizations is the site of the problem or interaction?
- Which organization(s) should deal with which problems and interactions?
- When some problems or interactions cut across organizations, who has the authority to

put a team together to deal with this interorganizational situation?
- Given the propagating aggravation, is it important to carry out corrective measures in some particular *sequence* that would have a much higher likelihood of succeeding through taking into account the propagating aggravation?

6.3   ENHANCEMENT STRUCTURE.

While the Problematique, discussed in Sec. 6.2, is useful in helping to define a complex situation; the Enhancement Structure is its conceptual opposite. The Problematique shows us how a set of problems are interrelated. The Enhancement Structure shows us how a set of proposed improvements are interrelated. To clarify the Enhancement Structure, the following questions will be treated in this section:

- What is an Enhancement Structure?
- How is an Enhancement Structure produced?
- Why is it produced in that way?
- What does an Enhancement Structure look like?
- What problems are encountered in interpreting it?
- How can the information in an Enhancement Structure be used?

■   *What is an Enhancement Structure ?* The elements of an Enhancement Structure typically are action options. The relationship is "will enhance the value of". The pattern developed tells us which action options, if chosen and carried out, will enhance the value of other action options when they are chosen and carried out. Like aggravation, enhancement propagates. Thus some action options may have a significantly favorable impact on others because of the propagation of enhancement.

■   *How is an Enhancement Structure produced ?* An Enhancement Structure is produced using the IM system. This means that a group of knowledgeable people is assembled and the group is facilitated according to the IM Workshop Plan, with the aid of selected methodologies, a well-chosen working environment, support staff, and support technology.

First the participants are asked to generate the set of action options that will be related in the Enhancement Structure, and to clarify each of them through dialog. If the set is very large, the group may be asked to identify those options believed to be more important than others.

In any case, after clarification is achieved, the set to be structured is placed in a computer file. The computer begins to present questions to the group, one at a time, designed to draw out the interrelationships among the options. At the conclusion of this work, the computer prints out the information needed to draw the structure. The computer may be able also to cause a printer to draw an initial version of the Enhancement Structure.

■   *Why is it important to produce it in that way ?*   Individually-produced Enhancement Structures are deficient, lacking important component action options, and overlooking or misinterpreting relationships. Groups, engaging in facilitated dialog, will collectively "purify" the information by reinforcing good ideas and gradually eliminating bad ideas, so that the final pattern does not reflect any individual's choice; but rather reflects the best thinking of the members of the group. The voluminous amount of information involved, and the need for focus, both reflect the importance of computer-sequenced questions; and the latter also enables the organized development of the information needed to construct the Enhancement Structure. Without the computer, human error would frequently invalidate the process. The computer also is able to make major savings in group time because of its efficiency in managing and inferring information.

■   *What does an Enhancement Structure look like ?*   An Enhancement Structure will look much like a Problematique. (See the discussion of Problematique for a description of the structure.) The only conceptual distinction between Problematique and Enhancement Structure is the difference between the nature of the elements and the nature of the relationships.

■   *What problems are encountered in interpreting it ?*   People may have trouble in reading and interpreting Enhancement Structures. What must be remembered is that if there is a path along the arrows from one box to another, the originating element for the path enhances all other members on the path. This is all that is shown. The intensity of the enhancement is *not* indicated.

It is common to hear people say that the action options at the left of a left-to-right Enhancement Structure are more fundamental than those at the right. Those on the right, they say, are just results of these more fundamental actions. Also it is now becoming common to hear people say that the action options at the left are "root benefits" associated with the situation. The first of these statements has some validity, in the sense that those members at the left enhance more members than do those on the right, as a rule. Their impact is, therefore more widely distributed across the situation. The second statement about "root benefits" has no validity, in general, but it may have in particular cases.

Before statements such as those mentioned can be given credence, additional work would have to be done to add quantification to the Enhancement Structure. This is perfectly possible in many situations.

■   *How can the information in an Enhancement Structure be used ?*   The kinds of questions that are supported when an Enhancement Structure is available are the following:

- In seeking a course of action in a situation, to what extent is the interaction among options important in setting action priorities?
- What interactions have been revealed that have not been systematically addressed, and what are the possible implications of overlooking such interactions?
- What action options and interactions do we already know how to deal with?
- What action options or interactions do we *not* know how to deal with, and what should be done to try to get the missing knowledge?
- How can the implications of large cycles in the structure be understood?
- What organization or group of organizations is the site of the action option or interaction?
- Which organization(s) should deal with which options and interactions?
- When some action options or interactions cut across organizations, who has the authority to put a team together to deal with this interorganizational situation?
- Given the propagating enhancement, is it important to carry out action options in some particular *sequence* that would have a much higher likelihood of succeeding through taking into account the propagating enhancement?

6.4   INTENT STRUCTURE.

In the early 1970's there was much interest attached to the formal development of objectives for organizations and for educational instruction. Curiously, many organizations and managers had tended to treat goals or objectives as though only one could be dealt with, and this did not recognize the fact that objectives of organizations are always intermingled with objectives of individuals in those organizations. Frequently organizational objectives conflicted with one another, and individual and organizational objectives were often also in conflict. Moreover, it was argued, educators who do not use formal statements of objectives often fail to clarify their own directions for educating students and also leave open the question of how to measure whether they had been successful or not.

Arguments arose as to whether it was more important to deal with objectives formally or to deal with conceived options formally. An objective, it was argued, may not be attainable; an option is something that is open to realization or achievement.

Whatever the point of view, it is important to know that it is possible to work with sets of objectives and show how they are interrelated. One way to do this is to work with an Intent Structure. To clarify the Intent Structure, the following questions will be treated in this section:

- What is an Intent Structure?
- How is an Intent Structure produced?
- Why is it produced in that way?

- What does an Intent Structure look like?
- What problems are encountered in interpreting it?
- How can the information in an Intent Structure be used?

■ ***What is an Intent Structure ?*** An intent structure is a pattern formed from the elements (which consist of a set of goals/objectives/aims, collectively called "intents") and a relationship "supports the attainment of". A typical statement read from an Intent Structure is Objective A (if achieved) supports the attainment of Objective B.

■ ***How is an Intent Structure produced ?*** An Intent Structure is produced using the IM system. This means that a group of knowledgeable people is assembled and their interaction is facilitated according to the IM Workshop Plan, with the aid of selected methodologies, a well-chosen working environment, support staff, and support technology.

First the participants are asked to generate the set of objectives that will be related in the Intent Structure, and to clarify each of them through dialog. If the set is very large, the group may be asked to identify those members believed to be more important than others.

In any case, after clarification is achieved, the set to be structured is placed in a computer file. The computer begins to present questions to the group, one at a time, designed to draw out the interrelationships among the objectives. At the conclusion of this work, the computer prints out the information needed to draw the structure. The computer may be able also to cause a printer to draw an initial version of the Intent Structure.

■ ***Why is it important to produce it in that way ?*** Individually-produced Intent Structures are deficient, lacking important component objectives, and overlooking or misinterpreting relationships. Groups, engaging in facilitated dialog, will collectively "purify" the information by reinforcing good ideas and gradually eliminating bad ideas, so that the final pattern does not reflect any individual's choice; but rather reflects the best thinking of the members of the group. The voluminous amount of information involved, and the need for focus, both reflect the importance of computer-sequenced questions; and the latter also enables the organized development of the information needed to construct the Intent Structure. Without the computer, human error would frequently invalidate the process. The computer also is able to make major savings in group time because of its efficiency in managing and inferring information.

■ ***What does an Intent Structure look like ?*** An Intent Structure will look much like a Problematique. (See the discussion of Problematique for a description of the structure.) The only conceptual distinction between Problematique and Intent Structure is the difference between the nature of the elements and the nature of the relationships.

■   *What problems are encountered in interpreting it ?* The reader of an Intent Structure sometimes does not understand exactly what the structure is intended to show. It is intended to show that if a certain objective were achieved, this would have a beneficial effect if one tries to achieve another objective, provided the latter is connected to the former by an arrow from the former to the latter.

■   *How can the information in an Intent Structure be used ?* The Intent Structure is helpful in answering questions of the following type:

- If a given objective is attained, what impact might this have on attaining another one?
- Which objectives are more fundamental than others?
- Should the highest level objectives be grouped into a mission statement?
- Should the intermediate level objectives be grouped into a policy statement?
- Should the lowest level objectives be grouped into a tactical statement?
- What action options should be considered to achieve the objectives, given the interdependence among the objectives?

6.5   CURRICULUM STRUCTURE.

Curriculum structures are produced to study the relationship among subjects of study; in particular to try to determine whether one subject, say A, should be studied before another subject, say B, in which case A would be prerequisite to B; or whether it is desirable to commingle the study of A and B, in effect treating them as co-requisites. In order to clarify the Curriculum Structure, the following questions will be treated in this section:

- What is a Curriculum Structure?
- How is a Curriculum Structure produced?
- Why is it produced in that way?
- What does a Curriculum Structure look like?
- What problems are encountered in interpreting it?
- How can the information in a Curriculum Structure be used?

■   *What is a Curriculum Structure ?* The elements of a curriculum structure are knowledge/experience packages, and the relationship is "should be learned before or corequisite with". When the temporal relationship between elements is understood, the curriculum structure forms a pattern for sequenced study and learning.

■   *How is a Curriculum Structure produced ?* A Curriculum Structure is produced using the IM system. This means that a group of knowledgeable people is assembled and their interaction is facilitated according to the IM Workshop Plan, with the aid of selected methodologies, a well-chosen working environment, support staff, and support technology.

First the participants are asked to generate the set of knowledge/experience packages that will be related in the Curriculum Structure, and to clarify each of them through dialog. If the set is very large, the group may be asked to identify those members believed to be more important than others.

In any case, after clarification is achieved, the set to be structured is placed in a computer file. The computer begins to present questions to the group, one at a time, designed to draw out the interrelationships among the packages. At the conclusion of this work, the computer prints out the information needed to draw the structure. The computer may be able also to cause a printer to draw an initial version of the Curriculum Structure.

■　　*Why is it important to produce it in that way ?* Individually-produced Curriculum Structures are deficient, lacking important packages, and overlooking or misinterpreting relationships. Groups, engaging in facilitated dialog, will collectively "purify" the information by reinforcing good ideas and gradually eliminating bad ideas, so that the final pattern does not reflect any individual's choice; but rather reflects the best thinking of the members of the group. The voluminous amount of information involved, and the need for focus, both reflect the importance of computer-sequenced questions; and the latter also enables the organized development of the information needed to construct the Curriculum Structure. Without the computer, human error would frequently invalidate the process. The computer also is able to make major savings in group time because of its efficiency in managing and inferring information.

■　　*What does a Curriculum Structure look like ?* A Curriculum Structure will look much like a Problematique. (See the discussion of Problematique for a description of the structure.) The only conceptual distinction between Problematique and Curriculum Structure is the difference between the nature of the elements and the nature of the relationships.

■　　*What problems are encountered in interpreting it ?* Educators are inexperienced in producing graphical representations of curriculum of the type developed using the IM process. Paths will need to be interpreted as learning sequences; parallel paths will need to be interpreted as representing parallel learning.

■　　*How can the information in a Curriculum Structure be used ?* The information in a Curriculum Structure is useful in answering questions of the following type:

• How many parallel learning sequences are needed?
• How can these be fit into academic time slots?
• Should innovative time-planning be used, driven by the learning requirements, so that

70

normal academic time slots might not be used?
- What staffing needs could blanket the curriculum sequence required?
- How can corequisites be integrated, so that the interdependent learning is most usefully attained by the student?

6.6 PRIORITY STRUCTURE.

Prioritization is encountered in budgets of governmental and private-sector organizations, as well as in family life. The budgets of some counties in the U. S., for example, incorporate several hundred million dollars. The budgets of states may be several billion dollars. Inability to prioritize may result in deficit financing or misuse of funds. The budgeting of time is also important. Prioritization can be studied with the aid of a Priority Structure. To clarify the Priority Structure, the following questions will be discussed:

- What is a Priority Structure?
- How is a Priority Structure produced?
- Why is it produced in that way?
- What does a Priority Structure look like?
- What problems are encountered in interpreting it?
- How can the information in a Priority Structure be used?

■ *What is a Priority Structure ?* A Priority Structure is a pattern such that for any (and every) two members, say A and B, there is a very clear indication on the pattern as to which of the following conditions is met:

- A has priority over B
- B has priority over A
- A and B are of equal priority

so that there is *never* an indication of this type: neither A nor B has priority. (Some of the early Priority Structures developed by people using Interpretive Structural Modeling had the defect that they did allow indications of the type: neither A nor B has priority.)

■ *How is a Priority Structure produced ?* A Priority Structure is produced using the IM system. This means that a group of knowledgeable people is assembled and their interaction is facilitated according to the IM Workshop Plan, with the aid of selected methodologies, a well-chosen working environment, support staff, and support technology.

First the participants are asked to generate the set of projects or other items that will be prioritized in the Priority Structure, and to clarify each of them through dialog. If the set is very large, the group may be asked to identify those members believed to be more important than others.

In any case, after clarification is achieved, the set to be structured is placed in a computer file. The computer begins to present questions to the group, one at a time, designed to draw out the interrelationships among the projects. At the conclusion of this work, the computer prints out the information needed to draw the structure. The computer may be able also to cause a printer to draw an initial version of the Priority Structure.

■   *Why is it important to produce it in that way ?* Individually-produced Priority Structures are deficient, lacking important packages, and overlooking or misinterpreting relationships. Groups, engaging in facilitated dialog, will collectively "purify" the information by reinforcing good ideas and gradually eliminating bad ideas, so that the final pattern does not reflect any individual's choice; but rather reflects the best thinking of the members of the group. The voluminous amount of information involved, and the need for focus, both reflect the importance of computer-sequenced questions; and the latter also enables the organized development of the information needed to construct the Priority Structure. Without the computer, human error would frequently invalidate the process. The computer also is able to make major savings in group time because of its efficiency in managing and inferring information.

■   *What does a Priority Structure look like ?* A Priority Structure will be a linear pattern in which all of the elements lie on a straight line. The structure may have cycles containing elements that have equal priority.

■   *What problems are encountered in interpreting it ?* If the Priority Structure is properly produced, there should be no problem in interpreting it, because of its simple structure. Problems will be encountered however, if the structure is not properly produced. The latter will be indicated by observing parallel paths on the structure caused by the failure to establish priority among some subset of the elements being prioritized.

■   *How can the information in a Priority Structure be used ?* As it stands, the Priority Structure shows clearly which elements have priority over which other elements. Going beyond this interpretation, one can add numerical values either before or after the structure has been developed, to assist in developing a course of action to be followed in recognition of the priority information.

6.7   FIELD REPRESENTATION (QUAD).

A Field Representation organizes information in a way that allows a large amount of information to be worked with effectively. Different types of Field are useful for different types of applications. The Field Representation is also called a Quad, because it places information into four levels. The information contained in a Quad has the same logical organization as would a four-level "Inclusion Structure". Anything in the fourth level of the Quad is included in something that lies at level three. Whatever lies at level three is part of what lies at level two. And everything that lies at level two is included in the single entity that lies at level one.

The distinction between a Quad and an Inclusion Structure is that the Quad is always drawn differently from the Inclusion Structure. An Inclusion Structure would be drawn much like the various other structures already discussed in this Chapter. The way in which a Quad is drawn provides a superior pattern for use in applications. For this reason the Inclusion Structure is not emphasized in this Chapter. Nonetheless it is important always to remember that, from a logical point of view, a Quad is an inclusion structure.

To clarify the Field Representation (Quad), the following questions will be treated in this section:

• What is a Field Representation (Quad)?
• How is a Field Representation produced?
• Why is it produced in that way?
• What does a Field Representation look like?
• What problems are encountered in interpreting it?
• What are the types of Field Representation?
• How can the information in a Field Structure be used?

■   *What is a Field Representation (Quad) ?*   A Field Representation shows a set of categories and the members of each of those sets. The members of a given category are all contained within that category (see, e.g., page 296).

The categories themselves may be categorized, with the categorization of the categories being dependent upon the nature of their individual members.

For example, suppose the elements of the situation are all action options. The categories will then represent different types of actions. If category A contains an option which, if elected, rules out the possibility of taking a certain option from category B, we say that categories A and B are *interdependent*.

In this situation, we can group interdependent categories into a third level and call the new categories by the name "clusters". We can then say that all the clusters are part of a higher level concept, the "design target".

Suppose the elements of the situation are all problems. The categories will then represent different types of problems. If category A contains a problem P1 that aggravates a problem P2 in category B and if problem P2 in category B also aggravates a problem P1 in category A, we can lump categories A and B into a cluster. Similarly we can say that all the clusters are part of a higher level concept, "the problem situation".

■ *How is a Field Representation produced ?* A Field Representation is produced using the IM system. This means that a group of knowledgeable people is assembled and their interaction is facilitated according to the IM Workshop Plan, with the aid of selected methodologies, a well-chosen working environment, support staff, and support technology.

First the participants are asked to generate the set of elements that will be the basis for the Field Representation, and to clarify each of them through dialog. If the set is very large, the group may be asked to identify those members believed to be more important than others.

In any case, after clarification is achieved, the set to be structured is placed in a computer file. The computer begins to present questions to the group, one at a time, designed to determine whether the subject elements lie in the same category . At the conclusion of this work, the computer prints out the members of each of the various categories.

The group is then asked to name the several categories, and to revise the membership in the categories as appropriate. Following this the categories themselves are entered in the computer, and the group is given a rule for placing categories into clusters. The group is then asked questions by the computer, the answers to which determine which categories fall into clusters. At the conclusion of this work, the computer prints out the relationships among categories.

■ *Why is it important to produce it in that way ?* Individually-produced Field Representations are idiosyncratic, lacking important elements. Groups, engaging in facilitated dialog, will collectively "purify" the information by reinforcing good ideas and gradually eliminating bad ideas, so that the final pattern does not reflect any individual's choice; but rather reflects the best thinking of the members of the group. The voluminous amount of information involved, and the need for focus, both reflect the importance of computer-sequenced questions; and the latter also enables the organized development of the information needed to construct the Field Representation. Without the computer, human error would frequently invalidate the process. The computer also is able to make major savings in group time because of its efficiency in managing and inferring information.

■ ***What does a Field Representation look like ?*** A Field Representation will look like a set of lists placed side by side, each list having a heading. Each member of a list is preceded by a bullet. At the head of the list is the category representing its list. Each category will be assigned a letter, such as A, B, C, etc.; except that if several categories are in a cluster they will be designed respectively A1, A2, A3, and B1, B2, etc., the numbers indicating membership in the cluster. (See Table A4.1 for an example of a Problem Field.)

■ ***What problems are encountered in interpreting it ?*** The primary difficulty in interpreting Field Representations has been associated with the failure to adhere to defined terminology. For example, the categories A, B, and C have sometimes been referred to as "clusters", even though the name "cluster" is specifically reserved to mean a *set of interdependent dimensions.*

■ ***What are the types of Field Representation ?*** Field representations are generally classified in one of two categories: descriptive or contingency. A descriptive field typically contains *attributes of a situation.* In applications, the attributes are often problems that are perceived within that situation. One may then speak of either an *attributes field* or a *problems field*, recognizing that the latter is a special case of the former. A contingency field contains elements that will normally not all be found in some future situation. For example, the elements may be action options, only some of which will eventually be selected for implementation. One may then speak of an *options field*. In addition to the elements mentioned (attributes, problems, options), the field will also contain *dimensions*, i.e., collections of elements grouped into like categories, all such categories being essential to encompass the situation.

■ ***How can the information in a Field Representation be used ?*** The information in a Field Representation is typically used in an intermediate way by a group to attain additional results that are closer to final application.

For example, if the Field is an Options Field, then it can be organized to meet the needs of design decision-making. If the field is a Problem Field, it can be organized to compare with a proposed Options Field generated to explore solutions.

6.8 TRIPLY-STRUCTURED QUAD.

To say that a set of elements is singly-structured means that the elements have been structured on the basis of a single relationship, e.g., "aggravates" or "precedes". Double-structuring means that two relationships are involved. A Field Representation (Quad) should always involve at least two relationships. The first relationship is always "is in the same category as", and results in partitioning the original set of elements into several subsets representing distinct categories. The second relationship is "is dependent upon", in which the categories are partitioned into clusters such that if two or more categories are in the same cluster they are interdependent.

The usefulness of a Quad is further enhanced, for design purposes, by introducing a third relationship, namely, "should be considered before". This relationship involves initially the clusters. The purpose is to determine the sequence in which clusters will be examined in order to make design choices. As soon as the clusters are sequenced, the same relationship is applied to the categories within each cluster, so that an ordering is achieved on all the categories.

This ordering will be used in laying out the triply-structured quad. The first component will be a category, namely the category to be examined first from the first cluster. The second component will be the category to be examined next from the first cluster, and so on.

Triple-structuring prepares the Quad to be used in a choice process, where individual members may be chosen from each of the categories for whatever purpose the activity entails.

If the Quad happens to be formed from design options, then the choices will be design options from each category (each design dimension). It may be that only one design option will be chosen from a given dimension, or several may be chosen. The choices that are made in this way make up an Options Profile, to be discussed in Sec. 6.10.

6.9   TAPESTRY OF QUADS.

A Quad can be viewed as the result of taking a single idea and breaking it up into constituent ideas organized in a four-level hierarchy. If the idea being broken up were, for example, an automobile, the first level of the hierarchy would consist only of the concept "automobile". The fourth level would include a large number of options to be chosen in designing an automobile. At the fourth level one might find, for example, the option "air conditioner".

If, in making design choices, the choice "air conditioner" were made, and if an already available air conditioner design were chosen, a relatively simple decision would have been made. If, however, it were decided that in order to meet competition or to resolve some environmental problem a totally new air conditioner design should be carried out, another Quad could be constructed in which the air conditioner is found at level 1 of a new hierarchy, and the options appearing at level 4 of this new hierarchy would be options for air conditioner components. For example, one such option might be "compressor".

This new Quad could be viewed as overlapping the first one. The Quad for air conditioner overlaps the Quad for automobile via the term "air conditioner". We then have a "tapestry" containing two Quads. If in designing the air conditioner an off-the-shelf compressor is chosen, a relatively simple decision is involved. If, however, a new compressor design is sought, a new Quad could be constructed which would overlap the second one via the term "compressor", and so on. The tapestry grows in this way, and can involve numerous overlapping Quads.

6.10 PROFILE REPRESENTATION.

The Field Representation (Quad) typically portrays a significant amount of information organized in a form that (a) is very suitable for use in decision-making and (b) is very suitable to maintain an ongoing, visible record of intermediate decision-making enroute to a final portrayal of the total set of choices that has been made. The ongoing and terminal portrayal of choices constitutes a Profile Representation.

Up to this point in the evolution of Interactive Management, the type of Field Representation that has been used in most applications is the triply-structured Options Field. Likewise, the type of Profile Representation that has been used the most is the Options Profile. Other types of Field Representation are likely to be used more frequently in the future. Such types will include the "Problems Field" and the "Attributes Field".

In constructing the Options Profile, a group will examine the first dimension of the Options Field (as determined in the sequence structuring: the third form of structuring in the triple-structuring) and make some choices of options from that dimension. Each choice that is made is represented graphically according to the following rule: draw a line from the bullet in front of a selected option down to the Tie Line. The Tie Line is a continuous line that is drawn at the base of the graphic. After all choices are made, all selected options will be connected to the Tie Line. (See Chapter 13 for some examples of an Options Profile with a Tie Line.) All options that have been ruled out will remain unconnected. In intermediate stages of decision-making, those options that have been chosen up to a particular point in time will be connected to the Tie Line. If a group must stop its work for a period of time, the Options Field should stay in place, with all chosen options portrayed by connections to the Tie Line. Then when the group returns, it can begin its work just where it left off. Multiple use of the working space would suggest that perhaps the group's work should be taken down and later returned in anticipation of their completing the work. One must compare the cost of dedicating a room to a particular complex activity against the cost of errors that may be made by staff in taking down elaborate displays and restoring them to their former status. Normally the dedicated room will win out in such comparisons. When the time comes that large electronic computer-controlled displays can be put in service (as opposed to small screens that are unsuitable for displaying much information), facilities may be used more flexibly. Until that time comes, when dealing with complexity, the dedicated facility has much to recommend it. It is the height of folly to spend significant amounts of valuable time of participants who are knowledgable about complex issues, only to have all their work invalidated by others who know nothing about the issue and are probably not expert in the nature of the large displays that are used to portray complex situations.

When an Options Profile is completed, it is also called a Design Alternative. If several Design Alternatives are constructed (perhaps by different groups concerned with the same issue), a decision normally must be made to try to choose the best Design Alternative.

6.11 RESOLUTION STRUCTURE [5].

While the Problematique, discussed in Sec. 6.2, is useful in helping to define a complex situation; the Enhancement Structure described in Sec. 6.3 is its conceptual opposite. The Problematique shows us how a set of problems are interrelated. The Enhancement Structure shows us how a set of proposed improvements are interrelated. The Resolution Structure combines a Problematique and some of the aspects of an Enhancement Structure. To clarify the Resolution Structure, the following questions will be discussed:

• What is a Resolution Structure?
• How is a Resolution Structure produced?
• Why is it produced in that way?
• What does a Resolution Structure look like?
• What problems are encountered in interpreting it?
• How can the information in a Resolution Structure be used?

■   *What is a Resolution Structure ?* The elements of a Resolution Structure are of two types. One type is problems. The other type is action options that may be useful in resolving the problems. Just as there are two different element sets (problems and options), there are also two relationships represented on the Resolution Structure. The first relationship is "aggravates". The problems are related by that relationship to form a Problematique. The second relationship is "may help resolve". This relationship is used to connect possible action options to the problematique. The Resolution Structure thereby connects graphically possible action options to the Problematique, making it possible to trace the potential impact of pursuing certain action options on the resolution of the Problematique. Thus some action options may have a significantly favorable impact in resolving certain problems, because of the propagation of help in resolving.

■   *How is a Resolution Structure produced ?* A Resolution Structure is produced using the IM system. This means that a group of knowledgeable people is assembled and their interaction is facilitated according to the IM Workshop Plan, with the aid of selected methodologies, a well-chosen working environment, support staff, and support technology.

First the participants are asked to generate the set of problems that are involved in the situation and to clarify each of them through dialog. If the set is very large, the group may be asked to identify those members believed to be more important than others.

In any case, after clarification is achieved, the set to be structured (which may be a subset of the total set, consisting of those thought to be most important) is placed in a computer file. The computer begins to present questions to the group, one at a time, designed to draw out the interrelationships among the options. At the conclusion of this work, the computer prints out the information needed to draw a partial structure. This partial structure will be a Problematique. The computer may be able also to cause a printer to draw an initial version of the Problematique.

Next the participants are asked to generate the set of action options that might help in resolving the situation, and to clarify each of them through dialog. If the set is very large, the group may be asked to identify those members believed to be more important than others.

In any case, after clarification is achieved, the set of action options to be connected to the Problematique (which may be a subset of the total set of options thought to be most important, or may be the set of categories under which the options were grouped in the Options Field) is placed in a computer file. Depending on the software system to be used, the options or option categories may be appended directly to the set of problems, beginning at the end of that set. Then the computer begins to present questions to the group, one at a time, designed to draw out the interrelationships among the options or option categories and the problems in the Problematique. At the conclusion of this work, the computer prints out the information needed to draw the Resolution Structure. The computer may be able also to cause a printer to draw an initial version of the Resolution Structure.

■ *Why is it important to produce it in that way ?* Individually-produced Resolution Structures are deficient, lacking important component action options, and overlooking or misinterpreting relationships. Groups, engaging in facilitated dialog, will collectively "purify" the information by reinforcing good ideas and gradually eliminating bad ideas, so that the final pattern does not reflect any individual's choice; but rather reflects the best thinking of the members of the group. The voluminous amount of information involved, and the need for focus, both reflect the importance of computer-sequenced questions; and the latter also enables the organized development of the information needed to construct the Resolution Structure. Without the computer, human error would frequently invalidate the process. The computer also is able to make major savings in group time because of its efficiency in managing and inferring information.

■   ***What does a Resolution Structure look like ?*** A Resolution Structure will look much like a Problematique, especially on the right hand side where a Problematique is a substructure of the Resolution Structure. On the left will appear either options or options categories connected directly to elements of the Problematique. (See the discussion of Problematique for a description of that structure.)

■   ***What problems are encountered in interpreting it ?*** People may have trouble in reading and interpreting Resolution Structures. What must be remembered is that if there is a path along the arrows from one box to another, the originating element for the path will be either a problem or an action option/category. The terminating element will be a problem. If the originating element is a problem, it will aggravate all other members on the path. If the originating element is an action option/category, it may help resolve all other members on the path. This is all that is shown. The intensity of the aggravation or resolution is **not** indicated.

■   ***How can the information in a Resolution Structure be used ?***   The kinds of questions that are supported when a Resolution Structure is available are the following:

• In seeking a course of action in a situation, to what extent is the interaction among problems important in setting action priorities?
• What interactions have been revealed that have not been systematically addressed, and what are the possible implications of overlooking such interactions?
• What action options and interactions do we already know how to deal with?
• What action options or interactions do we *not* know how to deal with, and what should be done to try to get the missing knowledge?
• How can the implications of large cycles in the structure be understood?
• What organization or group of organizations is the site of the action option or interaction?
• Which organization(s) should deal with which options and interactions?
• When some action options or interactions cut across organizations, who has the authority to put a team together to deal with this interorganizational situation?
• Given the propagating nature of aggravation and resolution potential, is it important to carry out action options in some particular *sequence* that would have a much higher likelihood of succeeding through taking into account the propagating resolution potential?

6.12   COMPARISON BAR CHARTS.

Comparison bar charts are used to compare two Design Alternatives following the application of a methodology used to select one over the other. One comparison bar chart will be constructed for each alternative. Each bar chart shows vertically, in descending order of numerical value, the weight attached by the group to a particular dimension of comparison of the two Design Alternatives. For one alternative, the largest weight will be shown at the left of its bar chart; while for the other the largest weight will be shown at the right of its bar chart. The two charts will be based on a common straight line, so that ready visual comparison of the relative weights can be made. The total score will appear above the bar chart for each Design Alternative.

6.13   UNIFIED PROGRAM PLANNING LINKED MATRICES.

When Unified Program Planning (UPP) was introduced in the period 1971-73, the aim was to incorporate in one large array relationships among all of the factors perceived to be relevant to planning any kind of program. The large array consists of a number of matrices, which can be triangular to show self-interactions among members of a given set or rectangular to show cross-interactions between one set and another set. By linking the matrices, a pattern of interactions can be produced that extends across a wide spectrum of concerns relevant e.g., to product development, product quality, and other factors having to do with the design or creation of new systems.

After developing the Unified Program Planning Linked Matrices, it was clear that while this scheme had many advantages, it also had some significant shortcomings: (a) the interrelationship of "interaction" was too general for many purposes; (b) while the matrices incorporated pattern-like information, it was much too difficult for the observer to see these patterns when they were, in effect, hidden in an array of matrix data; (c) there was no attendant methodology for constructing the matrices; (d) there was no attendant methodology for assuring that the data entered in the matrices were consistent across the large array; and (e) the array was more useful in motivating and portraying complex interrelationships than it was in aiding the systematic design of complex systems.

In spite of these disadvantages, one finds that some organizations have adopted UPP-like structures in their work with complex systems. This includes the Mitsubishi Shipyards in Japan, the Systems Engineering and Cybernetics Centre of the Tata Consultancy Services in India, and the Ford Motor Company in the U. S. A. Other large U. S. companies are said to be using or rumored to be planning to initiate this system in their design or quality-control activities.

The concept of using a pattern of linked matrices to couple consumer interests to product development and manufacturing (UPP), extending all the way back to the origins of the natural resources, was presented by Warfield to an international audience at Purdue University in 1972 at a conference on methodology, and the paper was published in the proceedings of that conference[6]. In the same year a paper on the subject, showing the application to planning for a short-takeoff-and-landing system was published by Hill and Warfield in an IEEE journal. At the same time as these articles were published, Warfield was already engaged in developing needed improvements. Some of the improvements seen as necessary were the following: (a) a process for eliciting the needed information from groups, (b) a way to insure logical consistency in the collected information, and (c) a superior way of representing the information to help assure that viewers of it could see visually the relationships involved, without having to try to imagine them in their minds while looking at a collection of matrices filled with information. The Interpretive Structural Modeling process (ISM) was developed by Warfield during the period 1972-74 and published in 1974, as a way of responding to these needed improvements, and the Nominal Group Technique (NGT) was subsequently chosen as the superior approach to eliciting the necessary information.

Both the UPP and ISM were subsequently discussed in Warfield's 1976 book, but the process aspects of UPP were subjugated to the discussion of ISM, since it was felt that it would be clear to readers that matrices could best be developed using ISM, and that the application of the ISM process to constructing UPP matrices would be evident. The latter assumption was dependent upon the quality of scholarship being applied to how to work with complex situations. In the light of experience, it is clear that one cannot count on the quality of scholarship in a world in which marketing and related factors have positions of dominance.

NOTES

1. See: J. N. Warfield and J. D. Hill, "The DELTA Chart: A Method for R&D Project Portrayal", <u>IEEE Transactions on Engineering Management</u> EM-18(4), Nov., 1971, 132-139.

2. See: Kaoru Ishikawa, Editor, <u>Reports of Statistical Application Research</u>, Union of Japanese Scientists and Engineers, Special Issue: "Seven Management Tools for QC", Vol. 33, No. 2, June, 1986 (60 pages).

3. See: J. N. Warfield, "Crossing Theory and Hierarchy Mapping", <u>IEEE Transactions on Systems, Man, and Cybernetics</u>, July, 1977, 505-523 and the followup work in Note 4.

4. See: K. Sugiyama, S. Tagawa, and M. Toda, "Methods for Visual Understanding of Hierarchical System Structures", <u>IEEE Transactions on Systems, Man, and Cybernetics</u> 11(2), February, 1981, 109-125. Also the same authors wrote an earlier report upon which their paper was based. The report was called "Effective Representations of Hierarchical Structures", produced as Research Report No. 8 from the (Fujitsu) International Institute for Advanced Study of Social Information Systems, September, 1979.

5. See: Appendix 2 for a discussion of relevant GMU PC ISM Software.

6. See: J. N. Warfield, "Participative Methodology for Public Systems Planning", <u>Proceedings of an International Symposium on Systems Engineering and Analysis,</u> West Lafayette, IN: Purdue University, October, 1972, 23-40 (reprinted in <u>Computers and Electrical Engineering</u> 1(1), 1973, 187-210 by invitation of the Editor) and J. D. Hill and J. N. Warfield, "Unified Program Planning", <u>IEEE Transactions on Systems, Man, and Cybernetics</u> SMC-2(5), November, 1972, 610-621.

STUDY QUESTIONS
CHAPTER 6. IM PRODUCTS (Application Structural Types)

1. What are the main tangible products of IM activity?

2. What distinguishes the Application Structural Types of IM from commonly-used structural graphics?

3. What is involved in becoming sensitized to graphics language?

4. What is a DELTA Chart?

5. What is a Problematique?

6. What is an Enhancement Structure?

7. What is an Intent Structure?

8. What is a Curriculum Structure?

9. What is a Priority Structure?

10. What is a Field Representation (Quad)?

11. What is a "triply-structured quad"?

12. What is a tapestry of quads?

13. What is a Profile Representation?

14. What is a Resolution Structure?

15. What is a Comparison Bar Chart, as used in IM?

16. What are Unified Program Planning Linked Matrices?

CHAPTER 7

IM PROCESSES

If processes are thought about at all, one imagines that they typically are thought to lie in specific applications involving particular contextual features. A particular process is seen as tied to some particular subarena, e.g., banking, electrical engineering, writing legislation, developing computer software, or designing power plants. If *all* processes are so perceived, the consequence will be that people working in one area will have little language or experience in common with people in another area, thereby creating instance after instance of difficulty in working across application areas. While it cannot be denied that areas such as those mentioned do possess some unique aspects, process uniqueness is much less than might be imagined. Processes can often be shared across vast territories. The differences are primarily in details which the processes encompass as discretionary options for process users.

We see this most clearly when we come to the realization that there is an area that is common to almost all human beings, no matter what kinds of activities occupy their attention. That area is the area of ideas and operations with ideas. There are just a few important, generic operations that are carried out with ideas. The primary types are as follows:

* *Generating* ideas
* *Clarifying* (interpreting) ideas
* *Amending* ideas
* *Structuring* ideas
* *Interpreting Structures* of Ideas
* *Amending Structures* of Ideas

This chapter will describe IM processes effective in supporting these six types of idea operations. The processes are related to the operations, so the reader can see which processes are helpful with which operations. The processes will be connected to the outcomes described in Chapter 6, so the reader can see which processes produce which products.

7.1 IDEAWRITING.

Ideawriting is an efficient process for eliciting many ideas relevant to a stated issue from one or more small groups in a fraction of an hour: in other words, an *idea-generating process.* It is self-documenting. Its use is appropriate for all efforts where collective idea generation is expected to be valuable. It is especially useful for issue formulation, including problem definition, and for identification of objectives and options. Also it provides a quick method for group evaluation of their immediately prior work results.

Ideawriting can be used whenever there is a need to collect ideas or elements relevant to some issue and little time available to do so. Other conditions for its use are: the information needed is spread among a variety of people, it is desired to eliminate the potentially inhibiting influence of dominant personalities in collecting the information, and people are available and willing to take part in the generation of ideas.

Ideawriting has the potential for spurring the generation of many ideas concerning organizational, behavioral, and other aspects of an issue. It will encourage contributions from those normally noted for reticence and quietness. It has the potential for stimulating greatly enhanced stakeholder input into a planning process.

Results of its use include the spontaneous occurrence of ideas, triggered by other ideas. Typically one may expect to gain a list of 50 to 150 ideas about an issue or question in 20 to 30 minutes. Also one can anticipate increased understanding of an issue as a result of the manner in which the ideas are produced.

To carry out Ideawriting, it is required that a specific *triggering question* be formulated. All ideas generated will be in response to this question.

A group leader who has some experience with the process will act as the process facilitator. No more than six people will take part in each instance of the process. However any number of these instances can be carried out simultaneously. Each individual group will need a table, chairs, paper, pencils, and a quiet room in which to work. Groups can share a single room.

The triggering question is displayed to the group throughout its working period, which will seldom exceed 30 minutes. Each participant is asked to carry out the silent generation of ideas in writing, in response to the triggering question. Exchange of sheets of paper is desired, after about each 5 minutes of writing, or at the convenience of the participants. When a participant gets a page from another participant, the page is read and will normally stimulate new ideas which can be written on the page presently in hand. Continued informal exchange takes place until all participants have examined all the written ideas and no further ideas come to mind.

Ideawriting terminates with the collection of the products of the group activity. Clearly a variety of actions might follow, either immediately or at a later date, but these actions are not part of the Ideawriting process itself.

7.2 NOMINAL GROUP TECHNIQUE (NGT).

The Nominal Group Technique has multiple properties. It is a process for: (1) generating ideas, (2) clarifying ideas, (3) doing a preliminary partitioning of the set of generated and clarified ideas, based on a criterion of relative saliency, and (4) helping to build a spirit of participation and teamwork or group morale. The NGT is self-documenting.

This process is more sophisticated than Ideawriting, and generally achieves considerably more. (Ideawriting has four attributes that will sometimes make it the method of choice for generating ideas. Ideawriting can be more easily learned by facilitators. It requires less time, perhaps only about 20% as much time as NGT. Many groups can carry out Ideawriting simultaneously, and it is less demanding on physical facilities and space availability for wall displays.)

A very-well written description of the NGT has been published by its inventors[1]. The following descriptions are intended to familiarize the reader with this process and with some results of analysis of its use, but not to substitute for the more encompassing description in the cited reference.

The use of the NGT is generally appropriate whenever collective idea generation is of value, and it is therefore especially useful for issue formulation. It is also useful in business and government planning, and for fostering stakeholder participation in planning. In these situations, controversy and uncertainty are often present concerning the nature of an issue or problem and its possible resolution. Frequently it is important to neutralize the effect of dominant individuals in small group meetings. Also it may be important to get an initial rough prioritization of problem elements in terms of relative importance. The NGT, when managed by a skilled facilitator who is sensitive to the behavioral design of this process, is highly effective in achieving all these ends.

On many occasions the NGT has demonstrated its potential to stimulate the generation of many ideas concerning organizational, behavioral, and other issues; and for encouraging contributions from those normally noted for quietness. Outcomes of this process will typically include a list of 20 to 150 ideas about an issue. There will be a greatly enhanced understanding of the components of the issue, an opportunity to assure that ideas of each member of the group become part of the context for future discussion, and a preliminary and rough assessment of the relative importance of the ideas that are produced.

Like the Ideawriting method, the NGT process is initiated by formulating carefully a *triggering question.* The ideas generated will be in response to this question. The ideas will be silently generated, and the written ideas will not be exchanged during the writing process. The quality and relevance of the generated ideas will be highly sensitive to thoughtful formulation of the triggering question.

After twenty to thirty minutes of writing of ideas, or whenever it appears that the participants have stopped writing, the facilitator will conduct a round robin recording of ideas, in which individuals present ideas one at a time. The facilitator will record the ideas on flip chart pages, and as each page is filled it is posted on the wall.

When all (or three rounds) of the ideas have been displayed, the process continues with sequential clarification of each idea. Criticism of ideas is foregone. Some editing may occur to add to the clarity of an idea. Ideas which appear to overlap or to be identical may be pooled, if it is clear that nothing is lost thereby.

After all ideas are clarified and new additions to the list (if any) have been made during the clarification discussion, participants are asked to vote by written ballot. In this voting each participant selects the five ideas in the set that are deemed to be most important in respect to the issue, and ranks them in order of importance. The facilitator collects and records these votes.

To carry out the NGT process, one requires a group leader trained as a facilitator who has some experience with the process. A carefully prepared triggering question drives the process. The participants consist (typically) of a group of between 6 and 12 individuals with issue-related expertise. Paper and pencils are required for each participant. A flip chart and felt-tipped pens are used by the facilitator. The meeting room should have table space for the group, comfortable chairs for all actors, and surfaces on which to tape the generated ideas where they will be in full view of the participants. A time period of about 3 hours for the process is the normal expectation.

Table 7.1 shows mean values of several NGT parameters derived from analysis of 43 applications:

TABLE 7.1
MEAN VALUES OF SOME NGT PROCESS PARAMETERS

Parameter	*Mean Value*
Duration of Session	*3.1 hours*
Number of Ideas Generated	*64 ideas*
Number of Ideas Selected in Top Five	*33 ideas*
Diversity	*5.6*

Typically there is great diversity in the views of participants as to which five ideas drawn from the set of ideas that is generated and clarified by the group are the most important in relation to the issue under study. A value of **zero** for Diversity means that the group is in *full agreement* about which of the ideas selected are the most important in relation to the issue being considered. A value exceeding five for Diversity typically indicates that the group is *closer to perfect disagreement* on relative importance than to perfect consensus. The mean value of Diversity is 5.6, which shows a significant and pervasive difference of view toward the issue, with this kind of difference tending to be present in any group that deals with any complex issue. For this reason, NGT is not the last step in the application of IM. Instead, it furnishes ideas for later steps when diversity is dispelled through learning.

"Enhanced NGT". The classical definition of NGT can be amended to produce what might be called "enhanced NGT". Enhanced NGT differs only modestly from classical NGT. The differences are changes in emphasis to reflect experience in observing many applications.

The enhanced version omits one part of the classical NGT and introduces a second part that reflects a different emphasis. The first aspect of the enhancement is to omit the very last part of the classical NGT. This last part is intended to produce a final ranking. This last part is omitted because when necessary to construct such a ranking it has been found that ISM is a more appropriate methodology to apply. The second part of the enhancement involves setting aside a specific time for amending ideas that have been generated and clarified using NGT. It appears that the inventors of NGT believed that facilitators of the process would be willing and capable to provide leadership in editing statements produced by the participants. Experience shows that one cannot rely on this assumption. Therefore what is proposed as the second component of enhanced NGT is as follows. Following the clarification, and during a break in the group work, the Scribe will provide to the IM Facilitator certain materials. These will consist of (a) a list of those statements that do not meet good standards of grammar and composition, (b) a list of those (compound) statements that incorporate more than one basic idea (and will usually include words like "and" and "or"), and (c) a list of statements proposed to replace the compound statements, in which each compound statement will have been partitioned into simple (one-idea) statements, adhering as closely as feasible to the participant's original statement.

There will be placed on the work table a set of specially-colored sheets specifically for use by participants to write proposed amendments to statements that are in the list (a) provided to the IM Facilitator. The IM Facilitator will lead the group in a process whereby the poorly written statements in list (a) will be amended just to meet good standards of grammar and English. This will be done by asking participants to write new versions on the special sheets and give them to the IM Facilitator. The work of amendment will continue until all of the list (a) statements have been upgraded in their power to communicate reliably.

During the break the Scribe will provide specially-colored sheets containing all the amended statements produced in list (c), and these will be posted for viewing by the participants. The participants will be asked either to accept the amended statements as presented by the Scribe, or to write new versions on the specially-colored sheets and provide them to the IM Facilitator as they did with the items in list (a). The work of amendment will continue until all of the list (c) statements have been upgraded in their power to communicate reliably a single primary idea.

7.3   DELPHI.

The DELPHI process, the oldest of the processes discussed in this chapter, is a means for generating, clarifying, structuring (in a limited way), and amending ideas. It is distinctive for its application when groups cannot or should not be in face-to-face communication, being served instead by a neutral information management group. As a rule, the DELPHI process is much slower in its use than the other methods, but it can be accelerated using modern communication and computer equipment at times. DELPHI is self-documenting.

The literature on DELPHI is extensive[2]. It has been found experimentally in studies extending over more than a decade that when groups are brought together, the benefits of direct interaction are great. Therefore DELPHI is seldom used in Interactive Management. When the circumstances require its use, it has been found to be helpful.

7.4 INTERPRETIVE STRUCTURAL MODELING (ISM).

The Interpretive Structural Modeling (ISM) process provides the means to enable groups to structure information with computer assistance, while simultaneously clarifying the component ideas. It also allows for amendment of preliminary structures, again with computer assistance. It is self-documenting.

In application, ISM provides the means to formulate a pattern or structure of elements associated with issue formulation. The elements may include needs, constraints, objectives, or options in a variety of fields such as education, public facility planning, city budget-cutting, or system design.

This method is useful when a complex issue is under study, and there are interactions among the diverse elements of the issue. A focused group discussion on the issue is needed on the way to the development of one or more relationship maps.

The elements that are structured as well as the relationships used to structure them are clarified by reasoning and discussion stimulated by the process. The quality of the results obtained depends upon skilled process leadership, which must be facilitative rather than issue-involved. ***Overemphasis upon the mechanistic and technical aspects of the process during its use is highly undesirable, while underestimation of the significance of its behavioral attributes by the facilitator may significantly weaken its utility.***

The use of ISM produces one or more documented models of element interrelationships. Part of the product will include a carefully refined language with which to describe or discuss an issue or system. There will be a significantly enhanced understanding of the issue, accompanied by modification and clarification of initially-formulated elements and relationships.

In the application of ISM, an issue and a structuring theme are identified. A group and a process leader are chosen. Elements of the issue will be available from prior work, frequently as a consequence of use of the Nominal Group Technique. Part or all of the element set that is developed from the NGT activity (or other means of developing such a set) will be entered in a computer. The machine will present inquiries visually to the group, which discusses them and makes judgments about relationships of the elements. Following the completion of the computer-questioning and group discussion of the questions, the computer computes information needed to construct and display a map of the relationship among the elements. A written interpretation of the map (keyed to the map) is developed by the IM Pattern Interpreter, who then gets assistance in developing the final version from the IM Broker. This is done separately from the group, and adequate time is allowed to ensure a quality interpretation. The map is then examined by the group and its interpretation is discussed. It may or may not then be amended (manually for simple amendments, or with computer assistance for more complex amendments).

To initiate the ISM process, one typically begins with the set of elements, and with a relationship chosen to be appropriate for exploration of the issue. The relationship chosen is then embedded in a ***generic question.*** There will be between 6 and 12 participants, an experienced group leader, a computer operator, and possibly other staff available to document key comments by the participants. The computer may be a time-sharing system, or may be a dedicated facility, but it must contain the software that supports and is part of the ISM process. A large wall display to present machine-generated questions to the group is achieved by a projection system driven from the computer. Copying facilities are needed to prepare and distribute results to the participants.

During this process the participants are asked to answer the questions presented by the computer, and the final answers to those questions are based on a democratic rule where the majority leads. It is also during this process when often the participants are asked to give the rationales for their individual decisions in order for the others to be exposed to different points of view and information, and then to have better basis for a final decision regarding the questions under consideration. It is in this "exchange" of points of view where most of the learning during the IM activity takes place among the participants.

The time required for an ISM process depends upon the number of elements in the set and their complexity. Time periods from two to eight hours have been experienced.

The ISM process is the formal replacement for previously-used heuristic methods of organizing information. It replaces "rearrange and tape" methods, or other methods in the literature that lack a sound behavioral design which takes account of human limitations and other behavioral aspects already discussed in earlier Chapters.

Table 7.2 shows mean values of certain ISM process parameters drawn from 31 sessions[3].

TABLE 7.2
MEAN VALUES OF SOME ISM PROCESS PARAMETERS

Parameter	Mean Value
Duration of Session	3.1 hours
Number of Ideas Structured	22 ideas

To summarize the discussion of ISM, it is a method for structuring ideas, and amending structures of ideas. The products of its use are beneficial in interpreting structures of ideas.

The discussion given here does not include aspects of ISM related to the interpretation and resolution of cycles. The reader who is interested in a more complete discussion will find it in the references, as well as in other parts of this Handbook.

7.5 FIELD DEVELOPMENT.

As mentioned, there are various types of field. This section deals with Options Fields, Problem Fields, and Attribute Fields.

7.5.1 Options Field. Processes for developing options fields provide means for thorough development of Design Situation descriptions and design Target descriptions. Self-documentation is inherent and incremental, providing a constantly updated status of all design decisions.

A Poly-Structure. The completed Options Field is a poly-structure. Its construction begins with the generation and clarification of a set of options. This set may be generated and clarified using the NGT, in response to a carefully formulated triggering question. This question defines the context and must, therefore, reflect substantial insight into the Design Situation. The question must be neither too broad nor too narrow. It must stimulate creative, productive responses, that do not stray from the topic under consideration.

Initial Structuring (Placing Options in Categories). Once a set is developed, using NGT, the initial structuring begins. The initial structuring is for the purpose of placing the options into categories. The ISM process is used to carry out the structuring. A relationship that may be used for this initial structuring is "is in the same category as".

Naming the Categories. Following the placing of the options into categories, the options are displayed as sets, arrayed vertically in anticipation of developing a name for each category that will be placed at the head of the appropriate column of options.

A standard comment that participants will make is that the categories should have been chosen first, and then the options should have been generated for each category separately. The standard response is that the disease called "hardening of the categories" is responsible for underconceptualization in many situations. To begin with the categories already specified will, no doubt, save time in options generation. The time spent in options generation is normally minuscule compared with the time spent later in designing, testing, installing, and operating the target system. *A primary reason for developing categories to characterize a set of previously-generated and clarified options is to fight underconceptualization at the outset of the design task.*

Identifying Design Dimensions. After the set of categories has been achieved, it is reasonable to believe that learning has occurred. At this point, it is appropriate to ask whether every category should be taken as a dimension of the design. The criterion for making this decision is to ask whether some option(s) in that category really *must be specified* in order to provide adequate definition of the alternative represented by choosing one or more options from each dimension, or whether any particular category is not essential to the definition of the Target. The purpose here is an economic one: to avoid using precious group time in working with a category that is non-essential to Target specification. Good processes leave room for groups to introduce superfluous information (within limits) in order to avoid cramping creative behavior, but later on provide opportunities to delete intermediate outcomes that are deemed not to require further consideration.

Discovering Clusters of Dependent Dimensions. Once the facilitated group has settled on the dimensions of the Target, a second structuring occurs. Now it is the set of dimensions that is structured. Again the ISM process is used. The relationship used is "is dependent on". Two dimensions are defined to be independent if a choice of one or more options in one of the dimensions does not rule out any choices in the other dimension. The kind of independence being dealt with is "decision-making independence". If two dimensions are dependent, the choice of options in one can be restricted by a choice of options in the other.

Because of this kind of dependence, this structuring forms clusters of dimensions such that any two dimensions in the same cluster are dependent. Clearly it is desirable that the choice of options in a cluster be made in light of the interdependency within the cluster.

Following this structuring, there is defined a set of clusters, each cluster consisting of a set of dimensions, and each dimension consisting of a set of similar options.

Establishing a Choice-Making Sequence for the Clusters. Now the third structuring begins. This structuring takes the clusters as the elements to be structured. The structuring relationship involves the sequence in which choices of options should be made. Once again the ISM process is used. A suitable relationship is "should be considered first in making choices of options". At the conclusion of this structuring, the clusters will have been placed in a linear sequence.

Sequencing Dimensions Within Clusters. A fourth structuring now is carried out, which normally will not require the use of the ISM process, but which can use it if it appears necessary. In this structuring, carried out separately for each cluster, the initial decision-making sequence among the dimensions in each cluster is defined. If, for example, a certain cluster consists of dimensions A1, A2, and A3; at the conclusion of the structuring for this cluster, it may have been decided to choose options first from dimension A2, then from dimension A3, and finally from dimension A1. With such ordering done for each cluster, a linear sequence involving all the dimensions is achieved.

Displaying the Completed Options Field. It is then appropriate to organize the Options Field by placing the dimensions in the order determined, with the name of each dimension heading a list of the options in that dimension, and with the clusters clearly identified. In the representation of the Options Field, each option is preceded by a "bullet". The bullets have been found to be very useful in helping to distinguish each option from each other option (especially to distinguish an option from one appearing immediately below it and from one appearing immediately above it); and also to maintain a high quality graphical readability in the Options Profile, to be discussed later.

7.5.2 Problems Field. Problems fields are organized much like options fields. A large set of problems is divided into categories for purposes of facilitating information management and interpretation.

7.5.3 Attributes Field. Attributes fields involve collection of the attributes of a situation and placing these attributes into categories for purposes of facilitating information management and interpretation.

7.6 PROFILE DEVELOPMENT.

While various types of profiles can be developed, the most common are the Options Profile (see, e.g., page 158) and the Attributes Profile.

7.6.1 Options Profile. The Options Profile is the visual representation of an Alternative, consisting of a set of chosen options, with at least one option coming from each Dimension in the Options Field. Each option that is selected is so designated by a line drawn from the bullet in front of the selected option down to the "tie line". Options chosen in a given dimension may be single or compound. A compound option is a set of individual members of the set of options that constitute a given dimension.

In applications, it is common to construct several Options Profiles for a given Options Field. Each Option Profile represents one design Alternative.

In choosing options, choices are made in the sequence determined in formulating the way the Options Field is represented.

If there are many options in a particular dimension, it may be deemed appropriate to use ISM to assist in constructing a Priority Structure for that particular dimension. The chosen option(s) for that dimension may then be selected in the light of the learning that occurred in constructing the Priority Structure for that dimension.

Choice is made in the first dimension in the order, and the selected options are "tied down" (by drawing a line from a chosen option to the tie line). Then choice is made in the second dimension, and so on. When an Options Field has many dimensions, it may occur that work will be interrupted at a point where choices have been made in the early dimensions in the sequence. These choices are designated by tying them to the tie line. When the group returns to resume work, they can see immediately the status of the work as they left it in a prior session, and can resume choice-making using the determined sequence.

Of course there is nothing to prevent the group from making modifications in the Options Field, as a consequence of the learning that goes on during the construction of the Options Profile.

When the decision is made that a sufficient set of Alternatives has been conceived, this set becomes the subject of tradeoff discussions, carried out using the Tradeoff Analysis process to be discussed in Section 7.7.

7.6.2 Attributes Profile. An Attributes Profile is constructed from an Attributes Field in the same way that an Options Profile is constructed from an Options Field. The basis for deciding which attributes to include in an Attributes Profile should be determined before the Profile is constructed. Some examples of bases are the following:

• Only those attributes will appear in an Attributes Profile that are seen as important to be *changed* through a process of implementation of an Options Profile
• Only those attributes will appear in an Attributes Profile that are seen as important to be *protected* **during any process of implementation of an Options Profile.**

7.7   TRADEOFF ANALYSIS.

The Tradeoff Analysis process offers a means of choosing systematically one alternative from a set of several that has been produced using the previously-described processes. Like the others, this process is self-documenting. It may also use (a) the NGT process as a component to develop criteria for making choices and (b) the ISM process as a component for use in prioritizing those criteria.

Starting Conditions. The starting conditions for the use of the Tradeoff Analysis Process are as follows. Two or more Alternatives (Options Profiles) are available. The group is prepared to choose one of these Alternatives as the recommended one to follow.

Development of Evaluation Criteria. The first step in the process is to generate ideas. The idea set that is desired is a set of Evaluation Criteria. These Criteria will be used as part of a systematic approach to the choice of a single Alternative. This set may be developed using any of the three processes described previously that produce sets of ideas in response to a suitable triggering question. The choice of which of the three will be used should be based on an understanding of the three processes and an awareness of the time available and relative complexity of the situation.

Criteria may be of two types: standard and non-standard. The standard criteria are those for which numbers are available that arise from a process of enumeration against accepted standards. For example, cost in dollars, area in acres, board-feet of timber, inches of topsoil, length of an artifact, number of horsepower, etc. The non-standard criteria are those criteria for which no suitable, accepted standards exist.

The non-standard criteria may be of two types: quantifiable and non-quantifiable. The former are those for which numerical values can be attained that reflect subjective opinion on a scale. The latter are those for which numerical values do not appear to have significance on any interpretable scale.

Then the criteria also can be said to fall into two other types: quantifiable and non-quantifiable. The former include both the standard criteria and the non-standard criteria which can be suitably quantified.

Choice of a Baseline Alternative. A single alternative can be arbitrarily chosen as a "baseline alternative", against which comparisons will be made.

Test for Dominance. Initially a table (matrix) will be constructed. The left side of this table will be indexed by the Alternatives, the Baseline Alternative being the first to appear in the index set. There will be one row in the table for each Alternative to be considered. Across the top of this table will appear the Evaluation Criteria. There will be one column in the table for each criterion. In the data cells of the table, there will be placed the quantified values for all those Evaluation Criteria that are quantifiable, one such value being tabulated for each Alternative.

For those Evaluation Criteria that are non-quantifiable, there will appear in each cell the rank of the particular Alternative in light of the particular criterion being applied. The ranks can be given in numerical form with 1 being the highest, and ties in rank must be permitted. Suppose, for example, that the criterion is "most beautiful". We know of no way to quantify beauty reliably. Nevertheless individuals may arbitrarily assign ranks, and the ranks may be averaged. What we are quantifying here is not beauty, but rather a perception that is likely to be different for each person. Nevertheless this practice allows the table to be filled with numbers.

It is now possible to inspect the completely filled-in table to search for any dominance that may occur among the set of Alternatives. Any one Alternative #1 is said to <u>dominate</u> another Alternative #2 if and only if every numerical entry in the row corresponding to alternative #1 is judged to be superior to or equivalent to the corresponding entry for alternative #2.

If one Alternative dominates another, then the Alternative that is dominated is removed from the set of Alternatives, leaving a reduced set. It is conceivable that one Alternative will dominate all the other Alternatives. Should this occur, the TAM terminates and the dominant Alternative is chosen.

Computer software can be used to drive a display unit that presents the table to the group in a large wall display so that as entries and comparisons are made, all of the relevant data are constantly in view.

If there are two or more Alternatives remaining after the dominance testing, and none of the remaining Alternatives dominates any of the other remaining Alternatives, the next step is to carry out difference ranking.

Difference Ranking. Select any two Alternatives for comparison. Each of the two Alternatives will now be examined by comparing them with respect to each Evaluation Criterion. Suppose the Alternatives are #1 and #2. Suppose that the Evaluation Criteria are A, B, C, and D.

Now examine the difference between alternatives #1 and #2 with respect to Criterion A. This difference can be designated DA. This difference will be considered very carefully with respect to how each of the options chosen in the several dimensions relates to this difference. A similar comparison can be made for the differences DB, DC, and DD. As this comparison is being made, it will become clear that it is possible to structure the differences according to their relative significance. It might turn out that differences are judged as of equal importance. In cases involving numerous criteria, the ISM process can be used to organize the structuring. A typical question might appear as follows:

"In the context of comparing Alternatives #1 and #2, is difference DA at least as significant as DB?"

Notice that if it should happen that the two differences were regarded as equally significant, they would then lie in a structural cycle.

This process of structuring the differences continues until all differences lie in a structure that represents their relative significance in assessing Alternatives #1 and #2.

Scaling the Ranked Differences. After the differences have been ranked, they are scaled. The items to be scaled may be individual differences or cycles containing more than one difference. The item ranked most significant is assigned a scale value of 100. The item ranked next highest is assigned a scale value between 0 and 100, by judging its relative significance compared to the highest-ranked item. The next most significant is then assigned a scale value less than (or possibly equal to) that just assigned, and so on, until all differences have attained a scale value between 0 and 100.

Scoring the Two Alternatives. Each of the two alternatives being compared can now be assigned a score for each of the scaled items. Suppose, for example, that Alternative #1 is taken as superior to Alternative #2 in respect to Evaluation Criterion A. Then there will be assigned to Alternative #1 the scaled value attached to the item DA, while a zero score would be assigned to Alternative #2 with respect to that item. Similarly, the scaled values given to each difference are assigned to whichever of the two Alternatives being compared is judged to be superior on that particular difference. Of course it could occur that for some particular criterion there would be no difference. If this should occur, the difference would always be ranked lowest in significance and assigned a scale value of 0.

When all the scale values representing the items have been assigned as indicated, the scaled values assigned to each Alternative may be added together to form the total score for each Alternative. The Alternative getting the highest score is then declared to be the superior Alternative. This conclusion should always be tested carefully against common sense, taking advantage of the audit trail that this process provides. Especially one should look to see whether there were very close judgments made that deserve more consideration.

Structuring the Set of Alternatives. Note that, when two Alternatives are compared, one normally emerges as the one with the higher score. This Alternative would then be preferred to the first. By continuing to compare Alternatives in pairs, using the process just described, a relationship of preference is built up on the Alternatives. This means that one can draw a tentative preference structure for the set of Alternatives based on the paired comparisons of Alternatives. If there were four Alternatives being compared, one might find, for example, a preference ordering as follows based on the total scores: 2,3,1,4. This type of ordering could be found, for example, by four comparisons: (1,2), (1,3), (2,3), and (1,4). Nevertheless one should not automatically assume that the preference ordering found by these four comparisons is the last word.

Nothing in this process assures that transitivity will apply to the ordering so found. Experience shows that transitivity almost always applies, but it should always be tested, because the mathematics of this process does not have a built-in guarantee of transitivity. This is because of the highly detailed process of comparison that is used. A thorough study of transitivity in relationships is required to control the quality of work using ISM or other ways of structuring[4].

7.8   PRODUCTS AND PROCESSES [5].

Chapter 6 identified thirteen prototypical "tangible" products of IM activity. In the preceding seven sections of Chapter 7, seven "IM Processes" were described. While the preceding sections have at least partially connected the products with the processes used to create them, it seems appropriate in this Section 7.8 to summarize the connection between products and processes. While there are several alternative ways to form product groups to produce the products, only the product(s) that is most commonly preferred is discussed in the following.

7.8.1 DELTA Chart. The DELTA Chart is produced using two of the seven processes. The ideas are generated and clarified using the NGT process. The result of using the NGT process is to create a set of activities, events, and decisions to be structured according to a time precedence relationship. In such structuring, it is to be expected that the product will be a hybrid structure, involving one or more cycles. Such cycles correspond to iteration. The structuring is done with ISM, but not merely to produce an initial structure. The cycles produced using the most commonly applied ISM algorithm leaves the cycles unresolved, showing merely that the elements lie in a cycle. What must be done to follow up is to create what is called an "inner cycle". The inner cycle is based on a non-transitive relationship. The cycle that is created using ISM is called an "outer cycle", and is formed from a transitive relationship.

What the user should appreciate is the following: the relationship "precedes" is transitive, but can be satisfied by members of an iterative cycle without saying anything more specific. The relationship "immediately precedes" is not transitive, but shows in detail the sequence that goes on in the iterative cycle. The ISM theory provides a straightforward way of deriving the inner cycle, once the outer cycle is available. Specifically, one can simply attach a weight to the relationship to show the immediacy of the precedence. A weight of ten can correspond to immediate precedence, while a weight of 0 can be used to show that the precedence is not immediate. From such a simple weighting matrix, the threshold structure can be created using an edge for a weight of ten and no edge for a weight of zero.

7.8.2 Problematique. The NGT process is used to generate and clarify the elements of the Problematique, and possibly to separate the elements into two categories of "most important" and "of lesser importance". The ISM process is then used to structure the problematique, using a relationship like "aggravates". If it is desired to delve deeply into any cycles that may be produced, this can be done in what is called "cycle resolution". In cycle resolution, weights are attached to each of the edges of the cycle, and threshold structures are created in which at first only the most heavily weighted edges are included, then the threshold is dropped down progressively to create a sequence of inner cycles. The inner cycles produced in this way are studied in order to interpret the meaning of the cycle as a whole. In addition, in very difficult instances, the method of geodetic cycles can be used to provide learning sequences for studying and interpreting cycles. The cycle resolution process is described in Section 9.5, which discusses appropriate resolution software.

7.8.3 Enhancement Structure. The NGT process is used to generate and clarify the elements of the Enhancement Structure, and possibly to separate the elements into two categories of "most important" and "of lesser importance". The ISM process is then used to develop the Enhancement Structure, using a relationship such as "enhances". The comments about cycle resolution in Sec. 7.8.2 apply equally to Enhancement Structures.

7.8.4 Intent Structure. The NGT process is used to generate and clarify the elements of the Intent Structure, which will be goals and/or objectives. The ISM process is used to structure the Intent Structure, using a relationship such as "supports the achievement of". Comments about cycle resolution in Sec. 7.8.2 apply equally to Intent Structures.

7.8.5 Curriculum Structure. The NGT process is used to generate and clarify the elements of a Curriculum Structure, and possibly to separate the elements into the categories "most important" and "of lesser importance". The ISM process is used to develop the Curriculum Structure using a relationship such as "should precede or be corequisite with". Comments about cycle resolution in Sec. 7.8.2 apply equally to Curriculum Structures.

7.8.6 Priority Structure. The NGT process is used to generate and clarify elements of a Priority Structure, and possibly to separate the elements into the categories of "most important" and "of lesser importance". The ISM process is used to develop the Priority Structure, using a relationship such as "is of equal or lesser priority than". Some users prefer to use two relationships, one of which can be "is of roughly equal priority with", and the other of which can be "is of distinctly higher priority than". The Priority Structure is more subtle than other structures, which explains why a technical paper[6] has been published to make very clear what is required to assure that a Priority Structure is properly developed using ISM.

7.8.7 Field Representation (Quad). The NGT process is used to generate and clarify the elements of the unstructured Quad. Then the ISM process is used to structure the

Quad, using a relationship like "is similar to".

7.8.8 Triply-Structured Quad. Section 7.5 describes the use of processes in developing the Triply-Structured Quad.

7.8.9 Tapestry of Quads. A Tapestry of Quads is produced by using the method for developing a single Quad repeatedly, once for each Quad. The representation of the Tapestry of Quads is achieved by overlapping the top of one Quad with one element lying at the lowest level of another Quad.

7.8.10 Profile. Sections 6.10 and 7.6 explain the development of a Profile.

7.8.11 Resolution Structure. The NGT process is used to generate and clarify the elements of a Resolution Structure, and possibly to separate the elements into the categories "of most importance" and "of lesser importance". The ISM process is used to structure the Resolution Structure, using two different relationships as described in Sec. 6.11. Comments about cycle resolution made in Sec. 7.8.2 apply equally to Resolution Structures.

7.8.12 Comparison Bar Charts. Comparison Bar Charts are constructed using the Tradeoff Analysis Methodology (TAM). Such Charts are made after relevant Profiles have been developed using the appropriate process discussed previously.

7.8.13 Unified Program Planning Linked Matrices. Each matrix component of the Unified Program Planning Linked Matrices is developed individually, using NGT to generate and clarify the elements, and using ISM to develop the structure. The relationship for each matrix will be selected through study of what kinds of elements are being related in the matrix. Linkages of matrices will be developed using ISM to connect the matrix elements of one matrix with the matrix elements of another.

NOTES

1. A. L. Delbecq, A. H. Van de Ven, and D. H. Gustafson, Group Techniques for Program Planning: A Guide to Nominal Group and DELPHI Processes, Glenview, IL: Scott, Foresman, 1975.

2. See for example: A. L. Delbecq, et al. above.

3. As given in Table A5.2 of A Science of Generic Design.

4. On this matter, the reader should consult references (e) and (f) in Note 5 below.

5. REFERENCES:

a) J. N. Warfield and J. D. Hill, "The DELTA Chart: A Method for R&D Project Portrayal", IEEE Trans. Engr. Mgt., EM18(4), 1971, 132-139.

b) T. Inagaki and E. M. Himmelblau, "Hierarchical Determination of Precedence Order and Representation of Digraphs", IEEE Trans. Syst., Man, and Cybern., 13(3), May/June, 1983, 406-413.

c) K. Sugiyama, S. Tagawa, and M. Toda, "Methods for Visual Understanding of Hierarchical System Structures", IEEE Trans. Syst., Man, and Cybern., Feb., 1981, 109-125.

d) A. L. Delbecq, A. H. Van De Ven and D. H. Gustafson, Group Techniques for Program Planning: A Guide to Nominal Group and DELPHI Processes, Glenview: Scott, Foresman, 1975.

e) J. N. Warfield, Societal Systems: Planning, Policy, and Complexity, New York: Wiley, 1976 (reprinted, Salinas, CA: Intersystems, 1989).

f) J. N. Warfield, "Interpretive Structural Modeling", Chap. 5 in Group Planning and Problem Solving Methods in Engineering, S. A. Olsen, Editor, New York: Wiley, 1982, 155-201.

g) Y. Sawaragi and K. Kawamura, Participatory Systems Approach: Methods and Applications, Tokyo: Daily Industrial Newspaper Company, 1982 (in Japanese).

h) N. Szyperski and M. Eul-Bischoff, Interpretative Strukturmodellierung (ISM), Braunschweig: Vieweg, 1983 (in German).

i) A. Ohuchi, M. Kurihara and I. Kaji, "An Efficient Procedure for Transitive Coupling in ISM", IEEE Trans. Syst., Man, and Cybern., SMC-15(3), May/June, 1985, 426-431.

j) J. N. Warfield, Interpretive Structural Modeling and Related Work (an annotated bibliography), Fairfax, VA: IASIS, May, 1990 (available through Interlibrary Loan from Fenwick Library, George Mason University, Fairfax, VA 22030-4444)..

k) J. N. Warfield, Generic Systems Design and Interactive Management (an annotated bibliography), Fairfax, VA: IASIS, August, 1990 (available through Interlibrary Loan from George Mason University, Fairfax, VA 22030-4444)..

l) J. N. Warfield, "Organizations and Systems Learning", General Systems 27, 1982, 5-74.

6. J. N. Warfield, "Priority Structures", Institute for Electrical and Electronics Engineers, Transactions on Systems, Man, and Cybernetics, SMC-10(10), Oct., 1980, 642-645.

STUDY QUESTIONS
CHAPTER 7. IM PROCESSES

1. What concept makes it possible to develop generic methodology (i.e., methodology that can be applied across disciplines and organizations, without regard to the specifics of the issue?

2. What are the primary operations that are carried out with ideas?

3. What is Ideawriting?

4. What is the Nominal Group Technique? How does it differ from Ideawriting?

5. On average, how long does an NGT session last?

6. On average, how many ideas are generated and clarified in an NGT session?

7. On average, how many ideas are selected by a Participant group as lying in the top five from among those generated and clarified?

8. What conclusion can be drawn about individual decision-making on complex issues from experience with voting for the top five ideas obtained from NGT work?

9. What is DELPHI?

10. What is Interpretive Structural Modeling (ISM)?

11. On average, how long does an ISM session last?

12. On average, how many ideas are structured in an ISM session?

13. What is a Field?

14. What is an Options Field?

15. What types of field can be structured other than an Options Field?

16. What is involved in developing an Options Profile?

17. What is the purpose of Tradeoff Analysis?

18. What process is used in developing any of the following Application Structural Types: DELTA Chart, Problematique, Enhancement Structure, Intent Structure, Curriculum Structure, Priority Structure, Field Representation, Triply-Structured Quad, Tapestry of Quads, Profile, Resolution Structure, and Unified Program Planning Linked Matrices?

CHAPTER 8

DEMOSOPHIA FACILITY

The working facility for carrying out IM activity is distinctive, and is carefully designed.

8.1   THE MEANING OF THE NAME.

The word "DEMOSOPHIA" is formed from two Greek words. The first refers to the people, and is recognizable as part of the word "democracy". The second refers to wisdom, and is recognizable as associated with the latter part of the word "philosophy". Put them together and you have a concept like "the wisdom of the people". Naming a facility in this way implies that it is tailored to help organize the collective wisdom of a group of people.

Ordinary, everyday experience leads people to believe that it is normal to carry out design and related activities such as planning in almost any environment. If the design encompasses physical artifacts, the working environment may be minimally altered to provide the most obviously essential accessories. In the computer age, ever-present publicity spurs the addition of computers to the working environment. The idea that the environment should be subjected to detailed design, taking into account the Laws of Generic Design, recognizing the potential benefits of creating a Working Environment that offers enhancements and minimizes detractions will only gradually be adopted. (This is the second aspect of DEMOSOPHIA.)

Nevertheless it is essential to design, construct, and maintain an environment that maximizes the likelihood of success in design activity. As the number of large system failures continues to grow, more and more evidence will accumulate to support the ideas given here.

8.2   THE NATURE OF THE WORKING ENVIRONMENT.

The working environment focuses on eliminating detractions and providing enhancements for people working there. The need exists for a variety of communication and cognitive assistance aids. The environment is designed in recognition of the need for personal comfort for human beings engaged in long, difficult tasks; for well-conceived, large displays; of the value in making protracted logic visible; and of the need to relieve actors of activities that distract from thinking, listening, and communicating. It recognizes the need for assistance in organizing knowledge, and for dialog to develop the capacity for teamwork.

The 1980 design incorporated key dimensions, ranging from "house- keeping" features (such as a coat rack to keep clothing out of the way of problem-solving activity) to communication facilities involving software that carries out inference with information.

The design was *not* carried out without relevant prior experience in environments that involved groups who were engaged in trying to solve complex problems or to design systems. Instead, a period of time extending from 1974 to 1979 had involved working in a variety of ad hoc settings, mostly consisting of rooms that were set aside as "meeting rooms", "conference rooms", or classrooms. Invariably these rooms had extremely bad attributes for problem-solving. It was after struggling to achieve results in group work under such unsatisfactory conditions that the insight needed to design an appropriate situation room was gained.

In short, two critical things went into the design of the room: (a) an understanding of the research results from social science revealing significant shortcomings that needed to be corrected in group work and (b) six years of experience working with groups in unsatisfactory environments.

In addition to the foregoing general benefits, the design was further informed by a number of specifics related primarily to processes for group problem-solving that were gathered, developed, and tested during the period from 1970 to 1979. While designing to incorporate the research results and the experience, specific aspects of the design related directly to the processes being used. Thus the design of the room involved considerations not likely to be found in most other problem-solving facilities.

In addition to the main facility, the design involved an anteroom specifically conceived to be a strong supporting facility for what goes on in the main room. Operations in the primary room are supported on a real-time basis by operations in the anteroom. The processes develop the necessary information. The actors who fill the various roles use the facilities of both rooms to provide the documentation in a real-time activity.

The first room to be developed was not completely faithful to the initial design. This was the decision-support facility at the University of Northern Iowa. There it was necessary to use an existing room that lacked some of the envisaged requirements. However many of the salient features were incorporated. Since its development in 1980, additional features have been added to make it more useful as a problem-solving environment. Also its use has not been limited to complex issues, but rather it has been applied to a variety of problems.

The second facility to be developed was almost totally done according to the original design insofar as the principal facility, the Demosophia, was concerned. The anteroom was considerably below desirable standards. Nevertheless this facility, developed at the University of Virginia, and placed in service in April of 1982, proved to be almost all that was hoped for in advancing the environmental needs for generic system design purposes.

As a result of experience gained with this design, its design was replicated by two client organizations in the period 1983-1985. These were the U. S. Forest Service Regional Office in Atlanta, Georgia, and the Southwest Fisheries Science Center in La Jolla, California (mentioned earlier). The former facility is no longer being used, because of a destructive fire in the building in which it was located. The latter facility continues to be used regularly by the Southwest Fisheries Science Center.

A room with most of the original design features and some new ones was created in the period 1984-1986 at the City University of London. This facility incorporated some improvements in the equipment and in graphical capabilities.

A well-equipped facility that was developed using the initial design was built at George Mason University in 1984-1985. This room had a much better anteroom than the one at the University of Virginia, providing for more efficient support services. It also had slightly more space, and its layout permitted better writing boards on the walls.

The Defense Systems Management College, Fort Belvoir, Virginia, modified one of its classrooms in the period 1989-90 to provide characteristics similar to those mentioned above. In 1991, the College continued to explore the creation of a new facility capable of providing support for IM (and, possibly, for other group activities).

The Ford Motor Company constructed such a room in 1993, after experiencing excessive problems in preparing for and conducting Interactive Management sessions in temporary space. As one example of a problem that was experienced while conducting a session at a four-star hotel, very early in the session the expensive rug on the ballroom floor caused static electricity to be produced, which migrated from the hand of one of the staff to one of the computers, disabling the computer and requiring extensive repairs.

The name "Demosophia" was chosen to distinguish it from other types of rooms that are also called "situation rooms" and to reflect the philosophy under which it was designed. Those who study situation rooms recognize that there are several types, characterized by different assumptions and underlying purposes.

The name "Demosophia" reflects the philosophy that the people who have difficult problems to deal with usually can do so with wisdom, provided they are supported by an appropriate environment, methodology based in sound theory, and staff people who are there to assist rather than to play out their own egos as superior problem solvers to those who "own" and who suffer from the problems.

While the design of Demosophia has been based on the background given in the preceding discussions, the original idea for such a room belongs to the late Harold Lasswell. This former Yale professor and political scientist was a well-known and well-respected scholar, teacher, and author.[1]

In his early days as a faculty member, Lasswell was very interested in group problem-solving activity. One of the experiences that he had together with two colleagues, took place in a Peruvian mountain village. For three months the small delegation of faculty tried to communicate with and assist the inhabitants of this poor village to try to help restore the viability of the community. This took place with Indians who did not speak English.

After several weeks, the discovery was made that communication could take place with a graphics language that was developed on the spot, using chalk drawings on the wall of a cave. Once this discovery was made, communication improved and significant progress was made toward restoring this village to health.

Years later, Lasswell articulated his concepts of a "decision seminar" and an "urban planetarium". The former was conceived as a specially designed room that emphasized major displays of information relating to policy development. In effect it was the modern version of the Peruvian cave. The urban planetarium was a larger concept. It would consist of a large building whose rooms and walls were so laid out and so covered with symbols, that a person could experience vicariously an entire urban center by simply walking through this building and experiencing its contents. In this way, it was thought that a citizen of a city could gain a feeling for the city as a whole and understand both its history and its current state, gaining an appreciation of the interdependence of its parts. By keeping an up-to-date status report, in graphical form, of numerous aspects of the city, citizens could know their city in a unique way. Even newcomers could gain rapidly an appreciation for the spirit and substance of the city. Possibly many of the self-serving actions that tend to destroy a city might be defeated if citizens perceived it more like an organism than only in terms of the individual's immediate situation. And possibly the individual might learn to appreciate the interdependence in the city and the possibilities for participation in its activities.

The vision of Lasswell was a significant motivation for the development of Demosophia, and the need for full information display was recognized as one of its main features.

Factors in the Design. By sorting out the room's attributes into principal design factors, it is possible to explain its concept and suggest how it is used. These are the main factors in its design:

• *Physical Comfort*. It should be possible for a person to sit in this room as a working participant for eight hours a day, and not be distracted from the task by any physical discomfort, the latter typically being found in "conference rooms" and most other settings where people are expected to work together. For achieving a minimum degree of physical comfort it is important to consider such aspects as lighting (artificial and natural), acoustics, chair design, etc.

- *Ample Table-Top Working Space.* In many rooms developed for group activity, no thought is given to maintaining ample table-top working space. In many rooms, there is no place for winter garments to be stored, so the working space is preempted by coats and hats. By providing proper space utilization, one helps assure productivity.

- *Flexible Table-Top Working Space.* Some large conference rooms have access to ancillary small rooms, where large groups can be broken up into small groups, one small group per room. However in a university and in many business environments such space cannot be made available. Also many organizations lack eating facilities near the working areas. By having several smaller tables that can be fit together to form one large one, it is possible to have a group working around the large one; and later by separating the tables and moving them to corners of the room, several small groups can be accommodated to work in parallel. It is also possible to use one of the small tables to hold a catered lunch. This economizes on the use of the group's time.

- *Design for Multiple Roles.* There is ample evidence that for effective group work, (a) the group should be small--perhaps 8 is the ideal size for effective verbal exchange--but the group can vary from 6 to 12 without introducing undue difficulty, (b) since there is often a need to accommodate more people than the "small group", space can be provided for observers who do not require as much space as the participants, (c) processes may provide for breaks during which "caucusing" among participants and observers can be carried out, (d) the group must have a facilitator, someone who is highly-skilled in working with groups using the methodologies that the room is designed to implement, (e) for certain kinds of group work the cognitive burden may be alleviated by using the computer, so that provision is made for a terminal and an operator, and (f) there is a need to record and duplicate in order to document what goes on for quick dissemination and amendment. Accordingly, the room should be designed to accommodate the various roles, which means it must have space for each that is appropriate to do what must be done in the role and to provide any necessary equipment support. In the Demosophia design, facilities are provided for about 10 participants, one or two facilitators, a computer operator, a computer terminal, up to twenty-five observers, and one or two scribes.

- *Design for Display.* Most of the walls are devoted to displaying information. The following modes are used: (a) manual display achieved by writing on butcher paper and taping it to the wall with masking tape, (b) manual display achieved by printing on cards, and either inserting the cards in magnetized holders, or using small rubberized magnets to place them manually on the magnetic wall-board which holds them, (c) augmenting the card display by drawing lines that connect the magnetic card holders to show relationships among the elements that are displayed on the cards, (d) projection displays on a bare wall, which can be produced from an overhead projector or more commonly from a computer driving a projection system (by this means, the computer can communicate with the group) which removes some of the cognitive overload that otherwise would weaken the capacity of the facilitator to perform in certain aspects of group work), and (e) direct writing, with a marker pen.

- *Design for Information Retention.* While the ordinary conference room seldom carries provision for retaining any information, and thus serves the purposes of the executive who doesn't intend to spend more than an hour in the room, complex issues demand prolonged periods of work, which may extend over several days, and typically may involve several periods separated by intervening days to catch up on normal work. For this reason, it is important to design for retaining information in the form it exists when the group has to interrupt its activity. Information is retained on the walls so that when a group returns it is visually cued immediately in detail about its prior work status. Members of the group may be able to walk through the displays in order to review graphically the work that has been done, and can resume work with little lost time. Information is also retained, when appropriate, in the computer, where it can be called on demand for refresher purposes, or to amend it by addition, deletion or other editing.

- *Production of Intermediate Results.* Group work is demanding. On complex issues, it is very important to reproduce intermediate results as soon as they have been achieved. This is done off line in the anteroom, using the drafting and copying facilities. Hard copy can then be provided to participants, giving a deserved feeling of accomplishment, and a record to study as needed as the work evolves.

- *Videotaping.* For certain purposes, such as summarizing results of a long project, for showing trainees how they perform in group work, and for archival reasons, it is desirable to be able to make and display videotapes, in which case audio design involving quality and placement of microphones is important.

- *Storing Possessions.* One corner of the room, near the door, is set aside for hanging coats and leaving bags so they do not use the work space and are available when leaving.

- *Telephones.* Persons using the room need to use telephones during breaks. Provision of them near but outside the working area is sometimes desirable.

- *Report Preparation.* Facilities are needed for preparing final reports on the work.

- *Access to On-Line Software.* Software for the ISM and TAM processes is needed to drive the processes, displaying questions and results. It has been demonstrated repeatedly that through activity in such a Laboratory Environment, following the steering provided by a Science of Generic Design, the best features of the separate Virtual Worlds of the participants can be brought forth and integrated, and that the interaction among the participants provides a learning experience that dissolves the potential negative impact of the initially-divergent views about issues.

NOTES:

1. Among his better known books is <u>A Pre-View of the Policy Sciences and Politics: Who Gets What, When, How?</u>

STUDY QUESTIONS
CHAPTER 8   DEMOSOPHIA FACILITY

1. What is the origin of the word "Demosophia"?

2. What does "Demosophia" mean?

3. What kind of working environment supports high-quality work on complex issues?

4. What factors support the design of a high-quality working environment?

5. What principle is supported by the Lasswell experience in Peru?

CHAPTER 9

IM SOFTWARE

Software appropriate for use with Interactive Management (IM) has been written in many places by many authors. Much, but not all, of this software has been written for the Interpretive Structural Modeling (ISM) process. Among the locations where ISM software has been written are the following: University of Hokkaido (Japan); Nippon Electric Company (Japan); IBM of Brazil (for the University of São Paulo); University of Dayton; Battelle Memorial Institute; City University, London; Tata Consultancy Services (India); GeneSys (India); Bell Northern Research[1] (Ottawa); Christakis, Whitehouse and Associates (CWA), Ltd. (Berwyn, PA); and the Instituto Tecnológico y de Estudios Superiores de Monterrey (ITESM, Monterrey, Mexico). In this handbook, just three versions of software for ISM are described, along with a discussion of software that would be useful for IM but which is not presently known to be available.

The version of ISM software to which most attention is given here was written for IBM PC compatible equipment at George Mason University. It is DOS-based (a Windows™ version is in preparation) and is referred to as the GMU ISM PC Software. It is described in detail in Appendix 2. CWA of Berwyn, PA, developed a version for IBM PC compatible equipment, embedded in the Windows™ applications, which is referred to as the Generic Problem Solving System (GPSS). It is incorporated in the Cogniscope™ instrument for problem-solving and design. At the Instituto Tecnológico y de Estudios Superiores de Monterrey (ITESM) a version of the software was developed for the NeXTstep environment, based on Object-Oriented programming, and is referred to as the Tlatocan software. This software incorporates many user-friendly features that are not contained in the GMU ISM PC software, expanding the ease with which workshop reports can be generated on line.

9.1 ISM SOFTWARE, INFERENCE, ISM ARITHMETIC.

ISM was developed in Columbus, Ohio, at Battelle Memorial Institute in 1972-74. Its use spread quickly to Japan and later to Brazil, Germany, England, India, and elsewhere. The ISM **process** is fundamentally a means to facilitate the construction of relationships among members of a set by a group of people engaged in dialog about the relationships. Intended as a learning process for the participants, the ISM **dialog** brings out and illuminates

---

[1] This development was initiated by Dr. Cliff Saunders, who chose to develop the software for use on the Apple MacIntosh line. He applied it within Bell Northern Research and, later, started his own consulting firm. He obtained an exclusive license to market and upgrade the software.

similarities and differences of views in a friendly environment, and in this way produces significant learning. ISM uses **machine inference** to make the process of development of relationships efficient, while assuring consistency in the logic. The tangible products of its use are maps of relationships (patterns) which permit significant interpretations to be drawn concerning complex issues.

The Arithmetic of Interpretive Structural Modeling. The **arithmetic** of ISM refers to how time is distributed in using the process and the implications of this for its utility. Data have been tabulated on 31 ISM sessions. These data are given in a table in the book: A Science of Generic Design, Appendix 5, page 495. The data relate to binary-matrix-filling, which is a mathematical description of the process of studying and modeling a relationship among members of a set. The following material is extracted from or estimated from that table.

TABLE 9.1
DATA ON THE INTERPRETIVE STRUCTURAL MODELING PROCESS

	Minimum	**Maximum**	**Mean**
Duration of ISM session	0.5 hours	6.0 hours	3.1 hours
Number of ideas structured	9	34	22
Number of matrix cells filled	72	1,122	485
Average time per query	0.5 minutes	7.5 minutes	2.44 minutes
Average time per cell filled	0.10 minutes	1.50 minutes	0.49 minutes

The average time per cell filled is found by dividing the total time spent in the session by the number of cells to be filled in a completed matrix. The numbers of 0.10, 1.50, and 0.49 are computed from known data under the assumption that the machine will infer 80% of the matrix entries. These numbers are just one-fifth of the numbers representing the average time per query. The assumed 80% figure is consistent with experience in running ISM sessions. .

It is known both from theory and from experience that the percent of inferred entries will vary from one session to the next, and we do not have data that enable us to determine how many entries were inferred in the above cases. In any session, the data can be taken if desired by using software sensitive to the need to get data on sessions and interpret it later.

The average time to conduct a working session with machine inference is represented by the foregoing data. If the assumed 80% inference were altogether absent, the time required would expand by a factor of five, as shown in the following:

Time to Complete a Session:

- minimum time ***with machine inference*** : 0.5 hours; minimum time ***without machine inference*** : 2.5 hours

- maximum time ***with machine inference*** : 6.0 hours; maximum time ***without machine inference*** : 30 hours

- mean time ***with machine inference*** : 3.1 hours; mean time ***without machine inference*** 15.5 hours.

9.2 GMU ISM SOFTWARE.

The DOS-based software developed at George Mason University (GMU ISM Software) has been widely used in more than 100 IM projects, and it is considered to be one of the most reliable versions though it doesn't present an interesting user interface. It is designed to run in an IBM PC or compatible machine provided that it has adequate RAM, a math co-processor and graphics capability.

The GMU ISM PC Software was designed in three versions, each one providing support for the generation of different Application Structural Types; the first two versions (DOCLUS and DOPRIOR) concentrate on particular cases, while the third one (DOMODEL) may be used for constructing most of the Application Structural Types that were discussed in Chapter 6; the distinction between these three versions lies in the relative efficiency of each one of them in helping to create the desired products.

Since at present the GMU ISM Software is believed to have been the most widely used in the USA, Appendix 2 presents a detailed explanation of how this software works. In spite of the extensive space devoted to this software in this book, the reader should appreciate that this version is over five years old, and a variety of newer software versions incorporate significant additions that go beyond the core aspects to include many new features, as well as having more friendly user interfaces. It is believed that many users would do well to begin with this software, because it is inexpensive and well-documented for beginner use. However for most applications a newer software package will be preferred.

9.3 GENERIC PROBLEM SOLVING SYSTEM SOFTWARE (GPSS).

The Generic Problem Solving System (Copyright © 1991 - CWA, Ltd.) is an integral component of the ***CogniScope***™ instrument. It provides a set of tools which are used to support IM sessions. The system runs on an IBM PC (or compatible) running Microsoft Windows™ 3.1 or higher, with at least 2 megabytes of RAM. It takes full advantage of the Windows graphical user interface through the use of menus, list boxes, push buttons, scroll bars, and a menu bar accessible from a mouse or keyboard; and supports such features as

117

printer setup, cutting, copying, and pasting texts between Windows applications (DTE).

Ideas which are generated by the participants of an IM session can be compared and structured in a variety of ways by the system. These methods include: classification of ideas into affinity groups, comparative structuring of ideas, influence structuring of ideas, MICMAC analysis of a structure's matrix, superposition of ideas onto an existing structure, and tradeoff analysis.

The system is able to produce a variety of reports including: lists of ideas, structure level reporting, logs of voting results, structural matrix reporting, and the structures themselves. The system provides online help for its features and a User's Manual is also available.

9.4 TLATOCAN SOFTWARE

The Tlatocan Software was developed in the Systems Engineering Department of the Campus Monterrey of ITESM, under the leadership of Professor Roxana Cárdenas, with support from other components of the Campus. The Tlatocan takes its name from the nahuatl word that was used to designate the Great Council that made the most important decisions in the Aztecd Empire. The Tlatocan's main purpose is to take advantage of state-of-the-art software engineering technology, in order to integrate most of the information management requirements of the Interactive Management process. The Object-Oriented programming technology used with the NeXTstep environment allows for the incorporation of some distinctive features that were not technically possible in a personal computer environment. Among these are: portability to different hardware platforms (e.g., INTEL, SPARC, and HP/PA), multi-user support, local area network presence (to support different concurrent activities for the IM support staff), excellent presentation features with PostScript Support, integrated multiple-font support, and multitasking advantages (such as the generation and printout of reports while working on the idea structuring processes and simultaneously producing backups and updates of data files).

Developed with the Interface-builder application, Tlatocan provides a user-friendly interface which includes a five-level support hierarchy for IM activity: (1) An IM Project (general information), (2) IM Workshops (information related to one or various workshops associated with one project), (3) Idea generation management (to support the management of one or more lists of ideas generated in each workshop, it incorporates full and flexible documentation capabilities as well as voting features with assignable criteria), (4) Structuring of ideas (for each list of ideas it is able to support the ISM process to produce the different basic types of structures that may be required, e.g., problematiques, priority structures, fields), and (5) Composite structure generation (providing for the generation of composite structures, such as a resolution structure). Also the system monitors the main variables of the IM activity, and generates a set of predefined performance indicators and statistics, according to the information developed in each level of the support hierarchy.

The outputs of the Tlatocan are available on the screen in the standardized format of each window. A number of reports are generated for each level of the support hierarchy, according to the information content of the level, which can be exported and presented in a word processor, where they can easily be modified and formatted according to particular needs, and thus are ready to prepare final reports about any IM project.

The main printed outputs include:

- General information about the projects and the workshops (e.g., objectives, context, names of participants)
- Lists of ideas generated
- Lists of ideas with their clarifying statements interspersed
- Individual idea statements presented with customized large fonts (one idea per page, ready to be displayed on a wall)
- Results of voting
- Full information concerning structures produced, including the relevant matrices
- Statistics related to the idea generation and structuring processes

Direct graphical printout is not yet available, but the relevant information is formatted in such a way that it can easily be exported to a drawing application. No known IM software presently contains high-quality graphical printouts, preconditioned to minimize crossings on structures, and to lay out structures so that straight lines can dominate the pattern to permit easy reading of the structures. A few IM software programs provide graphical printouts, but their utility is severely limited (not open at scale), and generally avoids internal software processing to lay out the structure according to high-readability criteria.

9.5 POTENTIALLY USEFUL SOFTWARE

Most, if not all, of the presently available software used with IM lacks some key features that would enhance significantly the potential for the use of this software to help deal with complex issues. The software can be described in two categories: software to help apply the Tradeoff Analysis process, and software to take full advantage of the ISM process. Software to assist in carrying out the Tradeoff Analysis process can be envisaged by reviewing how this process is conducted. The remainder of this section will deal with potentially useful additions to ISM Software to take full advantage of the ISM process..

9.5.1 Pattern Layout Capability. The theory required to permit software to be developed to provide pattern layout capability for patterns developed with the ISM process goes well beyond what has been incorporated in software so far. The goal of this work would be to produce layouts of patterns that incorporate text, and which are most easily read. Basic theoretical work was done by Warfield in 1977[1], followed by contributions to practical application presented by Sugiyama, Tagawa, and Toda at Fujitsu in 1978 and subsequently[2]. Additional work has been done by an Italian group involving Batini, Nardelli, and Tamassia, though they have been largely influenced by conventional computer-type structures that are not carefully based in mathematical theory and are not particularized to application structural types.

9.5.2 Cycle Resolution Capability. Very large cycles pose problems of interpretation. The ISM theory made provisions for this in terms of weights on edges, geodetic cycles, and threshold digraphs. After an early application of this theory (1976) by Zamerowski and colleagues[3] at the University of Dayton, most other practitioners ignored the problem of interpreting large cycles. Nevertheless it is straightforward to write and apply software for this purpose, using algorithms developed in the 1970's.

9.5.3 Quaternary Response Capability. In replying to a generic question in the querying portion of the ISM process, participants are almost always limited to responding "yes" or "no". However it was demonstrated in the mid 1970's that after a brief initial period during which questions were answered in that binary way, participants could learn how to respond with one of four answers: a) V, which meant that the question as shown on the screen could be answered "yes" (in the downward sense) and "no" in the reverse sense, b) A, which meant the the question as shown on the screen can be answered "no" (in the downward sense) and "yes" in the reverse sense (the upward sense), c) X, which meant that the question could be answered "yes" in both directions (upward and downward), and d) 0, which meant that the question could be answered "no" in both directions. Software with the capability to switch from the binary response to the quaternary response offers the potential to speed up significantly the ISM session, without diminishing the quality of the discussion.

9.5.4 Printout Capabilities. Many of the perhaps 50 or 60 versions of ISM software that have been developed are weak in printout capabilities. It should be possible to print out readily all key aspects of the work done. Much of the software uses the word "print" to mean "display on the screen", as though a screen display can somehow substitute for hard copy. In the first version of ISM software written at the Battelle Columbus Laboratories in 1972-73, hard copy was produced on line; showing the sequence of questions presented, the answers given, time required to arrive at a vote, and the voting results. Regrettably, much subsequently-developed ISM software elided this useful hard copy capability.

9.5.5 Re-Use Capability. It should be easily possible to re-use both sets of elements and previously-used generic questions. A library of generic questions built into the computer would be very beneficial for both instructional and application purposes. Much of the existing software makes it very difficult or almost impossible to enjoy the re-use capability.

9.5.6 Session Data Capability. In the interests of good housekeeping, it should be easy to enter in a pre-established format the data concerning all aspects of an IM session, the data to be printed out later in a format suitable for inclusion in a session report.

9.6 ISM SOFTWARE EVALUATION CRITERIA.

In order to make good decisions about how to upgrade existing ISM software or about how to choose from different versions of ISM software, a set of ISM Software Evaluation Criteria has been developed, and is presented in the following table. For illustrative purposes, the GMU ISM PC software is evaluated against these criteria.

The criteria fall into ten types, e.g., Input Criteria, Output Criteria, Inference Criteria, etc. A letter grade is assigned to the software for each particular type. The grades assignable are A, B, C, D, and F, with A being highest and F being lowest.

Within each of the criteria there are attributes, and the software is scored on each attribute. The score ranges from 10 (highest) to 0 (lowest) for that attribute. Not all attributes are equally significant, therefore the letter grade assigned to the type of criterion cannot be directly tied to the total attribute score for the type. (While a weighting system on attributes can be devised, it has not been deemed worthwhile to date.)

Acceptable software will receive a passing grade on all of the types. In other words, if software "flunks" on one type it becomes unacceptable.

It is not necessarily wise to use total scores in comparing two versions of the software. The judgment is more subtle than that. The value in the scores is in comparing the details of different versions, and making judgments about what is important.

TABLE 9.2
ISM SOFTWARE EVALUATION STANDARDS

CRITERIA	*GRADE OR SCORE FOR GMU PC ISM SOFTWARE*
1. Input Criteria	**C**

Ease of Loading ISM Software	**8**
Ease of Entering Elements	**5**
Ease of Entering Generic Questions	**8**
Ease of Entering Element Qualifications	**0**
Ease of Amending Elements	**7**
Ease of Amending Relationships	**7**
Ease of Amending a Previous Vote	**4**
Effective Use of Prior Information Following Amendments.	**7**

2. Output Criteria	**D**

Printout, individual elements	**0**
Printout, voting sequence results and timing	**0**
Printout, structures/structural data	**5**
Printout, fields	**0**
Printout, element list	**0**
Printout, generic question	**0**
Printout, element qualifications	**0**
Structural printout minimizes line crossings	**0**
Structural printout avoids diagonal lines	**0**
Structural printout avoids line/box intersections	**0**

3. *Inference Criteria* .... B

Optional structuring modes available	9
Selecting next question to ask	8
Minimizing the number of questions	9
Inference algorithm is correct	10

4. *Scale Criteria* .... B

Maintaining speed as number of elements grows	9
Maintaining usability of printouts as number of elements grows	7
Printing adequate documentation for checking as number of elements grows	7

5. *Operator Convenience Criteria* .... D

Readable screen displays	8
Unwanted queries can be switched off by operator	0
No operator penalty if operator wants to correct operator mistakes.	4
No unusable screen-operator interaction	7
Maximum use of helpful operator cues	2
Minimum demand on operator memory	3

6. *Literature for Learning* .... B

User Guide is free of enigmas	7
Step-by-step examples are included	10
Reference sources are provided when absolutely necessary	7
Software bugs are identified and operator is warned	9

7.   ***Query Scheme Doesn't Waste Group Time***   ....   ***C***

Alternative software modes make best use of inference	**8**
A given software mode makes best use of inference potential	**8**
Dual query scheme begins with binary responses and later can be switched to quaternary responses	**0**

8. *Cycle Resolution Capability*   ....   ***D***

Software permits cycle weighting for threshold structuring	**0**
Software permits identification of geodetic cycles	**0**
Software prints out interpretive material for cycle resolution	**0**

9.   ***Re-Use Convenience***   ....   ***D***

Old element set available for re-use	**0**
Old element set readily modifiable for re-use	**0**
Old problematique readily re-used in problem - option (resolution structure) joint diagram	**7**

10. *Performance Measures Included*   ....   ***D***

Time of session printed out	**0**
Number of queries printed out	**0**
Amount of inference printed out	**0**
Inference efficiency printed out	**0**
Details of voting printed out	**0**
Number of cycles printed out	**0**
Size of cycles printed out	**0**
Diversity printed out	**0**
Structural complexity printed out	**0**
Number of participants printed out	**0**
Objectives of session printed out	**0**
Comparison of results with objectives printed out	**0**

People information printed out	0
Equipment identification printed out	0
Working facility ID printed out	0

NOTES:

1. J. N. Warfield, "Crossing Theory and Hierarchy Mapping", <u>IEEE Transactions on Systems, Man, and Cybernetics</u> SMC-7(7), July, 1977, 505-523.

2. K. Sugiyama, S. Tagawa, and M. Toda, "Effective Representations of Hierarchical Structures", Fujitsu International Institute for Advanced Study of Social Information Science, Research Report Number 8, September, 1979.

3. E. Zamierowski, D. Hornbach, and R. Fitz, "Ecological Components of Climax Agriculture: An Example of Structuring Complex Feedback Systems", <u>Proceedings of the International Conference on Cybernetics and Society</u>, New York: Institute of Electrical and Electronics Engineers, 1976, 667-673.

STUDY QUESTIONS
CHAPTER 9. IM SOFTWARE

1. What is the principal process for which IM software has been written?

2. When and where was ISM developed?

3. Fundamentally, what is the ISM process?

4. To what does "the arithmetic of ISM" refer?

5. From data on past sessions, what is the average duration of an ISM session? What is the maximum? the minimum?

6. From data on past sessions, what is the average number of ideas structured in an ISM session? What is the maximum? the minimum?

7. How much time might a session take to structure the average number of elements if no machine inference were available?

8. What three versions of the GMU ISM PC Software exist?

9. Where was the Generic Problem Solving System developed?

10. Where was the Tlatocan software developed?

11. What are the principal features of the Tlatocan software?

12. What six additional features would improve most ISM software?

CHAPTER 10

IM PLANNING PHASE (PHASE 1)

The IM Planning Phase begins as soon as the need for an IM intervention is detected. The purpose of the Planning Phase is to make all the necessary arrangements for the conduct of the Workshop. Some who conduct IM Workshops do not really appreciate the importance of the Planning Phase in terms of its potential benefits to the Workshop Phase.

If the Planning Phase is defective, or if the conduct of the Workshop is defective, the time of the Participants will not be well-used. This should not come as a surprise. Everyone who goes to conventional meetings knows that most of the time spent in meetings is unproductive. Moreover, much of the time they spend in meetings can be conceptually very abusive.

Here is the abuse scenario. Someone calls a meeting and requires that you attend. A typical meeting might involve 10 to 20 people and last for 1 to 2 hours. Long division tells us that the average person attending will have between 3 and 12 minutes to say something. The rest of the time that average attendee will ostensibly be listening to others. Much of what the others have to say may be irrelevant to the interests of the listener, or irrelevant to the purpose of the meeting. If the person attending the meeting is highly motivated, all of the time spent in this unproductive mode will represent an abuse of that individual, using a part of that person's life in a way that the person would avoid if a choice were available.

On the other hand, if the person lacks motivation, and is just putting in time, that person will possibly be gratified to keep drawing a pay check while "hanging out". Any organization that caters to unmotivated people and abuses the others is headed for trouble. And any methodology or system of management that performs in this way deserves to be removed from the surface of the earth.

A critical purpose of planning is to make possible the productive use of the time of every participant in an Interactive Management Workshop. In striving to achieve this, the IM Facilitator controls the process completely; and is responsible for the efficient, effective use of the time of every participant. If, however, the planning is defective, participants themselves may frustrate the IM Facilitator's efforts by bringing up and pressing subject matter that should have been dealt with thoroughly by the IM Broker long before the meeting began.

Therefore, the conduct and follow up of Workshops is governed by an IM Plan. While a variety of individuals may be consulted about the plan during its preparation, the preparation of the plan is the joint responsibility of the IM Workshop Planner and the IM Broker. The former represents the organization that will be conducting the workshop. The latter represents the client organization.

127

The IM Plan consists of defined components. The names of these components are:

• Context
• Major Outcome Sought
• Products Sought
• Process Sequencing
• Triggering Questions
• Generic Questions
• Workshop Site
• Participants
• IM Staff
• Other Roles
• Budget and Schedule

This Chapter elaborates on each of these topics.

Experience with many applications shows that even individuals who are quite effective in conducting IM workshops may not accept the idea of planning. Planning is a subject of considerable confusion and controversy. The importance of how planning is viewed can be seen on an international scale. The idea of a "planned economy" was in vogue in Eastern Europe for decades, and has had intermittent support in many countries around the world. The practice of placing in direct opposition the ideas of "planned economy" and "free market" is very common. Intellectual wars between advocates of planned economies and free markets produce world-wide fallout, as people who have no taste for such intellectual wars become prisoners of one or the other of these overriding concepts.

The idea that individuals can be prisoners in either free market systems or planned economies is one that advocates of both systems might say is false. One must presume that they would argue this way because advocates of both systems have been so indifferent to the impact of these systems on individual lives.

Practitioners of IM can learn much from observing the events that transpire in relation to the international disagreements about the relative merits of planned economies and free markets. The lessons that can be learned can be translated into practice on a smaller scale in IM applications. What are some of these lessons?

■ *The planned economy-free market argument is a false dichotomy serving only the purposes of the fanatics on both sides of it, and damaging almost everyone else who encounters the fruits of this perpetual intellectual snakepit.* Why is it a false dichotomy? The answer is simple. No free economy can function without infrastructure, and no infrastructure can be created without planning. In the United States of America, the plans for the infrastructure are strongly embedded in the documents created by the Founding Fathers, and just as the infrastructure (whether explicit or implied) embedded in these documents creates opportunities, it also denies opportunities, as various Amendments amply illustrate. When infrastructure proves to be ineffective, plans are needed to decide how to improve that infrastructure. Laws themselves are plans. To the extent that they are poorly drawn, they are bad plans. Policy reflects planning, and to the extent that the planning is defective, policy is defective and people suffer. Planning is essential to good government everywhere. ***It is not planning that is bad; it is bad planning that is bad.***

■ ***The idea of a planned economy on a large scale is so absurd that it is amazing to realize how many contemptible acts have been justified by this rubric.*** Why is planned economy on a large scale absurd? The answer is that economic action on a large scale is sensitive to huge amounts of information and data--information and data that cannot possibly be collected in sufficient quantity, with sufficient accuracy, and made available with sufficient speed to allow its use in a planned way. If this were not enough, it is quite clear that the public is not comprised primarily of economists, but rather involves actors of all kinds and persuasions, and none of these actors will learn the economics in sufficient detail to make them viable players in any overall plan. So what we see in planned economies are attempts by the state to control these innocent actors to try to force them to behave in a pre- ordained way, or to punish them for behavior that does not come into congruence with plans.

Planning can be studied through research, and systems of planning can be conceived that serve a purpose that cannot be served in any other way: to educate the persons who will be involved in implementing a plan so that they are in the best position to make good decisions as they proceed. In this spirit, the concept of generic planning has been set forth[1] to clarify the requirements. Five factors are required in order to get successful change to take place in complex situations. These are:

• Research results that clarify the nature of generic planning
• Visible examples of successful application of generic planning
• Educated practitioners of generic planning
• Familiarization with research results on generic planning by people who have the power to effect change in how planning is carried out
• Willingness of those with power to take the necessary steps to bring about the change

As the article identified in Note 1 shows, the first two of these are readily available. There is a small but growing number of educated practitioners. It is the unpredictability of how the last two factors can or will evolve that leaves issues related to high-quality planning constantly in doubt. In any case, those who wish to practice IM but who do not take the Planning Phase seriously are indirectly contributing a small amount of comfort to those who fail to engage with high-quality planning, on whatever scale may be involved.

10.1 CONTEXT.

The word "context" refers to two quite different aspects of IM work. The first, Context 1, is the *situational context* in which the Client organization finds itself. The second, Context 2, refers to the *working environment* in which the Workshop will be carried out.

The scope of Context 1 must be well-understood before the Workshop begins, and it is the responsibility of the IM Broker to make this context clear to the IM Workshop Planner who, in turn, makes it clear to the IM Facilitator and other IM staff.

Context 2 demonstrates an understanding of the leverage that can be brought to bear in getting results from group work by providing a working space for the group that eliminates environmental factors conducive to poor work and provides environmental factors conducive to good group work. The IM Workshop Planner is responsible for making this context clear to the IM Broker. Context 2 was the topic of Chapter 8.

Context 1 is first approached in the formulation of a "context statement" in Phase 1. This context statement is formulated by the IM Broker, in collaboration with the IM Workshop Planner. It is a statement that typically involves just one or two sentences. The intention is that this context statement will:

• provide focus to the Workshop participants
• establish the outer limits of Workshop thinking
• reflect consideration of the extent to which the scope of activity must go in order to incorporate critical aspects of the situation and its possible resolution

All subsequent Workshop activity is governed by the context statement, so any flaws in this statement may have far-reaching impacts on the products of the Workshop. If the intended outcome of the first Workshop is a definition of the situation, the context statement will be elaborated in much detail in terms of the patterns developed during the Workshop and their subsequent interpretation. Products are very sensitive to the context statement. The elaboration that springs from it furnishes a significant test of its suitability, and offers the opportunity for amendment if the elaboration demonstrates shortcomings in it.

Moreover, as part of the Phase 1 interaction between IM Broker and potential participants, the Broker will have the opportunity to review this statement with each participant. This will (a) give the Broker feedback that might be useful in improving the statement and (b) educate the potential participants to the context so that they will have an opportunity to prepare for the Workshop and will not encounter any surprise with the scope of the Workshop activity.

10.2 MAJOR OUTCOME SOUGHT.

The Workshop Plan should make clear which of the major outcomes described in Chapter 2 is sought from the Workshop.

Definition Outcome. Normally the first IM Workshop on a subject will seek a Definition outcome. Some potential clients may be disturbed with the thought that a solution will not be found in the first Workshop. For these potential clients, one may note the following:
The use of IM is normally preceded by a significant time period in which other approaches to a solution or resolution have failed. This establishes several points. First, if the Client were an expert on the subject of processes for resolving complex issues, the Client would not have got to the point of trying IM because the Client would already have resolved the complex issue. Second, reams of experience teach us that if we do not understand the problem we are not very likely to solve it. Third, experience shows that normally almost all of the time and resources previously spent was expended in trying to find a solution, and very little of that time was spent in trying to define the issue.

One of the scientific findings from experimental work involving IM is encapsulated in a statement called the Law of Inherent Conflict. This Law reflects data that show that given any complex issue and any group of informed participants, the participants initially have quite different views on the relative importance of the factors involved in a complex issue. As a rule, there are as many different images of the issue as there are participants. For this reason, attempts to resolve issues are often struck down because people cannot cooperate to resolve an issue if they do not share a view of what the issue is.

Alternative Designs Outcome. If the outcome sought is a set of alternative designs, and if a prior Workshop has provided a definition of the issue within a fleshed-out context, the creation of alternative designs can be keyed directly (both scientifically and in group work details) to the patterns developed as part of the definitional work.

One of the scientific findings in the study of system design is called the Law of Requisite Variety. This Law states that in order to resolve a complex issue, one must match up the dimensions of the solution or resolution with the dimensions of the situation in which the issue is embedded. An excellent illustration of this Law was provided by Peter Senge in his book The Fifth Discipline, in which he discussed the famous DC-3 airplane.

"The Wright Brothers proved that powered flight was possible, but the McDonnell Douglas DC-3, introduced in 1935, ushered in the era of commercial air travel. The DC-3 was the first plane that supported itself economically as well as aerodynamically. During those intervening thirty years (a typical time period for incubating basic innovations), myriad experiments with commercial flight had failed. Like early experiments with learning organizations, the early planes were not reliable and cost effective on an appropriate scale. The DC-3, for the first time, brought together five critical component technologies that formed a successful ensemble. They were: the variable-pitch propeller, retractable landing gear, a type of light-weight molded body construction called 'monocque', radial air-cooled engine, and wing flaps. To succeed, the DC-3 needed all five; four were not enough. One year earlier, the Boeing 247 was introduced with all of them except wing flaps. Lacking wing flaps, Boeing's engineers found that the plane was unstable on take-off and landing and had to downsize the engine."[2]

Another illustration of the point was sharply described by Dr. John Kemeny [3], Chairman of the Three-Mile Island Commission, who pointed out that the control room of the reactor that failed was designed and the staff were trained to deal only with one-at-a-time problems. No training of the high-school graduates who were working in the control room recognized even the possibility that two things could go wrong at a time. (Three went wrong at a time in the accident at Three-Mile Island.)

In assessing possible remedial action to deal with complex issues of the type that seem to be increasing in incidence as time passes, Dr. Kemeny wrote about the Three-Mile Island nuclear power plant accident and the lessons to be learned from it:

"My conclusion is this: I've heard many times that although democracy is an imperfect system, we somehow always muddle through. The message I want to give you, after long and hard reflection, is that I'm very much afraid it is no longer possible to muddle through. The issues we deal with do not lend themselves to that kind of treatment. Therefore, I conclude that our democracy must grow up. What's principally lacking on the federal scene...is the existence of respected, nonpartisan, interdisciplinary teams..."

Still another illustration of the importance of the Law of Requisite Variety in complex situations was developed by Steve Landenberger when he and his colleagues solved a problem of production of a pump by attacking collectively five factors believed to be critical in pump rejection on the production line[4].

The central feature of this discussion is the need to think in terms of "sets", rather than in terms of "individuals". If there are e.g., 20 factors in a situation that can change and bring about problems in some context, a design that accounts for only 10 factors will leave to chance the behavior of the other 10 factors. On the other hand, if a design accounts for all 20 factors, it satisfies the Law of Requisite Variety and favorable results should be expected.

The IM products and processes (Chapters 6 and 7, respectively) are designed to facilitate the direct application of the Law of Requisite Variety, which means that the situational dimensions developed in the Definition Workshop can be matched to the design dimensions developed in the Design Alternatives Workshop.

Choice of a Design. If, previously, definitions and design alternatives have been developed, then the major outcome sought will be a choice of a design. As with the other two types of outcomes, the processes and products produced will be determined by the major outcome sought. If the major outcome sought is choice of a design, the Workshop Plan will provide for participant familiarity with outcomes of earlier Workshops. Generally speaking, there may be some variation of participants as the work proceeds from definition to design alternatives to choice of a design. This should be anticipated in the Workshop Plan. It will be desirable as a rule to have some overlap of participants from one Workshop to the next, and this should also be factored into the Workshop Plan.

It is the responsibility of the IM Workshop Planner to make very clear to the IM Broker the three alternatives described above. It is the joint responsibility of this pair of individuals to make sure that the plan reflects the right choice; and that the Client understands the choice, the rationale behind it, and the implications of the choice in terms of followup activity.

10.3 PRODUCTS SOUGHT.

What specific products should be sought from the Workshop? As a rule the products sought will be chosen from those "Application Structural Types" described in Chapter 6. Since these will normally be unfamilar to the IM Broker, the IM Workshop Planner will need to familiarize the IM Broker with them. Also the products sought will vary depending on which major outcome is sought. Past experience with numerous Workshops and a careful analysis of the situation under consideration will be the major guides to what is selected.

Definition. Definition Projects may be based on Success Level 1, 2, or 3. The products sought will depend on the anticipated Success Level, as indicated in Chapter 13. They will normally consist of a subset of the following list:

• Field Representation of the Situation (situational attributes, grouped into dimensions)
• Problem Field (set of component problems organized into categories)
• Problematique (component problems, arranged to show how some aggravate others)
• Intent Structure (set of objectives, structured to show antecedent support)
• Priority Structure (in what sequence should the component problems be attacked?)

Design Alternatives. If the major outcome sought is the creation of several design alternatives, (i.e., Success Level 4) the products may consist of the following:

• Options Field (corrective options, grouped into dimensions)
• Enhancement Structure (component options, arranged to show how adoption of some would enhance the likelihood of implementing others)
• Several Options Profiles (Triply-Structured Quads) (choices of one or more options in each dimension)
• Resolution Structure (showing how various options help resolve various problems)
• Several DELTA Charts (showing roles and sequences in implementation plans)

In addition, it is possible that one or more tapestries might be produced, to elaborate in depth on the nature of various options.

Choice of a Design. If choice of a design is the major outcome sought (i.e., Success Level 5), the products of this work may consist of the following:

- Criterion Priority Structures (what is the relative importance of criteria in comparing two alternative designs?)
- Comparison Bar Charts of Competing Designs
- Judgmental data provided by participants
- DELTA Chart for design implementation (what sequence of steps is needed to implement the design, what actors will be involved in each step, what intermediate decisions are needed in implementing?)

10.4 PROCESS SEQUENCING.

The sequencing of processes will depend on which major outcome is sought. For each of the various types of product to be developed, there is at least one corresponding process that facilitates the production of that product.

It is the responsibility of the IM Workshop Planner to explain to the Broker the nature of the process sequencing, and to illustrate it with past examples, so the Broker understands this information well enough to relay it to potential participants.

The connections between products sought and processes used are given in Section 7.8, following the discussion of products in Chapter 6 and processes in Chapter 7.

10.5 TRIGGERING QUESTIONS.

At any given time in an IM Workshop, the group of participants has before them a question that focuses their work. The questions are normally designed during Phase 1, through collaboration between IM Broker and IM Workshop Planner, and the questions appear in the Workshop Plan. One important type of question is called a "triggering question".

Triggering questions are stimuli to the generation of ideas. Successful triggering questions typically satisfy these criteria:

- Only a single focus is given to trigger the response; (do not ask for more than one kind of concept in a given work situation. If several different kinds of response are required, a separate question and a separate process should be used for each.)
- It is feasible both to understand and respond to the question; the question does not ask for something that is ambiguous, nor does it ask for something that the participants cannot reasonably be expected to provide.
- The words used to provide the focus for the request are neither so general that the responses are not likely to be to the point, nor so specific that the answers are likely to be overly restricted in utility. The focus should be neither too general nor too specific.
- The triggering question is *responsive to and correlated with the context in which the issue is embedded.*
- The *contextual implication* of the triggering question should be compatible with the background of the participants and the scope of the workshop[5].

10.6 GENERIC QUESTIONS.

During the ISM process, a generic question never appears unaltered before the participant group because the generic form is not content-specific. Nevertheless the group will see many questions that have the identical form to the generic question. For example, a generic question might be:

> *In context C,*
> *does*
> *problem A*
> *aggravate*
> *problem B*
> *?*

An example of what might appear before the group, based on this generic question, is the following:

> *In the context of a recession,*
> *does*
> *a high Federal Reserve discount rate*
> *aggravate*
> *difficulty in borrowing money*
> *?*

The Workshop Plan will contain the chosen generic questions. They will reflect the major outcome desired, and the products that are sought to achieve this outcome. It is the responsibility of the IM Workshop Planner to make clear to the IM Broker the purpose of the generic questions. The formulation of them is their joint responsibility.

10.7 WORKSHOP SITE.

Experience shows that the quality and utility of IM products, as well as the participant and IM staff satisfaction in the outcome, depend strongly on the working environment. The site should be chosen because it contains a specific facility tailored to the requirements for product development and display, participant and staff comfort, and technological support.

If a dedicated working environment is available, as described in Chapter 8, the attention given to the Workshop Site in the Workshop Plan can be minimal. If, however, there is no dedicated environment, part of the effort in Phase 1 must be to locate a suitable site, and to make local arrangements for the necessary capabilities.

It is the responsibility of the IM Workshop Planner to make clear to the IM Broker the importance of the Workshop Site, and the relevance of the characteristics sought in this site, so that the IM Broker can convey this explanation to the client, sponsor, and participants.

10.8 PARTICIPANTS.

The selection of potential participants, discussions with these potential participants, and the final acceptance/choice of participants should be reflected in the Workshop Plan. Participants should be chosen so that their collective knowledge and experience is comprehensive in relation to the context statement.

The choice of participants is the responsibility of the IM Broker, but the IM Workshop Planner should understand the choice and offer advice when appropriate.

10.9 IM STAFF.

IM staff are required, in order to fill the IM roles discussed in Chapter 5. The Workshop Plan should indicate which actors will fill which roles, and also have a contingency backup plan in the event of incapacity of individuals to serve.

Staff assignments are the responsibility of the IM Workshop Planner, but the IM Broker should be aware of the staff assignments.

10.10 OTHER ROLES.

Particular situations may have special requirements. For example, it is often desirable to have observers watching and listening to the group activity in a Workshop.

Observers may become participants in subsequent Workshops, or they may be involved in implementation of results. Sometimes they are new members of the organization who are learning from their observation of the Workshop. Sometimes they are IM trainees.

The Workshop Plan should show a consideration of the possibility of other roles, and make such provision for them as is necessary. For example, observers should be provided with appropriate space to watch, hear, and take notes; and not placed in positions where they cannot see or hear well what is going on.

10.11 BUDGET AND SCHEDULE.

The Workshop Plan should include a budget and schedule for the Workshop, and may include tentative projections for followup Workshops. This part of the Workshop Plan, like all other parts, is jointly worked out between IM Broker and IM Workshop Planner, with the IM Broker communicating with the Client and Sponsor as appropriate.

When planning for a Workshop it must be taken into consideration that the duration of an IM Workshop may vary from two to five days (there may be cases in which this duration could be enlarged), and thus time could become an important constraint in evaluating and designing the outcomes to be sought, the products to be developed, and the process sequencing.

In addition to the ideas presented in this Chapter concerning IM Workshops, Appendix 6 offers a check list of questions that can be considered systematically for the purpose of reviewing the status of a draft plan, or for the purpose of preparing to produce a plan.

Appendix 6 also offers an outline of a workshop plan that can be taken as a starting point for developing and publishing such a plan for the edification of potential participants, workshop staff, and others who have an interest in the workshop activity.

NOTES

1. John N. Warfield, "Generic Planning: Research Results and Applications", <u>Knowledge in Society: The International Journal of Knowledge Transfer</u>, Winter 3(4), 1990-91, 91-113.

2. See: Peter M. Senge, <u>The Fifth Discipline</u>, New York: Doubleday, 1990, page 6.

3. John Kemeny, "Chairing a Presidential Commission: Reflections", transcript of a talk given at the Massachusetts Institute of Technology, April 11, 1980.

4. See: John N. Warfield, <u>A Science of Generic Design,</u> Second Edition, Ames, Iowa: Iowa State University Press, 1994, pages 391-397, for a description of Landenberger's project.

5. The concept of "contextual implication" has been dealt with in a comprehensive way by K. L. Ketner in his report titled "An Emendation of R. G. Collingwood's Doctrine of Absolute Presuppositions", Graduate Studies Number 4, Lubbock, TX: Texas Tech Press, 1973; and in detail by Isabel Hungerland in her paper "Contextual Implication", <u>Inquiry 3,</u> 1960, 211-258. It has to do with what is presumed, for example, when a question is posed, about the knowledge that the recipient of the question might need to possess in order to answer the question; or, more generally, what is implied by a question that may or may not be valid. The concept is especially valuable in considering how to design and evaluate triggering questions.

STUDY QUESTIONS
CHAPTER 10. IM PLANNING PHASE (PHASE 1)

1. When does the IM Planning Phase begin?

2. What is the apparent purpose of the IM Planning Phase?

3. What is likely to happen if no IM Plan is produced?

4. What are the components of the IM Plan?

5. What five factors are required to get successful change to take place in complex situations?

6. What two contexts are explored in developing an IM Plan?

7. What are the three major types of outcome from which to choose in planning an IM Workshop?

8. What Law of Generic Design involves "thinking in sets"?

9. What products are sought from a Definition Workshop?

10. What products are sought from a Design Alternatives Workshop?

11. What product is sought from a Choice of a Design Workshop?

12. What criteria are satisfied by successful triggering questions?

13. What attributes does a generic question have that distinguish it from a triggering question?

14. Why may observers be included as part of an IM Plan?

15. How long might an ISM Workshop last?

CHAPTER 11

IM WORKSHOP PHASE (PHASE 2)

The IM Workshop Phase draws heavily on the plan that is developed in the Planning Phase, as explained in Chapter 10. In this chapter a discussion of the generic goals of an IM Workshop is offered, in which it is argued that certain goals will always be appropriate to any IM Workshop, which has some implications for effective education and training about the conduct of such workshops. The essential components of an IM Workshop are then discussed. This discussion lays a basis for an approach to evaluation of a workshop, and to an avoidance strategy aimed at preventing major mistakes in the conduct and reporting of a workshop.

11.1 WORKSHOP GENERIC GOALS.

What are the "generic goals" of the IM Workshop? That is, what goals would one hope to achieve from *every* IM Workshop; without regard to the situation being discussed, without regard to who the participants may be, without regard to the specific identity of external and internal personnel?

These are the goals to be sought universally from IM Workshops:

- *Maximize* the opportunity for high-quality contributions by every participant.
- *Maximize* treating the participants with much good will, thoughtfulness, and respect.
- *Maximize* the accessibility and effectiveness of all workshop communications, and especially of graphic communications.
- *Maximize* taking advantage of the documentation capabilities of the computer, developing hard copy to back up all staff activity involving information offered by the participants.
- *Maximize* the likelihood of high-quality workshop performance by having contingency plans for use in the unexpected unavailability of key workshop staff, equipment, or facilities; providing backup capability to deal with such contingencies
- *Avoid* fatigue resolution of any and all topics of discussion by assuring participant comfort and preventing overly long, continuous work activities.
- *Avoid* introducing untested ideas into high-stakes workshop activity; test out promising new process ideas in training activities or other in-house activities, in situations where participants want to improve the IM processes before using them in high-stakes activity.
- *Avoid* sacrificing the welfare and productivity of the group in order to cater to any uncooperative participant.
- *Avoid* abusing a cooperative participant in order to cater to the group.
- *Avoid* sacrificing quality in order to meet an arbitrary time deadline.

11.2 WORKSHOP COMPONENTS.

A typical IM Workshop will have certain components, which will be discussed separately. The primary focus of the discussion is the set of included events and the activity of the IM Facilitator in guiding the production of those events.

11.2.1 Workshop Preliminaries. At the outset of the IM Workshop, the IM Facilitator will have available an already-prepared set of *flip chart displays* for use in briefing the participants on the anticipated activities, their purpose, their sequence, the expected products, and the significance of those products in terms of the situation. For example, one flip chart will contain the context statement for the Workshop. Another will contain a brief outline of the Nominal Group Technique. Another will contain a brief outline of the Interpretive Structural Modeling Process. Another will contain a few goal statements for the Workshop. Still another will contain the anticipated schedule. There will be one flip chart per trigger question, and one flip chart per generic question.

At some point in the Workshop, each of these flip charts will be briefly explained to the participants, and responses will be made to any questions raised. However not all flip charts will be shown in the introductory part of the Workshop. Those that deal with the methodologies and the questions will be introduced at a time just before they are used.

The Facilitator will discuss the significance of the triad: *context, content, and process.* The *context statement*, the history of its preparation, and its meaning will be discussed until it is clear that there is good understanding of it. The Facilitator will explain that the *total control of the process* rests with the Facilitator; but that if it appears that there is a need to modify the planned process sequence, discussions will be held with the IM Broker, and the Facilitator and Broker will make the decision, after informal consultation with participants. The Facilitator will explain that *the participants control the content.* They are there for their content knowledge. It is not the role of the Facilitator to contribute any content knowledge.

The Facilitator's introduction to the workshop, using flip charts, will be followed by a *round-the-table activity* in which each participant is invited to give some personal identification and career information to other participants and workshop staff.

At the end of this preliminary work, the Facilitator will announce a break, and state the time at which work on the situation or issue will commence.

11.2.2 Idea Generation. Control of the workshop process generally is maintained by the constant presence of a question before the group, to which the Facilitator assures that the group will be trying to respond.

At the beginning of the work, there is no content available to work with, therefore the initial activity involves the generation of content developed by the participants in response to a triggering question. The ideas generated in response to the triggering question will be written on flip charts by the IM Facilitator for posting on the wall. (In the introductory part of the workshop the participants were invited by the Facilitator to comment on that question to make sure that they understood it. If necessary, it was amended at that time with the full support of the IM Broker, under leadership of the IM Facilitator).

The idea generation will produce content information to be used later in the clarification process.

11.2.3 Clarifying, Editing, and Recording. After all of the initial ideas are posted, they will be individually clarified. The Scribe will listen as the participants discuss the clarification of the numbered ideas, and the Scribe will type into a word processor the essence of the clarification discussion, for later use in helping participants and staff recall the intended meaning of each idea. While the ideas are being clarified, they will be edited as necessary, under leadership of the Facilitator. The Facilitator is not responsible for formulating revisions; however the Facilitator is responsible for insisting that the final version of each idea meet the requirements of good grammar, and that each idea contain a single primary thought. Ideas that contain two primary thoughts always cause difficulty in later work. The participants cannot be expected to anticipate the difficulty caused by compound statements of ideas; therefore the Facilitator must take the responsibility for stimulating the production of high-quality statements. The Scribe will be responsible for documenting both the edited form and the initial form of each generated statement.

During the idea generation and the clarification activities, the Facilitator must prevent the group from entering into an evaluative tone as the ideas are expressed and clarified. The ideas are not to be judged at that stage. It is important to stress the fact that the group has entered an open dialogue, and therefore their primary attitude should be focused on learning and understanding each other's ideas.

Both activities, idea generation and clarification, are based on the general prescriptions for the Nominal Group Technique Process described earlier in this Handbook.

11.2.4 Idea Structuring. Once a set of clearly enunciated elements is available, it is normally true that these ideas will be structured into patterns. Time is always at a premium in workshop activity, so a question that always arises has to do with how many of the ideas generated will be structured.

It is a basic concept in creativity theory that, when human beings are asked to be creative they should not be asked, during the period set aside for creative activity, to be constantly testing their thinking against a heavy set of constraints. The principle is to get the ideas out freely and save evaluation for a later time. One corollary of this principle is that some of the ideas produced will have no real merit, for any of a number of reasons. However the merit of the ideas is a content issue, not a process issue. The IM Facilitator needs a way to permit proceeding with structural work without the full set of elements. The strategy that is pursued to permit this is to use that part of the NGT process that calls for individual voting on what each individual sees as the top 5 ideas, with each individual ranking the top 5 according to relative importance. The IM Facilitator can collect the voting cards and organize the information they reveal. The results of the voting can be used to place the ideas into two subsets: (a) those that received at least one participant's vote as belonging in the top 5 and (b) those that no one voted to place in the top 5. The Facilitator can also order the members of subset (a) according to the numerical data accompanying the voting.

This strategy allows the Facilitator to sequence the ideas to be structured according to the judgments made by the participants, without using any participant time to discuss the relative merits or demerits of individual ideas.

In principle, all of the ideas can be structured, if it develops that there is enough time to do so. But if there is not sufficient time, at least the participants can know that those ideas they believed at the time of voting to be the most important have been included in the structuring activity. If it should develop that there is not enough time to structure enough elements, and if the participants feel that more should be structured, there is a basis established for a followup workshop at a later date, where the structuring can be completed.

One must realize that all workshops are generally confined to a specific period of time (e.g., 3 days). However there is no law that says followups cannot be scheduled if a good basis for doing so is found.

The idea structuring is done with computer assistance, using the Interpretive Structural Modeling software. During this process the computer operator will fulfill his main responsibilities and, depending on the software used, the computer operator must also keep track manually of the answers that the group is giving, in order to make it easier later on if there's a need to amend or change any of the decisions taken by the group.

11.2.5 Displays. The results of all idea generation, clarification, editing, and structuring are to be visible at all times to all participants. This requires that the walls be large enough to contain the information, and that the components of the displays be readable at a distance measured from any participant location to the wall. (The alternative of making all displays available on computer screens is not feasible, because the screens are too small.)

The information required to display the results on the walls is directly obtained from the

144

software, and the Display Arranger must pay particular attention to present the graphics as clearly as possible, trying to minimize the crossing arrows and keeping the standards of a good representation.

11.2.6 Interpretation. *It has been learned from experience that many participants are not generally able to interpret the patterns that they produce with computer assistance, in the absence of assistance from persons with long experience in interpreting such structures.* It is, however, necessary that participants become familiar with what the patterns convey, for two reasons: (a) to assure the quality of the display by either verifying its accuracy as presented initially or by amending it appropriately, and (b) to enable them to convey an interpretation of the structure to others who may also lack the capacity to interpret the structures.

Many professionals who produce graphical representations are insensitive to the problem of reading and interpreting those representations. The simple idea involved here is that when people have had training and experience with some concept, it becomes a part of their everyday life and they forget that it was hard for them initially.

After structures have been produced, some time must elapse to permit the Pattern Interpreter to develop a presentation for the participants to help them interpret and re-communicate to others. The possibility exists of using this time for a social break in which participants can relax and talk about the experiences they have had in the Workshop.

11.2.7 Pattern Amendment. Any pattern that is produced through an IM Workshop will have behind it a substantial amount of thought and effort by the participants. This offers a good reason to assume that the pattern is likely to be valid, even if it appears to be strange at first sight. One must remember that if conventional patterns of information had been adequate, the major issue being confronted would probably have been resolved. Therefore it is a sign of success that the pattern may appear at first glance to be outside the normal realm of thinking.

One should not assume that the pattern is valid, simply because of the foregoing. The time required to think through and judge a pattern is relatively small compared to other times involved in dealing with a complex issue. But this time is possibly the most critical time involved in working with a complex issue. To ask the participants to deal with a structure near the end of a long, hard session, is bad strategy. They are often tired, lack experience in reading and interpreting structures (though one or more may claim to have had such experience and, in some instances, might try to take control of the process to direct the group toward their interpretation), and there may not be time available to rethink the complex issue in the light of the structural patterns. Pattern amendment should be viewed as a matter to be considered, but only at the right time and after the right preparation.

11.3 WORKSHOP EVALUATION.

Evaluation of an IM Workshop is based on an understanding of the Science of Generic Design, and especially the foundations and the laws of that science. However it is possible to state the factors involved in workshop evaluation in a way that enables evaluation to be carried out without a thorough understanding of the science and its laws. This does require that someone who is involved in the evaluation should be available to provide oversight and guidance to workshop evaluation, in order to make sure that evaluators do not make serious mistakes that could stem from their lack of understanding.

Workshop evaluation is discussed in Chapter 13, where evaluation forms are given. To understand how to use these forms, it is particularly critical to realize that no plan showing what should be done in a workshop can do a very thorough job of saying what should not be done. Accordingly, special emphasis is given in this Chapter 11 to an avoidance strategy. This strategy focuses on three topical areas where it is especially important *not* to do certain things. As a part of the evaluation planning, errors of commission (i.e., doing things that should not be done) are given negative weights in evaluation. The three topical areas that are relevant are: the IM Facilitator, the IM Broker, and the documentation of the IM Workshop. Each of these areas will be discussed in the next section where, in evaluation, assignment of negative weights based on failure to follow the avoidance strategy is explained.

11.4 AN AVOIDANCE STRATEGY.

In observing IM Facilitators, IM Brokers, and the activities that go on in preparing documentation of results of IM workshops, certain critical mistakes have been seen. To prevent recurrence of these mistakes, or to encourage the various actors to become sensitized to them, an avoidance strategy is set forth. This strategy is buttressed by a practice of penalizing people who might violate this strategy when workshop evaluations are carried out.

11.4.1 The IM Broker. As shown in Section 13.8, the IM Broker can be "awarded" up to -30 points based on the performance of the IM Broker during an IM workshop.

The following are the primary conditions that the IM Broker must avoid in connection with IM workshops:

• *Avoid any violation of the Facilitator support role* of the IM Broker during an IM Workshop. This means that the broker must be present throughout the Workshop, be aware of the progress being made along the lines of the Workshop Plan, and be available to consult privately with the IM Facilitator concerning any possible need to change the workshop process as a result of conditions that may arise during the workshop. It further means that the IM Broker must not unilaterally intervene in the workshop activity except to consult privately with the IM Facilitator. While the Broker may and should listen to any comments made by participants during break periods, the Broker must support the Facilitator, while serving as ombudsperson for participants.

• *Avoid any violation of the Participant role* during the IM Workshop. This means that although the Broker judges that his or her views would be superior to those being stated, the Broker must remain outside the participant role. By self-denial of access to the role of participant, the Broker is not giving up an opportunity to correct mistakes that might be made by participants. Note that participant mistakes will almost always be corrected by other participants. If they are not, there will be an opportunity to inject new information at the conclusion of the workshop, and if particularly critical points need to be reviewed, the Broker may arrange with the Facilitator to inject commentary after the participants have completed their workshop activity, either before or after the group disbands.

• *Avoid taking on the role of process expert.*

The IM Broker who violates any one of these three components of the avoidance strategy should expect to see a negative 10 points assigned to that role during the evaluation of the workshop, with negative 30 points assigned if all three are violated.

11.4.2 The IM Facilitator. The avoidance strategy concerning the role of the IM Facilitator involves these components:

• *Avoid all forms of role usurpation.* This means that the IM Facilitator must be responsible to maintain ongoing oversight of role integrity for all parties to the Workshop, including the IM Facilitator. A particular instance involves the integrity of the role of Pattern Interpreter. IM Facilitators should not request participants to interpret or consider amending their products until there has been an opportunity for the Pattern Interpreter to carry out the duties of that role and prepare a report for the participants in which their products are interpreted. Another form of role usurpation that must be prevented is the case when the facilitator gets involved in the content of the situation and thus acts in ways that are mainly related with the participants' role.

• *Avoid any loss of symmetry among the participants.* Symmetry refers to the idea that every participant, at all times, is in an identical relationship to the IM Facilitator and to the other participants, and never assumes a process-directive role. Some IM Facilitators violate this when they pose process questions to groups (which should never be done).

• *Avoid any unilateral departure from the Workshop Plan.* The Workshop Plan has been developed jointly for very good reasons. If a departure from the plan seems warranted, the

IM Facilitator should call a halt to the group activity and meet privately with the IM Broker to consider such a departure.

• *Avoid any condition where (a) the preliminaries are over and (b) the group is at the table (not on a break), but where there is no task in front of the group.* Normally this means that there will be a question before the group during all of its working time, and every such question will have been determined in the Workshop Plan or through amendment of that Plan during the conduct of the Workshop.

• *Avoid any compromise in which quality of product is debased in order to meet time pressure.* As one example, in conducting NGT sessions, the IM Facilitator should ensure adequate editing of elements before concluding the NGT session.

In evaluating the performance of the IM Facilitator, ten negative points should be assessed for each of these avoidance factors that is violated by the Facilitator.

11.4.3 Documentation. In evaluating the documentation produced, two major concerns are involved.

Content Material. The first relates to the content material developed by the participants and injected into the computer by staff. This material will often be amended during the course of the workshop, and several documents may be produced that reflect changes to the original material. The strong possibility exists that confusion will develop concerning which document was developed first, or which takes precedence over another. Also, because the readability and quality of the report will depend strongly on the way the linguistic elements are finally presented, quality control over these linguistic elements is important in terms of the final outcome of the work. The following should be avoided but, if allowed to persist, should be assigned the negative weights shown in parentheses as part of the evaluation of the documentation:

• Compound elements, i.e., elements with more than one basic idea (-6)
• Elements reflecting faulty grammar (-6)
• Elements containing acronyms, abbreviations, or slashes (-6)
• Idiosyncratic, preemptive terminology that does not reflect common usage (-6)
• Documents that are not labeled on each page with title, date, start time of production, stop time of production, and the name or initials of the originating staff member (-6)

Computer-Held Data. Two important kinds of data are held in the computer. These are the computer-generated structural information that shows the information needed to produce the structural patterns arising from group activity, and the record of NGT voting. (Still other data have sometimes been collected in ISM software, depending on who wrote the software and what they put into it.)   These two types of data have special significance, and should be preserved to assure the absence of mistakes in later work involving interpretation. For this reason, the following should be avoided but, if allowed to persist, should be assessed the negative point totals shown in parentheses:

- No printout of NGT voting records for use in the report, accompanied by the relevant list of elements which was voted on by the participants (-10)
- No printout of the computer-generated structural data, identified by name, and accompanied by the relevant list of elements and generic question (-10)

With the foregoing arrangements, a total of 50 negative points could be assessed against the documentation in the worst case. On the other hand, if these various items are included, the corresponding numbers of positive points can be assigned.

STUDY QUESTIONS
CHAPTER 11. IM WORKSHOP PHASE (PHASE 2)

1. What are the universal goals of an IM Workshop?

2. What are seven components of an IM Workshop?

3. What is the purpose for each of the seven components?

4. Upon what is evaluation of an IM Workshop based?

5. What primary conditions should an IM Broker avoid in connection with IM Workshops?

6. What primary conditions should an IM Facilitator avoid in connection with IM Workshops?

7. What factors should be managed carefully in documenting the products of an IM Workshop?

CHAPTER 12

IM FOLLOWUP PHASE (PHASE 3)

When both a Planning Phase and a Workshop Phase in relation to some situation have been completed, what comes next? A variety of possibilities exists. This Chapter will present several of these possibilities, from which one or a variant may be thought appropriate.

12.1 FOLLOWUP TO A DEFINITION PROJECT.

If a successful Definition project has been concluded, the followup may consist of one of the following:

* A decision that the enhanced definition of the situation has made possible the resolution of the situation without further IM activity (so far, this has only been seen in a very small percentage of the applications)

* A decision to enter a new Planning Phase, with the aim of attaining a higher level of success (as defined in Chapter 3) (so far, this has been the result in the vast majority of applications)

Experience shows that the choice of one of these two decisions should normally not be made until the IM Broker has good assurance that the understanding of the results and potential significance of the previous work is solid. (Groupthink can still be at work in a negative way after the conduct of a Definition project.)

12.2 FOLLOWUP TO A DESIGN OF ALTERNATIVES PROJECT.

If a successful Design of Alternatives Project has been completed, the followup may consist of one of the following:

* A decision that the enhanced understanding of the possibilities has made further work with IM unnecessary (this has frequently been the result, following a Design of Alternatives Project).

* A decision to start a new Planning Phase aimed at the highest success level identified in Chapter 3, namely the choice of a particular design alternative (this has rarely been the result, following a successful Design of Alternatives Project).

There is a certain amount of euphoria associated with the completion of a Design of Alternatives project. Also there is considerable fatigue, stemming from the difficulty of the work. It may also be true that the Client and the IM Broker have gained substantial insight into the actions that are required to make progress toward resolution.

One may recall that IM is seldom called upon until a state of desperation has been reached (although this situation hopefully is changing). The visibility of potential design alternatives that appear to be capable of resolving the situation may be all that is required to return the actors to the same mode they were in before taking part in the IM activity; namely to proceed as individuals trying to bring about change through the practices with which they are familiar through long experience (the very practices which were not adequate for developing the design alternatives).

Accordingly, the recommended followup to a Design of Alternatives Project is twofold:

(a) Once again make sure that the personnel from the Client Organization have assimilated completely the interpretation of their products,

(b) Continue with a Planning Phase and Workshop Phase aimed at choosing the superior alternative from those arrived at previously.

A critical part of this choice will be to gain the process insight needed to carry out the implementation of the selected design. It may occur that a followup to the choice will be a new activity in which the development of the implementation process is the primary goal, and that this will be part of a new Definition Project.

12.3 CONCERNS FOR IMPLEMENTATION OF RESULTS.

Independently of the particular kind of followup that a project may require, when applying IM one must keep in mind that there was a group of people working hard during a period of several days, and that this group has developed a lot of learning related with the situation under consideration, as well as some expectations about the use of the results they produced. It is therefore extremely important that the Client and the Broker pay personal attention to the followup of those results, at least in the terms that were originally agreed upon. If the IM activity is not followed by any specific action related with its results, it is likely that the participants may become frustrated and demotivated, unwilling to cooperate and participate in any additional effort for group problem-solving; this is particularly dangerous when one considers that the kind of problems that are faced by a group using IM are normally related with very complex situations for which the organizations hadn't found any successful means to work with.

STUDY QUESTIONS
CHAPTER 12. IM FOLLOWUP PHASE (PHASE 3)

1. What is typically involved in followup to a successful Definition Workshop?

2. What is typically involved in followup to a successful Design of Alternatives Workshop?

3. What should the Client and Broker be concerned with in Followup activity?

CHAPTER 13

EVALUATION CRITERIA FOR IM APPLICATIONS

Establishing and controlling the quality of IM applications involves these concerns:

• Concern for the Client. In any professional service activity, concern that the client shall receive a high-quality effort and product is paramount.

• Concern for the Reputation of Interactive Management. The continued and growing use of Interactive Management in a wide variety of major problem areas depends on developing and sustaining a good reputation for Interactive Management.

• Concern for the Practitioners. The practitioners of Interactive Management can continue to perform only as long as the quality of their performance is established and sustained.

• Concern for the Participants. In a few applications, sanctioned by top management, the products developed by the participants did not fit the management's preconceived notions of what the content would be. Top management that is politically motivated to prevent the surfacing of potentially embarrassing information can invoke a "shoot the messenger" reaction. To protect the participants from such a syndrome, it is necessary to get a commitment from top management ahead of time that they will behave maturely in the face of results that may strike them as surprising or inconsistent with their preconceived notions of what should have emerged as products.

One must note that if the affected top management had been able to resolve the issue under exploration by applying those preconceived notions, it is unlikely that any effort to use Interactive Management would be in the planning stage. The client must understand that it is unethical to place employees in an untenable, vulnerable position when they are trying to find the truth about a problematic situation of long standing, by denying the impact of the factors that are among the principal causes of the issues facing the organization or client.

• Concern for the Society. Interactive Management was developed as a proposed answer to the need for a way for society to cope with the complexities of modern life. It would be the height of irony if Interactive Management held the keys to fulfill its intended function, only to see it fail to achieve it due to the lack of quality control in its application.

One of the Laws that underlies the practice of Interactive Management is the Law of Success and Failure. This Law recognizes that while overall success may require that a significant number of involved components are all successful; overall system failure may come from the failure of only one of a set of factors.

The Law teaches us that success cannot necessarily be achieved even if all of the many controllable factors are separately successful, because there are a few factors that are outside the control of the practitioners of Interactive Management.

The Law also teaches us the wisdom of applying knowledge to the fullest to each of the factors that can be controlled (or even partially influenced), because this helps to bolster many factors that might otherwise be directly responsible for failure.

In other words, the goal is to make every aspect of Interactive Management as high in quality as possible, even though it is not possible to guarantee success because not every factor is controllable through Interactive Management. It is also true that not everything that can be learned about control of quality has yet been learned. Nevertheless, many lessons about quality control have been learned from both theoretical and empirical sources, including the practice of Interactive Management for over a decade (during which time many of the quality factors to be discussed were discovered!). It is these lessons learned that form the knowledge base for the evaluation factors to be presented here.

A question that needs to be considered is this: how should the evaluation factors be organized? The answer that has been chosen is to organize these factors in a dyadic scheme. Evaluation will be done for each of the three major types of outcome of the application of Interactive Management that were discussed in Chapter 2; i.e., for the Definition outcome, the Design Alternatives outcome, and the Choice of a Design outcome. And each of the foregoing will be done for both of the first two phases discussed in Chapter 4, i.e., for Phase 1 (Planning) and Phase 2 (Workshop). In all, there will be six separate evaluation schemes:

• Definition--Phase 1 (Planning)
• Definition--Phase 2 (Workshop)
• Design Alternatives--Phase 1 (Planning)
• Design Alternatives--Phase 2 (Workshop)
• Choice of a Design--Phase 1 (Planning)
• Choice of a Design--Phase 2 (Workshop)

These schemes correspond to Success Levels 1, 4, and 5 described in Chapter 3.
No evaluation scheme is presented for Phase 3, the Followup Phase, because of the lack of adequate experience to give a comprehensive evaluation scheme. However most of the impetus that is needed to bring about a high-quality Followup Phase will already have been achieved in the first two Phases. Likewise, most of the direct contribution that can be made by the practice of Interactive Management will have been made in those two Phases.

It will be seen in the following that many of the evaluation factors will be very similar or even identical for these six schemes. In presenting each of the six, it is intended to make it unnecessary for the reader to sort out the components that are particularly relevant to a given application.

An Options Field for Interactive Management Planning will be used to introduce each of the six evaluation schemes. While the Field will be the same, each scheme will be distinguished by a particular Options Profile drawn to reflect the particuliar evaluation scheme. This helps summarize on one page what is being evaluated and, by facilitating comparisons, may help the reader distinguish one evaluation scheme from another.

13.1 EVALUATION OF THE PLANNING PHASE FOR A DEFINITION OUTCOME.

Figure 13.1 shows an options profile for evaluating the planning phase of a Definition Outcome, but more particularly, for that type of Definition Workshop in which Success Level 1 is sought. As discussed in Section 3.1, Level 1 Success is interpreted as beginning to make some order out of a very poorly-defined situation. In recognition of the sorry state of organization of knowledge relative to the situation to be considered, planning for this phase involves efforts to arrive at an initially coherent view of the situation.

13.1.1 Component Factors. The *component factors for this planning phase* include the following:

The *context statement*, which:

- may properly err on the side of being too inclusive (as opposed to too narrow), to avoid focusing the discussion so much that key factors might not be discovered in the Workshop Phase
- does not epitomize any assumptions that cannot be readily justified
- contains at most six lines

The *products sought* are:

- An *attributes field,* which represents the problematic situation by a set of attributes and the categories in which they fall (e.g., political, social, technological, etc.) deemed to be relevant to the situation
- A **problems field,** which represents the problematic situation by a set of problems that are categorized according to their nature.

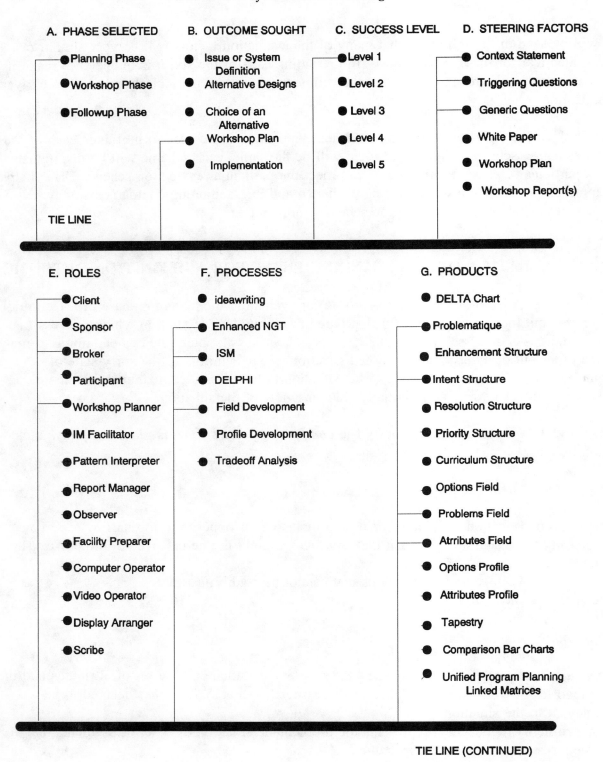

Figure 13.1 Options Profile--**Planning Phase** for a **Definition** Outcome at Success Level 1

- A **problematique**, which shows the structure at least of that subset of the problem set deemed to be most important (or, if the problem set is quite large, containing perhaps 100 members, shows the structure of the problem categories).
- An **intent structure**, which shows the relationship among the objectives that would be sought in trying to resolve the situation being studied.

The *processes* to be used are:

- The **Nominal Group Technique** to produce (a) a set of situational attributes, (b) a set of problems, and (c) a set of objectives.
- The **Interpretive Structural Modeling** process to produce (a) Attributes Field, (b) Problem Field, (c) Problematique, and (d) Intent Structure, in the order just listed.

Three *triggering questions* are required for using the NGT, to generate the three sets needed in order to produce the four products identified above. These questions may read as follows:

- In context X, what attributes characterize the situation?
- In context X, what problems are causing difficulty?
- In context X, what objectives, if satisfied, might be helpful in alleviating the situation?

The following four *generic questions* may be useful in arriving at the mentioned products:

- In context X, is Attribute Y similar to (in the same category with) Attribute Z?
- In context X, is Problem Y similar to (in the same category with) Problem Z?
- In context X, does Problem Y aggravate Problem Z?
- In context X, could the achievement of objective Y help to achieve objective Z?

      13.1.2 Evaluation Factors. In light of the discussion of components, the following are important evaluation factors:

- the *Context Statement*.
- the *Client's attitude* (See Section 5.1.1 for a discussion of the Client role).
- the *Broker's capability* (See Sect. 5.1.3 for discussion of the Broker role).
- the *breadth of knowledge and experience of the proposed participants*, individually, and as a group in relation to the anticipated Level of Success.
- the *triggering questions*, in relation to (a) the context statement, (b) the anticipated Level of Success, and (c) the anticipated knowledge and experience of the proposed participants.
- the *generic questions*, in relation to (a) the context statement, (b) the anticipated Level of Success, and (c) the anticipated breadth of knowledge and experience

of the proposed participants.
*   Evaluation of the proposed *workshop facility*, in terms of its potential for enhancing or detracting from the workshop activity
*   Evaluation of the *planned sequence* of work in the workshop
*   Evaluation of the completeness and adequacy of *workshop supporting role assignments.*
*   Evaluation of the *match between the workshop plan and the IM facilitator's expectations and experience.*
*   Evaluation of the *congruence between the time requirements to produce the anticipated workshop products and the time allotted to conduct the workshop.*
*   Evaluation of *contingency plans*.
*   Evaluation of the *written workshop plan* for quality and completeness of communication.

The above list of 13 evaluation factors offers an opportunity to review most of the key aspects of a workshop plan. If 10 points are chosen as the maximum score to be assigned to each of the factors, a perfect workshop plan as defined through these factors would produce a score of 130. It is good practice to develop such scores and to use them as a basis for discussing lessons learned in planning and conducting workshops. The concreteness provided by scores in this situation helps sharpen the evaluation, whose principal purposes are twofold:

*   to assess a plan before the workshop and make improvements in the plan if the evaluation suggests that they are needed, and
*   to serve retrospectively as a basis for learning how to do better in the future.

13.2 EVALUATION OF THE WORKSHOP PHASE FOR A DEFINITION OUTCOME.

Figure 13.2 shows an options profile for evaluating the Workshop Phase of a Definition Outcome, but more particularly, for that type of Definition Workshop in which Success Level 1 is sought. As discussed in Section 3.1, Level 1 Success is interpreted as beginning to make some order out of a very poorly-defined situation. In recognition of the sorry state of organization of knowledge relative to the situation to be considered, planning for this phase involves efforts to arrive at an initially coherent view of the situation.

13.2.1 Component Factors from the Planning Phase. The component factors that are available for conducting the Workshop and which come from the Planning Phase include the following:

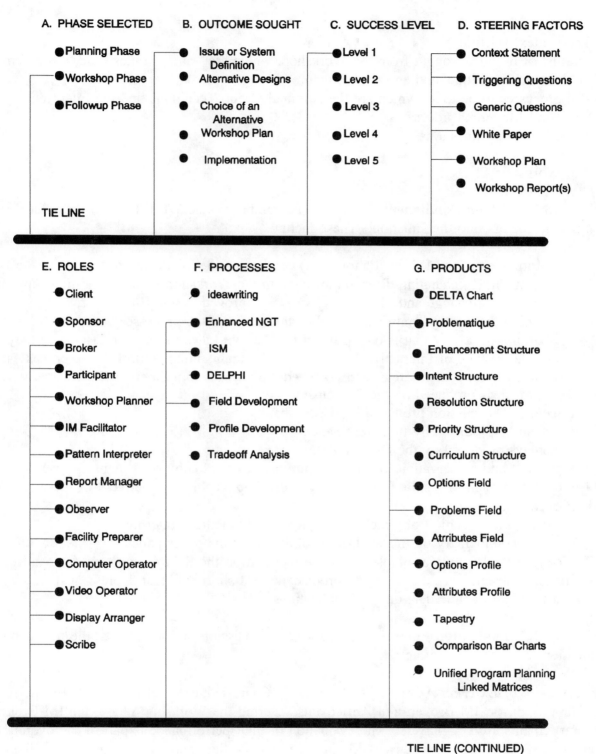

A. PHASE SELECTED
- Planning Phase
- Workshop Phase
- Followup Phase

TIE LINE

B. OUTCOME SOUGHT
- Issue or System Definition
- Alternative Designs
- Choice of an Alternative
- Workshop Plan
- Implementation

C. SUCCESS LEVEL
- Level 1
- Level 2
- Level 3
- Level 4
- Level 5

D. STEERING FACTORS
- Context Statement
- Triggering Questions
- Generic Questions
- White Paper
- Workshop Plan
- Workshop Report(s)

E. ROLES
- Client
- Sponsor
- Broker
- Participant
- Workshop Planner
- IM Facilitator
- Pattern Interpreter
- Report Manager
- Observer
- Facility Preparer
- Computer Operator
- Video Operator
- Display Arranger
- Scribe

F. PROCESSES
- ideawriting
- Enhanced NGT
- ISM
- DELPHI
- Field Development
- Profile Development
- Tradeoff Analysis

G. PRODUCTS
- DELTA Chart
- Problematique
- Enhancement Structure
- Intent Structure
- Resolution Structure
- Priority Structure
- Curriculum Structure
- Options Field
- Problems Field
- Atrributes Field
- Options Profile
- Attributes Profile
- Tapestry
- Comparison Bar Charts
- Unified Program Planning Linked Matrices

TIE LINE (CONTINUED)

Figure 13.2 Options Profile--**Workshop Phase** for a **Definition** Outcome at Success Level 1

161

- The context statement
- The list of products sought from the Workshop, which are: an attributes field, a problem field, a problematique, and an intent structure.
- The processes to be used, which are the Nominal Group Technique and the Interpretive Structural Modeling process.
- Three triggering questions.
- Four generic questions
- The Workshop Plan.

13.2.2 Other Component Factors. The conduct of the Workshop will introduce new component factors into the situation. These include:

- The performance of the IM Facilitator in (a) conducting the Workshop according to the Workshop Plan, (b) changing direction away from the Workshop Plan if conditions appear to warrant such a change and, if such a change is approved by the IM Broker, (c) sustaining the quality-control factors that are built into the processes used, (d) performing in a way that is cognizant of the Twelve Laws of Generic Design as they relate to the practice of Interactive Management, (e) maintaining control of the processes, while not invading content areas, and (f) scheduling breaks in a timely and sensitive way.
- The sets of ideas produced by the Participants.
- The record of discussion produced by the Scribe.
- The structures produced by the Participants.
- The displays produced by the Display Arranger.
- The printout and preservation for archival purposes of hard copy of structuring results.
- The documentation of results for use in the Workshop Report, and delivery of these to the Report Manager.
- The written interpretation of structures prepared by the Pattern Interpreter.
- The verbal commentary on the workshop coming from the participants.
- The congruency of time available with time required, in the light of concerns for quality control and absence of fatigue resolution or expedient short cuts that depress quality, and in the light of time data on past applications.

13.2.3 Evaluation Factors. In light of the discussion of components, the following evaluation factors are important:

Performance of External Actors. As identified in Chapter 5, external actors will fill the roles of Client, Sponsor, IM Broker, and Participants. During the Workshop Phase, the IM Broker and Participants are key players. The evaluation of their performance is part of the overall evaluation of the Workshop. Discussion of the roles that they play appears in Chapter 5 and Chapter 11. The weights assigned to the evaluation are as follows:

- To the IM Broker, a negative weight whose value can be as poor as (-30). Other evaluations with positive weights will reflect good performance by the IM Broker. Therefore in evaluating the IM Broker (as well as the IM Facilitator to be discussed shortly), a value of 0 will be an excellent score, and negative points will be assigned for failing to perform in certain ways, as discussed in Chapter 11.
- To the Participants as a group, a weight of 30.

Performance of Internal Professional Actors. As identified in Chapter 5, the Internal Professional Actors are the IM Workshop Planner, the IM Facilitator, the Pattern Interpreter, and the Report Manager. All of these except the IM Workshop Planner play important roles in the Workshop Phase. The weights assigned to the evaluation are as follows:

- To the IM Facilitator, a negative weight whose maximum value can be as poor as (-50). Other evaluations with positive weights will reflect good performance by the Facilitator. Therefore in evaluating the IM Facilitator, a value of 0 will be an excellent score. A negative assessment may be assigned for failing to perform in certain ways, as discussed in Chapter 11.
- To the Pattern Interpreter, a maximum weight of 30.
- To the Report Manager, a maximum weight of 30.

Performance of Internal Support Staff. As discussed in Chapter 5, the Internal Support Staff includes the Facilities Preparation Manager, the Computer Operator, the Scribe, the Display Arranger, and the Video Tape Operator. Each of these can be given a maximum weight of 10, so that the maximum score attainable by the Internal Support Staff is 50.

Quality of Documentation. The quality of documentation is dependent on the performance of numerous actors. The Report Manager is responsible for collecting, organizing, and reporting the information; but several other actors are responsible for preparing documentation, and the assessment of the Quality of the Documentation is best seen not as an assessment of actors, but rather as a prima facie assessment of the quality of what is provided for use in the report. Each major component of documentation can receive up to 10 points for quality, with an upper limit of 50 points for the documentation as a whole. However it is also appropriate to assign a negative value of 10 points for each important component of documentation that is missing. Specifically, 20 points should be assessed against the quality of documentation if the following printouts are not available for the report: the printout of the information needed to construct any structure and the printout of the record of participant voting in response to queries.

Finally, a review of the evaluation of the Planning Phase may prove worthwhile.

13.3 EVALUATION OF THE PLANNING PHASE FOR A DESIGN ALTERNATIVES OUTCOME.

Figure 13.3 shows an options profile for evaluating the Planning Phase for a Design Alternatives Outcome, i.e., for that type of Workshop in which Success Level 4 is sought. As discussed in Section 3.1, Level 4 Success is interpreted as finding good alterntive designs for resolving the issue (which will be compared later, enroute to a choice of one of them to be implemented.)

13.3.1 Component Factors. The component factors for this Planning Phase include the following:

The *context statement*, which:

- may properly err on the side of being too inclusive (as opposed to too narrow), to avoid focusing the discussion so much that key factors might not be discovered in the Workshop Phase
- does not epitomize any assumptions that cannot be readily justified
- contains at most six lines

The *products sought* are:

- An **options field,** which represents and organizes conceivable options for resolving the problematic situation, and portrays them in the categories under which they fall.
- Several **options profiles (design alternatives),** each of which represents one design alternative for resolving the problematic situation or issue.
- **A resolution structure,** which connects structurally to the problematique the categories discovered in producing the options field , showing how the implementation of options will help resolve the problems portrayed in the problematique
- Several **DELTA Charts,** one to accompany each options profile, showing the process sequence proposed to implement the options profile, along with the other relevant information normally appearing on DELTA Charts.

The *processes* to be used are:

- The **Nominal Group Technique** to produce (a) sets of options and (b) sets of activities and/or events
- The **Interpretive Structural Modeling** process to produce the various application structural types (the products mentioned above).

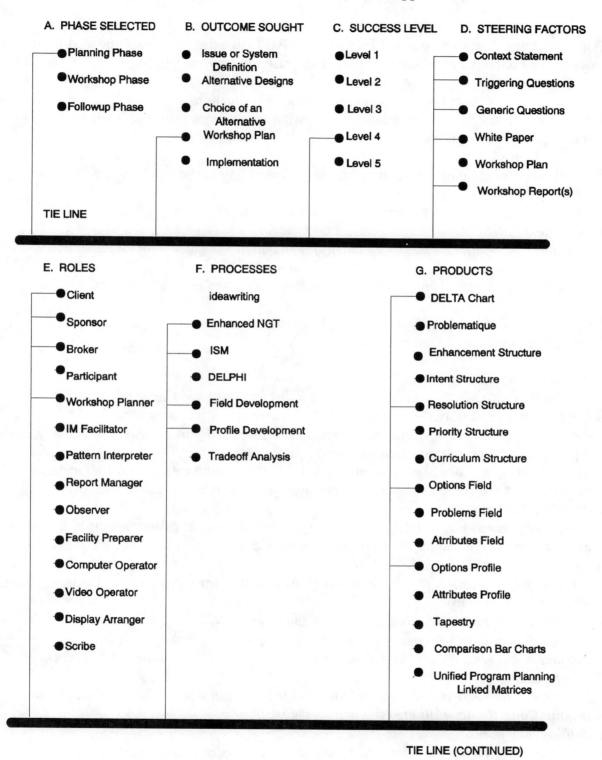

A. PHASE SELECTED
- Planning Phase
- Workshop Phase
- Followup Phase

B. OUTCOME SOUGHT
- Issue or System Definition
- Alternative Designs
- Choice of an Alternative
- Workshop Plan
- Implementation

C. SUCCESS LEVEL
- Level 1
- Level 2
- Level 3
- Level 4
- Level 5

D. STEERING FACTORS
- Context Statement
- Triggering Questions
- Generic Questions
- White Paper
- Workshop Plan
- Workshop Report(s)

TIE LINE

E. ROLES
- Client
- Sponsor
- Broker
- Participant
- Workshop Planner
- IM Facilitator
- Pattern Interpreter
- Report Manager
- Observer
- Facility Preparer
- Computer Operator
- Video Operator
- Display Arranger
- Scribe

F. PROCESSES
- ideawriting
- Enhanced NGT
- ISM
- DELPHI
- Field Development
- Profile Development
- Tradeoff Analysis

G. PRODUCTS
- DELTA Chart
- Problematique
- Enhancement Structure
- Intent Structure
- Resolution Structure
- Priority Structure
- Curriculum Structure
- Options Field
- Problems Field
- Atributes Field
- Options Profile
- Attributes Profile
- Tapestry
- Comparison Bar Charts
- Unified Program Planning Linked Matrices

TIE LINE (CONTINUED)

Figure 13.3 Options Profile--**Planning Phase** for a **Design of Alternatives** Outcome

165

Triggering questions are required for using the NGT, to generate the sets needed in order to produce the products identified above. These questions may read as follows:

- In context X, what options might help alleviate the situation?
- In context X, for the given options profile, what activities or events should occur in implementing the options profile?

The following *generic questions* may be useful in arriving at the mentioned products:

- In context X, is Option Y similar to (in the same category with) Option Z?
- In context X, is Category Y dependent on Category Z?
- In context X, should a choice of option(s) be made in Category Y before a choice is made in Category Z?
- In context X, should Event Y occur before Event Z in the first iteration?

      13.3.2 Evaluation Factors. In light of the discussion of components, the following are important evaluation factors:

- the *Context Statement.*
- the *Client's attitude* (See Section 5.1.1 for a discussion of the Client role).
- the *Broker's capability* (See Sect. 5.1.3 for discussion of the Broker role).
- the breadth of *knowledge and experience of the proposed participants*, individually, and as a group in relation to the anticipated Level of Success.
- the *triggering questions,* in relation to (a) the context statement, (b) the anticipated Level of Success, and (c) the anticipated knowledge and experience of the proposed participants.
- the *generic questions*, in relation to (a) the context statement, (b) the anticipated Level of Success, and (c) the anticipated breadth of knowledge and experience of the participants.
- the proposed *workshop facility*, in terms of its potential for enhancing or detracting from the workshop activity
- the *planned sequence* of work in the workshop
- the completeness and adequacy of *workshop supporting role assignments.*
- *the match between the workshop plan and the IM facilitator's expectations and experience.*
- the *congruence between the time requirements to produce the anticipated workshop products and the time allotted* to conduct the workshop.
- *contingency plans.*
- the *written workshop plan* for quality and completeness of communication.

The above list of 13 evaluation factors offers an opportunity to review most of the key aspects of a workshop plan. If 10 points are chosen as the maximum score to be assigned to each of the factors, a perfect workshop plan as defined through these factors would produce a score of 130. It is good practice to develop such scores and to use them as a basis for discussing lessons learned in planning and conducting workshops. The concreteness provided by scores in this situation helps sharpen the evaluation, whose principal purposes are twofold: (a) to assess a plan before the workshop and make improvements in the plan if the evaluation suggests that they are needed, and (b) to serve retrospectively as a basis for learning how to do better in the future.

13.4 EVALUATION OF THE WORKSHOP PHASE FOR A DESIGN ALTERNATIVES OUTCOME.

Figure 13.4 shows an options profile for evaluating the Workshop Phase for a Design Alternatives Outcome, i.e., for the type of Workshop in which Success Level 4 is sought. As discussed in Section 3.1, Level 4 success is interpreted as arriving at several potential design alternatives, as described by options profiles and their related documentation.

13.4.1 Component Factors from the Planning Phase. The component factors that are available for conducting the Workshop and which come from the Planning Phase include:
- The **context statement**
- The **list of products sought** from the workshop, which are an options field, several options profiles, a resolution structure, and several DELTA Charts (one for each options field)
- The **processes** to be used, which are the Nominal Group Technique and Interpretive Structural Modeling
- The **triggering questions**
- The **generic questions**
- The **Workshop Plan**

13.4.2 Other Component Factors. The conduct of the Workshop will introduce new components factors into the situation. These include:

- The *performance of the IM Facilitator* in (a) conducting the Workshop according to the Workshop Plan, (b) changing direction away from the Workshop Plan if conditions appear to warrant such a change, and if such a change is approved by the IM Broker, (c) observing the quality-control factors that are built into the processes used, (d) performing in a way that is cognizant of the Twelve Laws of Generic Design as they relate to the practice of Interactive Management, (e) maintaining control of the processes, but not invading the content areas, and (f) scheduling timely breaks

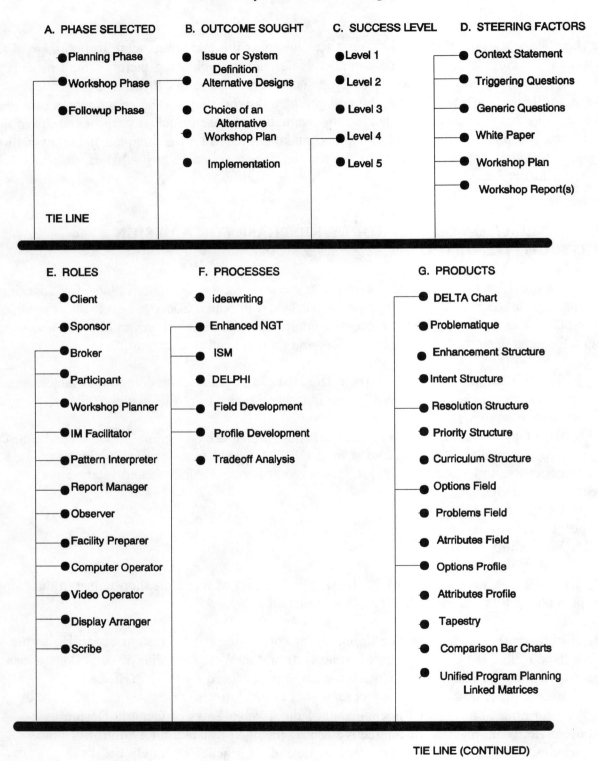

A. PHASE SELECTED

- Planning Phase
- Workshop Phase
- Followup Phase

TIE LINE

B. OUTCOME SOUGHT

- Issue or System Definition
- Alternative Designs
- Choice of an Alternative
- Workshop Plan
- Implementation

C. SUCCESS LEVEL

- Level 1
- Level 2
- Level 3
- Level 4
- Level 5

D. STEERING FACTORS

- Context Statement
- Triggering Questions
- Generic Questions
- White Paper
- Workshop Plan
- Workshop Report(s)

E. ROLES

- Client
- Sponsor
- Broker
- Participant
- Workshop Planner
- IM Facilitator
- Pattern Interpreter
- Report Manager
- Observer
- Facility Preparer
- Computer Operator
- Video Operator
- Display Arranger
- Scribe

F. PROCESSES

- ideawriting
- Enhanced NGT
- ISM
- DELPHI
- Field Development
- Profile Development
- Tradeoff Analysis

G. PRODUCTS

- DELTA Chart
- Problematique
- Enhancement Structure
- Intent Structure
- Resolution Structure
- Priority Structure
- Curriculum Structure
- Options Field
- Problems Field
- Attributes Field
- Options Profile
- Attributes Profile
- Tapestry
- Comparison Bar Charts
- Unified Program Planning Linked Matrices

TIE LINE (CONTINUED)

Figure 13.4 Options Profile--**Workshop Phase** for a **Design of Alternatives** Outcome

- The *sets of ideas* produced by the Participants
- The *record of discussion* produced by the Scribe
- The *structures* produced by the Participants
- The *displays* produced by the Display Arranger
- The *printout and preservation for archival purposes* of hard copy of structuring results
- The *documentation of results* for use in the Workshop Report, and delivery of these to the Report Manager
- The *written interpretation of structures* prepared by the Pattern Interpreter
- The *verbal commentary* on the workshop coming from the participants
- The *congruency of time available with time required,* in the light of concerns for quality control and absence of fatigue resolution or expedient short cuts that depress quality, and in the light of time data on past applications.

13.4.3 Evaluation Factors. In light of the discussion of components, the following evaluation factors are important:

Performance of External Actors. As identified in Chapter 5, external actors will fill the roles of Client, Sponsor, IM Broker, and Participants. During the Workshop Phase, the IM Broker and Participants are key players. The evaluation of their performance is part of the overall evaluation of the Workshop. Discussion of the roles that they play appears in Chapter 5 and Chapter 11. The weights assigned to the evaluation are as follows:

- To the IM Broker, a negative weight whose value can be as poor as (-30). Other evaluations with positive weights will reflect good performance by the IM Broker. Therefore in evaluating the IM Broker (as well as the IM Facilitator to be discussed shortly), a value of 0 will be an excellent score, and negative points will be assigned for failing to perform in certain ways, as discussed in Chapter 11.
- To the Participants as a group, a weight of 30.

Performance of Internal Professional Actors. As identified in Chapter 5, the Internal Professional Actors are the IM Workshop Planner, the IM Facilitator, the Pattern Interpreter, and the Report Manager. All of these except the IM Workshop Planner play important roles in the Workshop Phase. The weights assigned to the evaluation are as follows:

- To the IM Facilitator, a negative weight whose maximum value can be as poor as (-50). Other evaluations with positive weights will reflect good performance by the Facilitator. Therefore in evaluating the IM Facilitator, a value of 0 will be an excellent score. A negative assessment may be assigned for failing to perform in certain ways (Chap. 11).
- To the Pattern Interpreter, a maximum weight of 30.
- To the Report Manager, a maximum weight of 30.

Performance of Internal Support Staff. As discussed in Chapter 5, the Internal Support Staff includes the Facilities Preparation Manager, the Computer Operator, the Scribe, the Display Arranger, and the Video Tape Operator. Each of these can be given a maximum weight of 10, so that the maximum score attainable by the Internal Support Staff is 50.

Quality of Documentation. The quality of documentation is dependent on the performance of numerous actors. The Report Manager is responsible for collecting, organizing, and reporting the information; but several other actors are responsible for preparing documentation, and the assessment of the Quality of the Documentation is best seen not as an assessment of actors, but rather as a *prima facie* assessment of the quality of what is provided for use in the report. Each major component of documentation can receive up to 10 points for quality, with an upper limit of 50 points for the documentation as a whole. However it is also appropriate to assign a negative value of 10 points for each important component of documentation that is missing. Specifically, 20 points should be assessed against the quality of documentation if the following printouts are not available for the report: the printout of information needed to construct a structure and the printout of participant voting in response to queries.

Finally, a review of the evaluation of the Planning Phase may prove worthwhile.

13.5 EVALUATION OF THE PLANNING PHASE FOR A CHOICE OF ALTERNATIVES OUTCOME.

Figure 13.5 shows an options profile for evaluating the planning phase of a Choice of Alternatives, i.e., for the type of Workshop in which Success Level 5 is sought. As discussed in Section 3.1, Success Level 5 is interpreted as arriving at a choice of a good design which, if implemented, is likely to resolve the situation or issue being considered.

13.5.1 Component Factors. The component factors for this planning phase include the following:

The ***context statement***, which:

- may properly err on the side of being too inclusive, as opposed to being too narrow, to avoid focusing the discussion so much that key factors may not be discovered in the Workshop Phase
- does not epitomize any assumptions that cannot be readily justified
- contains at most six lines

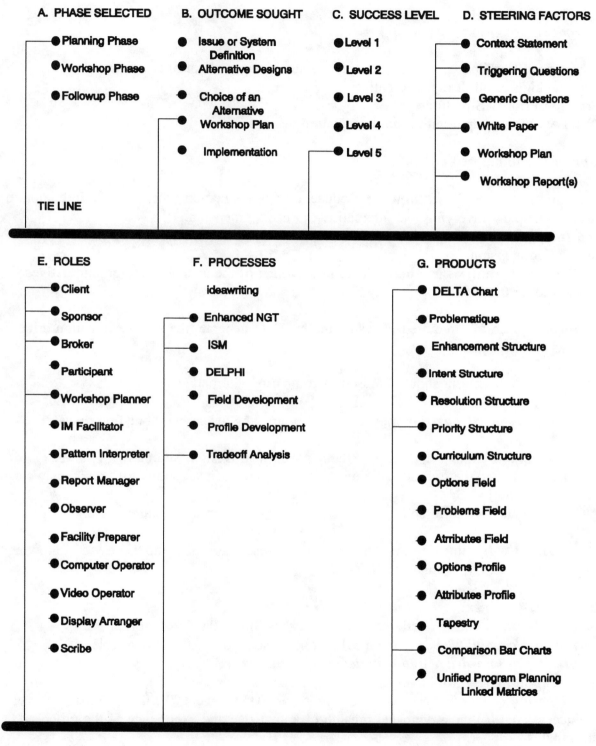

Figure 13.5 Options Profile--**Planning Phase** for a **Choice of Alternatives** Outcome

The ***products sought*** are:

* Comparison Bar Charts, to portray comparisons among pairs of alternatives.
* Final ranking of all design alternatives.
* Criterion Priority Structures
* DELTA Chart(s) representing implementation designs

The ***processes*** to be used are:

* The **Nominal Group Technique** to produce a set of evaluation criteria to use in comparing all possible pairs involving two alternatives, in each dimension.
* The **Interpretive Structural Modeling** process to produce rankings of alternatives on each individual dimension.
* The **Tradeoff Analysis Method** to determine which of the available design alternatives appears to be the best.

The ***triggering question*** required for using the NGT, to generate the set of evaluation criteria may be as follows:

* What evaluation criteria should be used in comparing alternatives?

The following ***generic question*** may be useful in arriving at the mentioned products:

* In the context of comparing Design Alternative X with Design Alternative Y, is the difference between the two on criterion A at least as significant as the difference between the two on criterion B?
  (Note that if the two differences are equal, they would lie in a structural cycle.)

13.5.2 Evaluation Factors. In light of the discussion of components, the following are important factors in evaluation:

* the ***context statement***.
* the ***client's attitude*** (See Section 5.1.1 for a discussion of the Client role).
* the ***broker's capability*** (See Section 5.1.3 for a discussion of the Broker role).
* the ***breadth of knowledge and experience of the proposed participants***, individually, and as a group in relation to the anticipated Level of Success.
* the ***triggering questions,*** in relation to (a) the context statement, (b) the anticipated Level of Success, and (c) the anticipated breadth of knowledge and experience of the proposed participants.
* the ***generic questions***, in relation to (a) the context statement, (b) the anticipated Level of

Success, and (c) the anticipated breadth of knowledge and experience of the proposed participants.

- the proposed *workshop facility*, in terms of its potential for enhancing or detracting from the workshop activity
- the *planned sequence of work* in the workshop
- the completeness and adequacy of *workshop supporting role assignments*
- *the match between the workshop plan and the IM facilitator's expectations and experience*
- the *congruence between the time requirements* to produce the anticipated workshop products *and the time allotted to conduct the workshop*.
- the *contingency plans*.
- the *written plan* for the Workshop for the quality and completeness of its communication.

The above list of 13 evaluation factors offers an opportunity to review most of the key aspects of a workshop plan. If 10 points are chosen as the maximum score to be assigned to each of the factors, a perfect workshop plan as defined through these factors would produce a score of 130. It is good practice to develop such scores and to use them as a basis for discussing lessons learned in planning and conducting workshops. The concreteness provided by scores, in this situation, helps sharpen the evaluation, whose principal purposes are twofold:

(a) to assess a plan before the workshop and make improvements in the plan if the evaluation suggests that they are needed, and

(b) to serve retrospectively as a basis for learning how to do better in the future.

13.6. EVALUATION OF THE WORKSHOP PHASE FOR A CHOICE OF ALTERNATIVES OUTCOME.

Figure 13.6 shows an options profile for evaluating the Workshop Phase for a Choice of Alternatives Outcome, i.e., for the type of Workshop in which Success Level 5 is sought. As discussed in Section 3.1, Level 5 success refers to arriving at a choice of a good design which, if implemented, is likely to resolve the problematic situation or issue .

13.6.1 Component Factors from the Planning Phase. The component factors that are available for conducting the Workshop and which come from the Planning Phase include the following:

- The *context statement*
- The list of products sought from the workshop, which are *Comparison Bar Charts* and *a ranking of the Design Alternatives*.

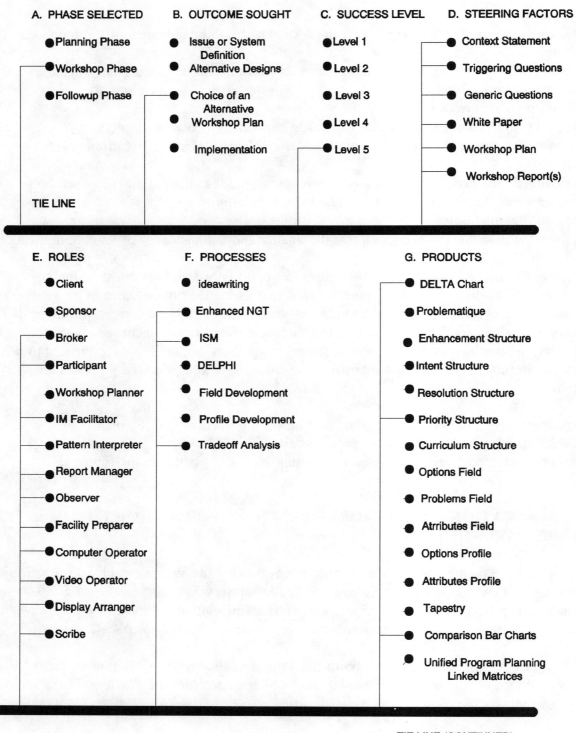

A. PHASE SELECTED
- Planning Phase
- Workshop Phase
- Followup Phase

B. OUTCOME SOUGHT
- Issue or System Definition
- Alternative Designs
- Choice of an Alternative
- Workshop Plan
- Implementation

C. SUCCESS LEVEL
- Level 1
- Level 2
- Level 3
- Level 4
- Level 5

D. STEERING FACTORS
- Context Statement
- Triggering Questions
- Generic Questions
- White Paper
- Workshop Plan
- Workshop Report(s)

TIE LINE

E. ROLES
- Client
- Sponsor
- Broker
- Participant
- Workshop Planner
- IM Facilitator
- Pattern Interpreter
- Report Manager
- Observer
- Facility Preparer
- Computer Operator
- Video Operator
- Display Arranger
- Scribe

F. PROCESSES
- ideawriting
- Enhanced NGT
- ISM
- DELPHI
- Field Development
- Profile Development
- Tradeoff Analysis

G. PRODUCTS
- DELTA Chart
- Problematique
- Enhancement Structure
- Intent Structure
- Resolution Structure
- Priority Structure
- Curriculum Structure
- Options Field
- Problems Field
- Attributes Field
- Options Profile
- Attributes Profile
- Tapestry
- Comparison Bar Charts
- Unified Program Planning Linked Matrices

TIE LINE (CONTINUED)

Figure 13.6 Options Profile--**Workshop Phase** for a **Choice of Alternatives** Outcome

- The processes to be used, which are the *Nominal Group Technique, Interpretive Structural Modeling, and the Tradeoff Analysis Method*
- The *triggering question*
- The *generic question*
- The *Workshop Plan*

13.6.2 Other Component Factors. The conduct of the Workshop will introduce new components factors into the situation. These include:

- The *performance of the IM Facilitator* in (a) conducting the Workshop according to the Workshop Plan, (b) changing direction away from the Workshop Plan if conditions appear to warrant such a change, and if such a change is approved by the IM Broker, (c) observing the quality-control factors that are built into the processes used, (d) performing in a way that is cognizant of the Twelve Laws of Generic Design as they relate to the practice of Interactive Management, (e) maintaining control of the processes, while not invading the content areas, and (f) scheduling breaks in a timely and sensitive way.
- The *sets of ideas* produced by the Participants.
- The *record of discussion* produced by the Scribe.
- The *products* produced by the Participants.
- The *displays* produced by the Display Arranger.
- The *printout and preservation for archival purposes* of hard copy of structuring results.
- The *documentation of results* for use in the Workshop Report, and delivery of these to the Report Manager.
- The *written interpretation of products* prepared by the Pattern Interpreter.
- The *verbal commentary* on the workshop coming from the participants.
- The *congruency* of time available with time required, in the light of concerns for quality control and absence of fatigue resolution or expedient short cuts that depress quality, and in the light of time data on past applications.

13.6.3 Evaluation Factors. In light of the discussion of components, the following evaluation factors are important:

Performance of External Actors. As identified in Chapter 5, external actors will fill the roles of Client, Sponsor, IM Broker, and Participants. During the Workshop Phase, the IM Broker and Participants are key players. The evaluation of their performance is part of the overall evaluation of the Workshop. Discussion of the roles that they play appears in Chapter 5 and Chapter 11. The weights assigned to the evaluation are as follows:

- To the IM Broker, a negative weight whose value can be as poor as (-30). Other evaluations with positive weights will reflect good performance by the IM Broker.

Therefore in evaluating the IM Broker (as well as the IM Facilitator to be discussed shortly), a value of 0 will be an excellent score, and negative points will be assigned for failing to perform in certain ways, as discussed in Chapter 11.

- To the Participants as a group, a weight of 30.

Performance of Internal Professional Actors. As identified in Chapter 5, the Internal Professional Actors are the IM Workshop Planner, the IM Facilitator, the Pattern Interpreter, and the Report Manager. All of these except the IM Workshop Planner play important roles in the Workshop Phase. The weights assigned to the evaluation are as follows:

- To the IM Facilitator, a negative weight whose maximum value can be as poor as (-50). Other evaluations with positive weights will reflect good performance by the Facilitator. Therefore in evaluating the IM Facilitator, a value of 0 will be an excellent score. A negative assessment may be assigned for failing to perform in certain ways, as discussed in Chapter 11.
- To the Pattern Interpreter, a maximum weight of 30.
- To the Report Manager, a maximum weight of 30.

Performance of Internal Support Staff. As discussed in Chapter 5, the Internal Support Staff includes the Facilities Preparation Manager, the Computer Operator, the Scribe, the Display Arranger, and the Video Tape Operator. Each of these can be given a maximum weight of 10, so that the maximum score attainable by the Internal Support Staff is 50.

Quality of Documentation. The quality of documentation is dependent on the performance of numerous actors. The Report Manager is responsible for collecting, organizing, and reporting the information; but several other actors are responsible for preparing documentation, and the assessment of the Quality of the Documentation is best seen not as an assessment of actors, but rather as a *prima facie* assessment of the quality of what is provided for use in the report. Each major component of documentation can receive up to 10 points for quality, with an upper limit of 50 points for the documentation as a whole. However it is also appropriate to assign a negative value of 10 points for each important component of documentation that is missing. Specifically, 20 points should be assessed against the quality of documentation if the following printouts are not available for the report: the printout of the information needed to construct any structure and the printout of the record of participant voting in response to queries.

Finally, a review of the evaluation of the Planning Phase may prove worthwhile.

13.7 SUMMARY EVALUATION FORM FOR PLANNING PHASE.

Table 13.1 is a summary evaluation form for the Planning Phase of Interactive Management.

TABLE 13.1
SUMMARY EVALUATION FORM FOR PLANNING PHASE

No.	FACTOR	POINTS
1	The Context Statement	0 to 10
2	The Client's Attitude	0 to 10
3	The Broker's Capability	0 to 10
4	The Correlation Between Proposed Participants' Capabilities and the Anticipated Level of Success	0 to 10
5	The Triggering Questions	0 to 10
6	The Generic Questions	0 to 10
7	The Workshop Physical Facility	0 to 10
8	The Planned Work Sequence	0 to 10
9	Workshop Supporting Role Assignments	0 to 10
10	Match Between Workshop Plan and Facilitator's Expectations and Experience	0 to 10
11	Match Between Time Allotted and Time Required to Produce Products	0 to 10
12	Contingency Plans	0 to 10
13	The Written Plan in its entirety	0 to 10

13.8 SUMMARY EVALUATION FORM FOR WORKSHOP PHASE

Table 13.2 is a Summary Evaluation Form for the Workshop Phase of Interactive Management.

TABLE 13.2
SUMMARY EVALUATION FORM FOR WORKSHOP PHASE

No.	*FACTOR*	*POINTS*
1	The IM Broker	0 to - 30
2	The Participants	0 to 30
3	The IM Facilitator	0 to - 50
4	The Pattern Interpreter	0 to 30
5	The Report Manager	0 to 30
6	The Support Staff	0 to 50
7	The Documentation	-50 to 50

With this arrangement, it is possible for a workshop score to be as low as -130 and as high as +190, the former representing a complete debacle, and the latter representing an outstanding effort that produces outstanding products.

To review the components of the evaluation factors for the IM Facilitator, the IM Broker, and the Documentation, please refer to Section 11.4.

13.9 EVALUATION FOR SUCCESS LEVELS 2 AND 3.

Evaluation, as discussed in the foregoing, has been tailored to Success Levels 1, 4, and 5. In this Section, evaluation for Success Levels 2 and 3 will be considered briefly, and regarded as variations on the evaluation for Success Level 1.

Section 13.1 dealt with the Planning Phase for Success Level 1, while Section 13.2 dealt with the Workshop Phase for Success Level 1.

At the outset of the comparison, it can be said that the evaluation factors will be the same as for Success Level 1. What will be different in the comparison is the component factors, and in particular the products sought.

For Success Level 1, the products sought, as specified in the Planning Phase, are: an attributes field, a problem field, a problematique, and an intent structure. In the Planning Phase for both Success Level 2 and Success Level 3, the intent structure is removed as a product to be sought, but a priority structure replaces it as a product. The primary rationale is twofold: (a) in dealing with Success Level 1, where there is a high level of uncertainty involved in the issue or situation, considerable clarification can be achieved by discussing objectives; but this same focus is less relevant for Success Levels 2 and 3, and (b) the time can better be spent in planning for Success Levels 2 and 3 by giving more attention and time to the other products.

The Workshop Phase for Success Levels 2 and 3 is basically the same as for Success Level 1, except that what is supplied at the outset of the Workshop does not include an intent structure.

13.10 LARGE NUMBERS OF ELEMENTS.

When the number of elements to be structured is very large, it will often be found both expedient and of sufficient quality to use the cited methodologies to structure up to 30 or more elements and then, after interpreting the structures, to place the remaining elements in the structures manually with facilitator assistance. Following this activity, participants are asked to survey the new structure (which must be appropriately displayed), and to place "magnetic question marks" on each element whose location is questioned. The IM Facilitator can then work with the group to deal with all of the question marks that appear, using ISM amendment procedures if necessary, to finalize the group products.

STUDY QUESTIONS
CHAPTER 13. EVALUATION CRITERIA FOR IM APPLICATIONS

1. What five types of concerns are significant in quality control of IM applications?

2. In evaluating IM activity, how should the evaluation factors be organized?

3. What are the component factors of an evaluation of the Planning Phase for a Definition outcome?

4. What products are sought for a Definition outcome?

5. What processes are used in a Definition Workshop?

6. What is a typical format for a triggering question to use in a Definition Workshop?

7. What is a typical format for a generic question to accompany the triggering question identified in Question 6?

8. What evaluation factors are important for a Definition Workshop?

9. What are the component factors of an evaluation of the Workshop Phase for a Definition outcome? What percentage of these come from the Planning Phase?

10. What are evaluation factors for the Workshop Phase for a Definition outcome?

11. What are the component factors of an evaluation of the Workshop Phase for a Design Alternatives outcome?

12. What products are sought for a Design of Alternatives outcome?

13. What processes are used in a Design of Alternatives Workshop?

14. What is a typical format for a triggering question to use in a Design of Alternatives Workshop?

15. What is a typical format for a generic question to accompany the triggering question identified in Question 14?

16. What evaluation factors are important for a Design of Alternatives Workshop?

180

17. What are the component factors of an evaluation of the Workshop Phase for a Design of Alternatives outcome?

18. What component factors are important in evaluating the Planning Phase for a Choice of Alternatives outcome?

19. What component factors are important in evaluating the Workshop Phase for a Choice of Alternatives outcome?

20. What is the maximum possible score for evaluating the Planning Phase of IM, attained if everything is done at the best possible level of quality?

21. What is the maximum possible score for evaluating the Workshop Phase of IM, attained if everything is done at the best possible level of quality?

22. What is the minimum possible score for evaluating the Workshop Phase of IM, attained if everything is done at the worst possible level of quality?

23. What special conditions can be considered when the number of elements in the sets are very large?

CHAPTER 14

COMPARING IM WITH METHODS WIDELY USED IN JAPAN

This chapter compares IM with practices widely associated with Japanese organizations and, especially, with Japanese manufacturing firms that have a long history of dedicated application of quality-engendering practices in design and manufacturing. To designate these methodologies by country is not necessarily sensible, but rather reflects prevailing opinions and ways of discussing them. This document will shed some light on origins, but only to correct misperceptions that have tended to become pervasive in the available literature.

In this chapter, the relevant literature to be used as part of the basis for comparisons is comprised of two types: (a) **scientific literature**, which has undergone rigorous review by qualified referees, and which reflects the importance of sustaining continuity in the apparent flow of scientific development in order to maintain an adequate perspective, and to provide for the needs of evaluators and students; and (b) **venture literature,** in which rigorous review is not seen as relevant, and there is little obligation displayed for the student or to sustain the apparent flow of scientific development. That such literature exists is beyond argument. The quality of venture literature varies widely. Some of it is outstanding, but on the whole it suffers from the fact that much higher priority is given to its marketing value than to its scientific basis. Venture literature dominates American design and manufacturing, as reflected in the very large sales of such literature when contrasted to sales of the scientific literature. A similar domination occurs in many conferences and meetings ranging from purely marketing meetings to so-called scientific or professional meetings, where the venture literature is often uncritically taken as the starting point for conference design, and those who contribute to that literature are often prominent speakers. Venture literature is especially prominent in the management field. Those few scholars of organizations that facilitate access to prior scientific work are often ignored by faculty of business schools.

The purpose of this chapter is to provide a comparison of several methodologies that are useful or potentially useful in the general area of system design and, especially, in system design and manufacturing, with the view that some readers may want to consider changing their approach to design--or to manufacturing--or to design and manufacturing as a unit.

14.1 METHODS TO BE COMPARED.

Three methods (or more accurately, systems of methods) will be compared in what follows. For convenience, and comparison with existing literature, they are described under three headings. These three have all been applied to design of complex systems, yet they differ significantly in their approach. The comparisons will highlight differences.

There is considerable confusion in the literature as to where some of these systems of methods originated. In this chapter, some of the confusion may be mitigated, in order to make it somewhat easier for diligent scholars to improve on the weak historical background currently available to them.

14.1.1 Interactive Management. Interactive Management (IM), the subject of this Handbook, is one of the systems of methods to be compared.

14.1.2 The Japanese Tool Box. As defined here, the "Japanese Tool Box" (JTB) is a collection of what are often described as "tools" in the Japanese literature, and which have become very well-known in the United States, largely through the venture literature and short courses allied with this literature. Fourteen of these tools have been heavily publicized. Seven relate directly to design, and the other seven relate to manufacturing. All are identified in later sections of this chapter. Evidence indicates that these tools have been used extensively in Japan, especially in manufacturing sectors of the economy.

14.1.3 Quality Function Deployment. Quality Function Deployment (QFD) is a system of benchmarking product designs and manufacturing processes against standards of comparison. It has been used both in Japan and in the United States, although presumably much more so in Japan than in the U. S.

14.2 CATEGORIES OF REFERENCES.

A fairly extensive set of references is presented at the end of this chapter, to support some of the statements made in the text. For reader convenience, these references have been grouped into five categories. These categories are: *System Failure* (designated SF), *Japanese or German publications* relating to structural modeling (designated JG), *Organizational Cultures* (designated OC); *Design Processes* (designated DP), and *Prescriptions* (designated P). For example, the notation DP-3 refers to the third publication on Design Processes in the alphabetical sequence by author; and the notation OC-6 refers to the sixth publication on Organizational Cultures in the alphabetical sequence by author.

In several instances, papers listed under Organizational Culture are put there not because they specifically deal with Organizational Culture, but rather because they are, so to speak, concrete examples of the impact of Organizational Culture on the topics with which they deal. For example, reference OC-18 which deals with diagramming techniques, illustrates an organizational culture that has little emphasis on connecting the subject with any scientific historical development. As a consequence, it is sorely deficient in terms of foundations for what is recommended, but in that respect it is like much of what comes out of today's American corporations--and especially out of small businesses who are striving to succeed in some niche area. The reason for bringing up this subject is that many of the inhibitors to successful application of design science relate to organizational cultures, as well as to the vested interests of technological organizational components in sustaining an image in which they have invested, even though this acts to the detriment of the general welfare.

14.3 NOMENCLATURE.

There is little standardization of the nomenclature applied to the areas being studied. It is easy to be misunderstood, simply because the names are often interchanged, at least in part. Therefore the following practice will be followed in this report: the nomenclature relative to the processes to be compared will be derived from only these references: King [DP-8, 1989], Brassard [DP-2, 1989], Ishikawa [DP-6, 1986], Warfield [DP-31, 1994], and Warfield and Cárdenas [DP-32, 1994]. If the reader wants to check up on nomenclature, these sources should be consulted. In a few places, the terminology used in DP-2 and DP-6 will be presented side by side for comparison, showing where the names are the same as well as where they differ.

Acronyms will be used to represent what is being compared. The acronym **QFD** represents the Quality Function Deployment process and its related literature. The 14 members contained in the **7-QC**-Tools (Seven-Quality Control-Tools) and **7-M**-Tools (Seven-Management-Tools) and the related literature are referred to here as **JTB**, the "Japanese Tool Box". The seven members of JTB that pertain directly to design, as opposed to quality control in manufacturing, identified in Table 14.5 (i.e., the <u>qualitative component</u> of the JTB and its related literature), will be referred to as **7JDT**, the Seven Japanese *Design* Tools. The Interactive Management system and its related literature will be referred to as **IM**. These notations are used to cut down on the verbiage involved in carrying out comparisons.

14.4 CONTEXT.

The context in which this chapter is written is one of a highly competitive world in which expensive systems are designed and manufactured, and in which there is a history of significant failures of systems. Such failures may be technical or economic, or a mix of technical and economic; and they may involve products or services or both. Working within such a context, it is appropriate to consider policies, strategies, and goals for becoming more competitive. One of the approaches to becoming more competitive is to apply what is known as ***competitive benchmarking.***

14.4.1 Competitive Benchmarking as Seen from the Ivory Tower. Today it is argued by many that competitive benchmarking must be used to upgrade competitiveness. As observed from the Ivory Tower, competitive benchmarking involves a company studying a competitor's product and comparing the company's product to that of the competitor. (Such studies tend to emphasize the use of customer-generated criteria as a basis for comparisons, and refer to such criteria as "the voice of the customer".) Following this competitive benchmarking, the company strives to improve its own product in areas where the competitor's product is vulnerable, or in areas where the company's product is vulnerable. (While the word "product" is used generically in this discussion, the word "service" can be substituted for it, because the production of high-quality services involves similar philosophies and methodologies as the production of tangible products.)

In order to facilitate an ongoing continuous improvement effort, companies may choose and implement *design and manufacturing processes* (DM-Processes) to help guarantee continued attention to such improvements, and they may invest significantly in such processes.

What companies have <u>*not*</u> *done is to apply competitive benchmarking in the choice and implementation of DM-*<u>*processes*</u> *that they use to determine how to upgrade their* <u>*products*</u>.

Companies who manufacture products are seldom expert in design processes. As a result, they are not naturally inclined to do competitive benchmarking concerning design processes. This makes them vulnerable to getting and accepting bad advice on such matters. This is especially true concerning design processes, because the latter are not generally understood. While these reasons may explain why companies are not necessarily able to apply competitive benchmarking to the choice and implementation of DM-Processes, this does not relieve them of the responsibility to consider this idea: *if competitive benchmarking is a good thing to apply to see how to improve their manufactured* <u>*product*</u>, *why is it not equally a good thing to apply in the choice of the DM-*<u>*processes*</u> *applied to improve design and manufacturing?*

The nature of competitive benchmarking on DM-Processes is a little different from that on products. The origin of benchmarks for products is the competitors, but the potential origin of benchmarks on DM-processes is the *scientific and technical literature*, plus a new kind of commercial *venture literature* in which entrepreneurs put together a collection of ideas that they did not invent and may not even use, but which they are prepared to market as a publishing venture. The "venture literature" seems to have taken over in many fields. Much of what passes for potential benchmarking in software design has been based in venture literature, and now it seems that the same kind of literature has gained a strong foothold in the design area, with reference to quality control. Venture literature, by its very nature, can never be a means to get ahead of competitors, but its use can give the appearance that something is being done to get improvement.

■ *System Failures.* Many system failures have been studied over the past seven years as part of a program of assessment of design practices. A substantial percentage of those failures is traceable to bad design practices. In considering what disciplines large-scale systems design, a number of such failures were mentioned, involving large and well-known organizations [Warfield, SF-5, 1987]. A few of these are described in the References in that paper [Alpert, SF-1, 1984; Brooks, SF-2, l987; and Kemeny, SF-4, 1980].

■ *Japanese and German Literature on Interactive Management.* One of the systems of D-M processes being considered in comparisons in this report is Interactive Management (IM). There exists both Japanese and German literature on this subject, mainly emphasizing the Interpretive Structural Modeling Process. The Japanese literature includes [Arai, et al, JG-1, 1981; Haruna and Komoda, JG-2, 1978; Komoda and Haruna, JG-3, 1978; Kawamura, JG-4, 1977; Komaya and Fukuda, JG-5, 1980; Mizoguchi et al, JG-6, 1978; Nakao, et al, JG-7, 1978; Nishikawa and Udo, JG-8, 1978; Ohuchi et al, JG-9, 1988; Sato, JG-10, 1978 and JG-11, 1979; Sawaragi and Kawamura, JG-12, 1982; and Sugiyama, et al, JG-13, 1981]. It is known that much of this material is being taught in Japanese universities, generally in systems or engineering curricula. The small German literature is well-represented by Szyperski and Eul-Bischoff, JG-14, 1983.

■ *Organizational Cultures.* It is agreed by most scholars that organizational cultures, as reflected in decision-making and behavior in general, present severe obstacles to change in organizational processes and practices. Even when efforts are made with the best of intentions to change organizations, failure can be encountered [Bushe, OC-5, 1988]. An extensive literature exists that not only discusses the organizational culture issues, but also illustrates the kind of thinking that stems from dysfunctional cultures [OC-1 through OC-28]. Unfortunately, scholars still tend to propose only partial solutions to organizational cultural change. For example, Senge [P-7, 1990] offers many good rationales and perspectives on the kind of change that is needed but, unfortunately, has little to say about what specific steps to take and what specific agenda to follow to bring about such changes in organizations.

■ *Diagnostics and Prescriptions.* Diagnostics and prescriptions separately are not nearly as valuable as when they are combined and integrated. In the U. S. A. one finds three major geographical locations from which diagnostics and prescriptions arise. These are the Cambridge area in Massachusetts, the Pittsburgh area in Pennsylvania, and the federal government in Washington, D. C.. In Cambridge, both Harvard University and M. I. T. are notable for providing a variety of diagnostics and prescriptions, but they tend to be unintegrated. In Pittsburgh, Carnegie-Mellon is well-funded to make diagnostics and prescriptions. Unfortunately, the recent track record there indicates that their interest in diagnosing difficulties seems greatly to exceed their ability to make prescriptions and, especially, to make prescriptions that are based in competitive benchmarking. At the federal level, U. S. Governmental action is rationalized in terms of international competition but (regrettably) is dominated by members of the Congress who believe that newly-developed organizations or new parts of old organizations in their own jurisdictions, if given funds in areas new to them, can somehow quickly gain significant knowledge in areas of system design, manufacturing, benchmarking, quality control, software design, etc. Such organizations typically ignore all the available literature, write uninformed reports, and put out public relations newsletters and/or newspaper blurbs to present the appearance that they are truly making headway.

14.4.2 Three Possible Temporal Strategies. For comparative purposes, three possible strategies for companies to adopt to deal with the international competition are:

A. Decrease the rate of falling behind, while continuing to lag.
B. Decrease the rate of falling behind to zero.

C. Catch up and pass the competition.

Even if none of these is specifically stated as a company-adopted strategy, it may be possible to find clues as to which of these mutually-incompatible strategies appears to be at work in a given organization. Some of the ways to determine the implicit strategy are the following:

i) Compare elapsed time from concept origination to manufactured product with that of competitors

ii) Compare data on components of large design and manufacturing processes to see where the most critical lags are found, and study whether these are being heavily acted on

iii) See if the company is doing competitive benchmarking on the methods being used to enhance design and manufacturing

iv) See if the company is aware of and is engaged in careful assessment of the scholarly products of design and manufacturing research

14.4.3 A Singular Goal. If the "Catch Up and Pass Strategy" is chosen, the available ways to proceed and the possible goals to be sought are dramatically restricted. In fact, **a singular goal becomes appropriate, this being to apply strict quality controls to the choice and implementation of all decision, design, and manufacturing processes, and especially to those processes that involve the conceptual aspects of design.**

14.4.4 A Two-Factor Policy. If the singular goal is chosen, the high-level policy required to support that goal involves two overriding factors. The first factor is:

#1, speed with quality,

regarded not as two distinct items, but as a single factor. The second factor is:

#2, the application of the first factor not only to product decisions that are made in design and manufacturing but, more significantly, to the choice and implementation of DM-processes and the documentary representations that these processes produce, and which are to be used to develop and communicate about product decisions. Such a policy will act indirectly to change the organization for the better.

Previously attention has been focused on working to get product quality, but the standards that are being applied to quality of product are not being applied to choice and management of the processes whereby that product is designed and produced. It is not possible to support the speed and quality factor by concentrating on the product alone.

14.5 FIVE-FACTOR PROCESS COMPARISONS.

In this section, comparisons will be made between QFD, 7JDT, and IM on the basis of five factors, all having to do with information. These factors are:

- Generating Information
- Organizing Information
- Displaying Information
- Interpreting Information
- Applying Information

■ **Ways of Generating Information.** The literature differs greatly in terms of how it deals with ways of generating information, depending on which of the three systems (QFD, 7JDT, or IM) is being discussed. There is relatively little available literature on QFD and what is available emphasizes the form in which the information is presented. While there is more information on 7JDT, it is not up to archival standards. There is a great deal of information on IM, and it is generally up to archival standards.

14.5.1 Generating Information for Quality Function Deployment. Generating information for QFD is described in [DP-1]. This is the only source discovered that is sensitive to the process issues related to the use of QFD. (A telephone communiction with the organization that produced this report suggests that a later version than the one referenced may be seen in their organization's library.) The following quotation from page 8-1 of this document deals with generating the information:

"Based on Japanese experience, the complete QFD process will require 50-60 hours of team meetings and team work for each member. Most of the work will normally be done outside the meetings. The team meetings are principally for the purpose of coordinating activities, updating charts, analyzing information and deciding on the information which must be gathered outside these meetings by individual team members. This individual time will normally far outweigh the 50-60 hours spent in the team process."

It is also asserted (Chapter 4) that information should be gained in a variety of ways, including surveys, clinics, focus groups, individual interviews, listening, and the use of existing information. It is recommended that design engineers, particularly, be involved in surveys and interviews to develop a <u>real understanding</u> of the voice of their customer.

14.5.2 Generating Information for 7JDT. Generating information for 7JDT is described in Brassard's publication which indicates that over a million copies of it have been sold. This publication is more stringent in denying use of excerpts from it than the "fair usage" copyright standards, stating that: "Any reproduction of any part of this publication without the written permission of GOAL/QPC is prohibited". Why is it so restrictive?

■ Pages 20-23 of [DP-2] describe (ambiguously) the information generation process for the **Affinity Diagram.** The description does not distinguish between "Brainstorming" and the Nominal Group Technique, even though these are very different processes from a behavioral and quality control point of view. A triggering question is used. The information is recorded, as in NGT. The description of NGT given on page 298 is quite different from the definitive definition given by the inventors of NGT [DP-3].

■ Page 45 of [DP-2] suggests that the primary ideas for use in producing the **Interrelationship Digraph** are those already generated in producing the Affinity Diagram, although others may be added through brainstorming.

■ Pages 83ff of [DP-2] are ambiguous about precisely what course to pursue in generating information for use in a **Tree Diagram**, but it is clear that much of what is to be used will come from information generated previously, e.g., in developing an Affinity Diagram and an Interrelationship Digraph. Several triggering questions may be formulated based upon the form of the previously-developed diagrams.

■ Pages 164-165 of [DP-2] highlight the choice of symbols to be used, and what the symbols will show. The symbols are to be entered into the **Matrix Diagram**. Symbols are suggested to be used in lieu of numbers. Presumably individuals enter these symbols into the matrix without any particular pattern of group activity.

■ Page 176 of [DP-2] suggests that Brainstorming is the preferred generation method to use in getting information for the **Process Decision Program Chart.**

■ Page 217 of [DP-2] again suggests Brainstorming or data gathering to obtain the information needed to develop an **Activity Network.**

■ Page 275 of [DP-2] gives information about the **Cause & Effect Diagram** (the Fishbone Diagram, or the Ishikawa Diagram). While two different methods of generating information are given, it appears that "Structured Brainstorming" is the normal procedure for use with groups. Structured Brainstorming is described on page 297, where the actual generation of information is not mentioned; instead the round-robin recording is mentioned (which is normally the second step in NGT).

In summary, it appears that there are two principal means of generating information for the 7JDT, which are Brainstorming in a group, and Data-Gathering outside the group process.

14.5.3 Generating Information for IM. Three alternative means of generating information are available in Interactive Management. These are: (a) Ideawriting, (b) Nominal Group Technique, and (c) DELPHI. Each of these means is discussed extensively in the literature. Of these three, the most common by far in applications is the Nominal Group Technique (NGT) [DP-2, 1975]. Moreover, NGT is *more than just a way of generating information.* It also provides for the *formal clarification of the information generated,* and for *an initial assessment of relative importance of what has been produced.* This allows a record to be produced that can be inspected later when revisions in the information may be considered, and also it offers some ways of prioritizing later effort. Brainstorming is specifically ruled out for use in IM, although some of the original behavioral aspects of the Brainstorming process are retained in both Ideawriting and the Nominal Group

Technique. The NGT Process requires a formal clarification process, and a preliminary assessment of relative importance, while Brainstorming requires neither.

■ *The Nominal Group Technique (NGT)*. The NGT process is always driven by a single, carefully formulated question, called a "triggering question". For example, such a question might be: "What do buyers of automobiles desire in a rear-view mirror?" or, a more open question of this type would be: "what do automobile drivers need in order to have adequate rear-view vision?" Table 14.1 presents data from 43 applications of NGT [Warfield, DP-31, Appendix 5, 1994].

TABLE 14.1
DATA ON THE NOMINAL GROUP TECHNIQUE

■ Average duration of working session	3.1 hours
■ Average number of ideas generated in response to the triggering question	64 ideas
■ The average number of ideas generated that were viewed by at least one participant as being among the five most important from the whole set	33 ideas

Two major points are based on these data: *(a) In around 3 hours, most of the significant ideas about a complex issue can usually be extracted, clarified, and initially assessed for relative importance,* **and** *(b) it is typical that members of the group that produce the large set of ideas will differ substantially in points of view concerning relative importance of the ideas produced.*

■ *Benefits of the Nominal Group Technique*. From the use of this process, it has been discovered that as a rule there is widespread difference of opinion among participants about the relative importance of the various factors involved in whatever design situation is being considered. The use of the process not only generates and clarifies the ideas, but also exposes the wide differences of opinion, which has two beneficial effects: *(a) it prevents premature acceptance of any individual's point of view,* **and** *(b) it motivates additional process activity aimed at helping the participants learn more about the issue involved, so that the divergent views can be modified and so that better decisions can be reached about the design issues involved. The clarification component of NGT is indispensable to good followup work.*

14.5.4 Comparisons (Generating Information). Both QFD and 7JDT require qualitative information (such as the factors involved in considering a design question) and quantitative information (such as the intensity of relationships among the factors). IM reflects the following point of view. The need for and utility of quantitative information can only be clearly seen when the underlying qualitative information is well-organized and high in quality. **In the absence of quality control on both the content and organization of the relevant** <u>**qualitative**</u> **information,** <u>**quantitative**</u> **information will be misused.**

Interactive Management requires that an experienced NGT group facilitator be available to conduct the process, and also requires that the working facility have a large wall space for use in displaying information to the participants. The information on QFD and 7JDT is too vaguely written to allow a careful comparison. Experience with NGT shows that clarification is absolutely essential, as most of the ideas generated are not clear to persons in the group who did not generate them. ***The idea that individual experts can consistently produce very clear statements in areas of complexity (even when they are specialists in these areas) has been repeatedly demonstrated to be false.*** This is why NGT is the preferred method of generating information for use with IM. One may also observe that in the Brassard description of the use of the 7JDT's, what is done in developing an early structure is then used in developing later structures, making the quality of the processes dependent on the quality of the information generated in the early work.

■ **Ways of Organizing Information.** Organization of information is often done manually in an ad hoc way. The habit of doing things this way is responsible for many problems in dealing with information. Many mistakes can be made in organizing a large amount of information. It is for this reason that some believe that it is very important to exercise quality control on how information is organized, and provide documentation to permit retracement of all decisions having to do with the organization of information.

14.5.5 Organizing Information for QFD. Chapter Four (Page 4-20) of [DP-1] "Quality Function Deployment QFD" training materials discusses the organization of information for use in QFD. (King [DP-8, 1989] shows a wide variety of forms that may emerge as a result of the work done to organize the information.)

This document [DP-1] asserts that information gathered concerning QFD should usually be organized in an Affinity Diagram. Six steps are given for manually grouping the cards or "post-its" on a large table in a group process. It is stated that "experience shows that this team process is best accomplished when there is a minimum of discussion so that members do not get involved in semantic battles". After the cards are piled into categories, names are chosen for the categories. Normally these would be customer wants. The technical information offering options for satisfying the wants is placed on one side of the matrix with the needs on the other side. It is suggested that numbers be assigned to all the matrix indexes for convenience of reference. Customer complaint histories are gathered and organized as inputs to the matrix system.

14.5.6 Organizing Information for 7JDT. Somewhat different processes of organizing information can be expected for the 7JDT, depending on which tool is involved. (The origin of the organizing information to be discussed here is Brassard [DP-2])

■ Pages 20-23 of [DP-2] describe the construction process for the **Affinity Diagram**. The process is entirely manual, involving sorting of cards without talking, and continues until people stop moving cards around.

■ Pages 44-53 of [DP-2] describe the construction process for the **Interrelationship Digraph**. The description suggests that the process involves people placing "post-it" notes on a table, and that the group is expected to reach consensus. There is no consideration of such issues as how the process might provide for consistency in the logic; nor is there any discussion of inference. Some talking is allowed.

- Pages 82-97 of [DP-2] describe the construction process for the **Tree Diagram**. The method seems to be to get the ideas on cards and move the cards around manually.

- Pages 158-167 of [DP-2] describe construction processes for the **Matrix Diagram**. Different shapes of Matrix Diagram are discussed.

- Pages 179-195 of [DP-2] describe construction processes for the Process Decision Program Chart.

- Pages 216-232 of [DP-2] describe construction processes for the **Activity Network.**

- Page 275 of [DP-2] gives steps in constructing a **Cause and Effect Diagram.**

14.5.7 Organizing Information for IM. Interactive Management stresses the organization of information by a group led by a facilitator, and using computer assistance. (The computer assistance does **not** involve participants sitting at computer terminals.) Beginning with the information generated using the NGT process discussed in Sections 7.2 and 14.5.3, the specific relationships that are important in organizing the information are determined. Then a group of participants, under the leadership of an experienced facilitator, is presented with a sequence of questions, the responses to which will provide the information needed for the organization of the relationships among the relevant factors. The questions are presented to the design group by a computer-driven display. The computer sequences the questions, keeps track of the answers and, ultimately, computes the organization of the information. **In the process of responding to the questions the members of the design group, in effect, educate one another concerning the nature of the relationships.**

The discussion can be documented and preserved for later interpretation by managers, manufacturing people, or designers who may wish to modify an earlier design. The computerized system that provides the services mentioned is a software program that instruments a process called Interpretive Structural Modeling (ISM). The process algorithm does **not** ensure that group decisions are correct, but **it does ensure that they are logically consistent.**

It is also a requirement of the Interactive Management system that all representations, whether they are networks, digraphs, diagrams, or matrices, shall have the property of *unambiguous translatability into prose.* To attain this desirable state, it is necessary to be attentive to design of the graphical representations.

- *Interpretive Structural Modeling (ISM).* The ISM process is very heavily documented in the literature [Warfield, DP-21, 1976]. It has been converted into software programs at many different places, using different programming languages, and installed on many different kinds of machines. For a long time it could only be used on a mainframe. However in the 1987-88 time frame it became feasible to use this process with software written for a microprocessor. At present, ISM software exists for IBM-PC compatible machines as well as for the Apple McIntosh series and the NeXT machine. With the present state of the software, almost all of the programs provide for organizing qualitative relationships, and some of the programs provide a printed graphical display of the pattern of the relationships that is suitable for working with small numbers of design factors (20 to 25). For more involved designs, almost all the existing software will compute the pattern and provide the information needed to construct it manually.

Table 14.2 shows data gathered from 31 applications of ISM:

TABLE 14.2
DATA ON INTERPRETIVE STRUCTURAL MODELING (ISM)

■ Average duration of a session	3.1 hours
■ Average number of ideas structured	22 ideas
■ Average length of the hierarchical component of the structure produced	6.3
■ Average length of the longest cycle in the structure produced	7.1
■ Average length of the sum of the lengths of the longest cycle and the hierarchical component	13.4

The interpretation of these data is given in Warfield [DP-31, 1994].

■ ***Benefits of Interpretive Structural Modeling.*** The primary benefits of using ISM are the following: (a) the process drives the design group systematically through a detailed consideration of important relationships; (b) the process facilitates the learning process of the participants (which may include manufacturing people), helping them to avoid design errors, and to correct mistaken ideas; (c) the process is self-documenting for later reference, (d) the process is highly-efficient in the use of participant time compared with all other known forms of high-quality information management, and (e) consistency in relationships is maintained by the computer programming.

14.5.8 Comparisons (Organizing Information). Processes QFD and 7JDT cannot be associated with any specific organizing system. Relationships typically can be qualitative, quantitative, or (in the best scheme) a well-defined combination. The premature introduction of high quantitative content usually serves to obscure the qualitative nature of the information behind it, contributing to all kinds of problems. The IM process facilitates the development and understanding of the qualitative relationships, while providing quality control on the details of the relationships. This not only allows discovery of the patterns of relationships, but also gives substantial insight into what kind of quantitative information and how much is needed. There is considerable reason to question the translatability into prose of the representations constructed with QFD and 7JDT. Facilitation, while recommended for some of the processes of organizing information used with QFD and 7JDT, is certainly not stressed in the literature of these processes. Since a skilled facilitator can do much to exert process quality control in group work, the relatively little attention given to this in the literature of QFD and 7JDT **suggests that the latter work is not applying quality control to processes that are supposed to assist in quality control of design and manufacturing.**

■ **Ways of Displaying Information.** A useful perspective on displaying information demands that displays be considered apart from all other aspects of information management.

Interactive Management, QFD, and the 7JDT, all involve organizing information relevant to design and manufacturing. It is important to understand that **a means of organizing information should not be thought of as being the same as the means of displaying information.** The process of organizing information should always have, as its principal purpose, to discover the relationships among information components. A normal followup to the discovery would be **to display the discovered relationships in a form most suitable for human interpretation and decision making relevant to design and manufacturing.** The design and manufacturing culture in the U. S. A. has overlooked this vital distinction.

The history of design for manufacturing in the U. S. A. is one whereby most mechanical design was done at a drawing board, and the education of designers was one that stressed the production of a blueprint that conveyed the shape and measurements of the object to be manufactured. In terms of the distinctions being made here between organizing information and displaying it, there has not been historically any distinction between the two. **Engineering practice embodied (more pointedly, enshrined) the assumption that organization and display of relationships are done simultaneously.** Consequently the logical basis for the organization of information into critical relationships has almost always been considered a byproduct of work done to create the presentation of the visual display.

With the advent of the computer as an aid to designers, a similar practice has usually been followed.

The most evident consequence of overweighting the display to the exclusion of the organization of information is the historical one that has always plagued the relationship of manufacturing people to engineering people. Designers have supplied manufacturers with the quantitative information, but not the logical basis, for what is to be manufactured. Since the manufacturing people have often not understood the logical basis that underpinned the organization of information, and have had to rely only on the displays, costly mistakes have often been made in manufacturing.

One example on a very large scale of this kind of problem is found in the design of nuclear plants. Organizations that design these plans have historically "thrown the blueprints over the wall" to be used by clients who contract for construction of the plants. There can hardly be any informed individual who is not aware of the huge cost overruns incurred by utilities and others in the construction of nuclear plants driven only by displays of configurations as opposed to the logic behind design decisions. It is well-known in the nuclear industry, for example, that the amount of paper created to describe the design of nuclear plants was very small for the early licensing compared to what would be required today for relicensing, in the

195

absence of any change of regulations. The fact that the original plant designers have retired or otherwise vanished from sight poses significant problems for utilities to try to reconstruct the logical basis for plant design in order to get license renewals. The expenses incurred in trying to reconstruct the logic are very large. What we see today reflects willingness of early managers and designers to pass costs off into the future, rather than paying the price required to provide high-quality design information at the earlier time.

14.5.9 Displaying Information for QFD. The display of information in QFD reflects the organizing concept, i.e., to develop several matrices and show side by side those that are equivalently indexed. There is an implicit assumption that must be questioned, which is that because the information is initially organized in matrix form, it must necessarily be displayed in that same form (i.e., automatically the form of generation must be the form of display).

Experience indicates that the information displays for QFD largely consist of screen displays on computer monitors. The information density of these displays can be very high. The displays are in the form of matrices (the same form in which they are produced).

14.5.10 Displaying Information for 7JDT. The mode of displaying information differs among the 7JDT components, but no rationale has been developed to say why each of the representations used has been chosen. The Affinity Diagram is displayed much like a Venn Diagram, with information entered into the separate geometric components of the Affinity Diagram. Other 7JDT components use a digraph-like representation, or a matrix representation.

14.5.11 Displaying Information for IM. The importance of choosing the best display scheme has been stressed in the development of Interactive Management [Warfield, Figure 1, P-8, 1979]. Four different constituent options were considered in this paper. They were:

- A prose sentence
- A graphics sentence
- A set theory model
- A Venn diagram model

It was explained that of these four, only the graphics sentence met the communication requirements. The shortcomings of the other three were stated. In later discussions, the concept of methodology that was "open at scale" was enunciated [Warfield, DP-31, 1994]. The Venn diagram model, frequently used in 7JDT, is explicitly ruled out in IM because it loses its display advantages as soon as the complexity of the display goes beyond a few entries.

196

The typical displays used with IM are located on large walls, where there is ample room for examining these displays, and large lettering to make them easily readable. All such displays are translatable into prose, following the criteria applied in their development.

The displays generally are either digraph-like or field-like (including profiles). Many examples of such displays are found in Warfield [DP-31, 1994] and the circumstances under which they are developed are described in Warfield and Cárdenas [DP-32, 1994].

14.5.12 Comparisons (Displaying Information). Neither QFD nor 7JDT literature gives any significant discussion of how best to display the information developed. The display recommended for the Affinity Diagram, for example, is just a Venn diagram model, even though it is not open at scale, and lacks the advantages of the field and profile representations that are used in IM.

The graphics sentence has become the building block for all IM representations except the field and profile representations. While these two representations can be shown with graphics sentences as building blocks, and if so shown are open at scale in that respect, there are overriding advantages to using the dimensional representation [Warfield, DP-31, 1994] that were not foreseen in the paper dealing with constituent options [Warfield, P-8, 1979]. While the graphics sentence can be thought to be the basis for representing most of the 7JDT tools, the failure to comprehend and apply the concept of translatability to the graphic deprives those representations of a valuable communication capability.

■ **Ways of Interpreting Information. Background.** The ability of design and manufacturing personnel to interpret information is heavily conditioned by their experience with certain specific modes of communication. Americans who attend school and college are given a massive workload involving <u>prose documentation</u>. A smaller subset, those who take part in engineering or technical programs are given a very heavy dose of <u>blueprint graphics</u> instruction, of the type required in developing and reading blueprints. Another subset is introduced to what might be called <u>venture graphics</u> of the type very widely used in PERT and in flow-charting. This class of graphics cannot be called "scientific" because typically this type of graphics grew out of ad hoc commercial usage, often in a situation where the developer and promoter gained a financial advantage by adopting an idiosyncratic graphic communication system. Whenever documentation is produced to describe a design, certain communication issues ought to be paramount. If the modes of communication are restricted to those three types underlined in this paragraph, severe constraints are automatically incurred upon understanding and interpreting the information that is represented.

14.5.13 Interpreting Information for QFD. Here is how the American Supplier Institute report [DP-1] describing QFD deals with the issue of interpreting the information contained in the QFD matrices (and see also, for reference, [Staley and Vora, DP-10, 1990]).

"What to Look For"

From the viewpoint of a manager examining QFD matrices, there are some basic areas you can look for which will help you in discussing and questioning the process.

- Any blank row indicates that there are no requirements for that customer want. This can be the case if the requirements were based on past experience and the customers' inputs were not a driving force in these [sic] previous planning. If the row is blank, action needs to be taken.

- Similarly, blank columns represent requirements that have no customer want as a basis. These requirements should be carefully examined to verify their necessity.

- If any row of [sic] column has only triangles in it indicating weak relationships, there is reason to question the unfulfilled customer want or the apparently unnecessary requirement.

- The 'hows' need top [sic] be quantifiable to the largest extent possible. Look for unmeasurable hows.

- As a rule of thumb, there should be [sic] less than 50% 'white space' in the matrix relationship area. Too little white space makes it extremely difficult to prioritize items. It is better [sic] to have 70-90% white space.

- In examining the competitive assessment both in terms of customer/owner satisfaction and the comparison relative to quantitative requirements, look for areas where the customer says the issue is important and the competition is not meeting the demand well enough. [sic] this may be a sales point, an opportunity to excel and therefore, an area to explore.

- In the correlation matrix (under the roof of the house of quality) look for negative correlations and try to determine ways to eliminate them. If they can not be eliminated, carefully examine the trade-offs for the best approach.

- Look for areas where the customer wants are in conflict with the requirements we have established for meeting those wants. If the customer want has a high level of priority in his view and the engineering specifications give it a low priority, then investigation is needed to resolve this conflict."

14.5.14 Interpreting Information for 7JDT. The interpretation of the representations associated with the 7JDT seems to be regarded by Brassard [DP-2] as a highly intuitive activity. Page 37, for example, in discussing the Affinity Diagram says that:

- "The important thing is that participants allow their creative juices to flow and distill them into the key elements which they must address. An Affinity [sic] is a 'mine of minds' that yields both jewels and junk that can be refined in the remaining tools or through group discussion."

- The Interrelationship Digraph interpretation scheme recommended on page 62 of [DP-2] involves a count of entering and leaving arrows. The view expressed is that if outgoing arrows are dominant, the element may be a basic cause, while if incoming arrows are dominant, the element may be a "secondary issue or bottleneck".

Generally speaking the interpretation of the 7JDT is treated through a series of unsupported assertions.

14.5.15 Interpreting Information for IM. The interpretation of the structures produced with IM involves first of all the recognition that the graphics are translatable into prose. This means that there is no ambiguity in extracting information from the structures. Whatever ambiguity may be present in interpreting the graphics stems from the choice of language of the participants. No process can substitute for careful expression of ideas. The NGT Process specifically requires a period of clarification, and inevitably this period of time exposes the folly of trying to use raw information coming from participants that has not been subjected to review and clarification. If the review and clarification is followed by careful editing, the patterns produced in the IM graphics outputs contain much information, all of which can be extracted. In fact, it is possible for the computer to print out every single statement that is represented in these graphics. What is normally appropriate, however, is for a person who is highly skilled in reading the carefully-designed graphics that emerge from IM activity to develop a written interpretation of the graphic, keyed to make the interpretation both very accurate and very readable. Sometimes a complex graphic will be replaced by a simpler graphic by combining elements of the complex graphic that fit into a common concept. Examples from past work illustrate these points, e.g., the Case Study in Appendix 4.

When a person skilled in interpreting these graphics prepares an interpretation, it is presented to the participants verbally and in writing, whereupon they (a) have a chance to see how what they did is interpreted and (b) have an opportunity to correct or improve upon the interpretation rendered by the person with honed skills in reading graphics.

Technical people who are accustomed to constructing or interpreting PERT charts often confuse **any** graphic with a PERT Chart. They may have more trouble interpreting a graphic product than a novice who has listened to and understood the basis for developing a graphic, free of influence from prior narrow experience in reading graphics.

14.5.16 Comparisons (Interpreting Information). Graphics communication, properly organized, can display a significant amount of relational information in a relatively small space. The density of information is much greater than in typical prose discourse. Prose discourse generally hides the structural relationships contained in the prose. It is for this reason that all three systems, QFD, 7JDT, and IM place a high premium on the use of modes of communication where prose is used only in small packets; and all three rely on non-prose representations to present the information.

The QFD representation hides all the structure that may be present by forcing information to be displayed in the matrix form. The 7JDT representations leave the interpretation to the imagination of the participants, because there is sufficient ambiguity in the development and representation of the structures to demand that the participants develop their own perspectives. The IM system sees ambiguity as a quality degrading factor, and in all parts of the IM system, controls are incorporated to eliminate as much ambiguity as is possible.

QFD and 7JDT treat as natural the predominant use of quantitative information or quantum levels that are roughly akin to quantitative levels. IM treats quantitative information as information to be used only when absolutely necessary to enhance the precision of qualitative relationships that are exposed in the IM representations.

Interpretation may be different from one participant to another in both QFD and 7JDT, while interpretation must be very similar (though not identical) for all IM participants.

■ **Ways of Applying Information.** Whatever methods are employed in the context being considered here, the singular "Catch Up and Pass the Competition Strategy" outlined in Sec. 14.4.2 is the basic recourse for decision making. This strategy has to be tempered by certain constraints, and the clear understanding of those constraints is essential in order to allow the best decisions to be made. The information obtained from QFD, 7JDT, or IM, or some combination will be considered in detail in an effort to make the greatest gains in the face of the given constraints. This demands ultimately that numerical values be used because some of the constraints will inherently be quantitative.

14.5.17 Applying Information for QFD. The information gained from QFD is applied to do Product Planning, Parts Deployment, Process Planning, and Production Planning; and all four of these activities are discussed in detail in two references [DP-1 and King, DP-8]. The activities that are carried out in applying the information are those having to do with decision making and tradeoffs, with the aim of gaining competitive advantage.

14.5.18 Applying Information for 7JDT. Brassard [DP-2] offers several summary sections that provide significant guidance on how to apply the information gained from the 7JDT, in some instances tying them into the total Japanese Tool Box.

On page 266, six tasks are set forth, and the appropriate techniques to be used to deal with these tasks are indicated. The techniques shown in this Technique Selection Guide include a number of tools that are not part of the Japanese Tool Box, such as the NGT.

Appendix A of [DP-2] shows a flow chart contained on pages 252-254 inclusive that indicates where the 7-M-Tools may be used in a process. Appendix B of [DP-2] shows an integration of the 7-M-Tools with the 7-QC-Tools, but also incorporates material from the Kepner-Tregoe method. Part of the admonition given by Brassard is to the effect that good decision making balances knowledge and data; a middle ground that isn't blinded to the logic or to the numbers, but recognizes the importance of reconciling what is known with available data is urged.

Direct comparison of 7JDT with QFD and IM is <u>not</u> facilitated by the materials mentioned, because Brassard has chosen to import other methods **into his summary material!**; specifically, methods that fall outside of the Japanese Tool Box. It is surely not a bad thing to be open to other sources, but to see them for the first time in a summary is odd, except possibly in venture literature. The following are some of the consequences: (a) the reader may be led to believe that Brassard is very familiar with all of the available methods (which he clearly is not); and (b) the specific uses of individual 7JDT items are not readily disassociated for comparison.

14.5.19 Applying Information for IM. All IM work is aimed at two end results: (a) the selection of the best design, whether it be a process or a product, based on specified criteria and (b) the synthesis of a process for producing the specified design. Much of the IM work done so far has stopped short of these results. This is not because the information needed could not be developed. Instead it is because many clients are accustomed to non-systematic, non-participative work, with decisions being undocumented. It is only when this approach fails that clients tend to turn to IM. As soon as IM enables them to see the light at the end of the tunnel, they revert to their former ways. This is partly because their organizational culture is not able to absorb the new ways. Fortunately not all clients have this kind of problem. Significant benefits have been obtained in many IM applications.

14.5.20 Comparisons (Applying Information). People are generally most efficient in using information which they are familiar with in ways they are familiar with. When learning new methods, there is often a tendency to try to make the methods so easy to use that quality and saliency are allowed to play a lesser role than expediency in interpreting or using information in familiar ways.

QFD is not a particularly easy method to learn to use, but by committing it to software, many of the problems in using it can be suppressed from the user, leaving it to the user only to do those things that the software can't do, which is usually to provide substantive information and interpret it. The use of large data matrices clearly suppresses structural information that may be important, so in that respect QFD is deficient. On the other hand, QFD helps considerably with product competitive benchmarking, which seems vital to improvement of competitiveness. There is no evident means in QFD to assure consistency of relational information. In the absence of such a means, there is no good way to assess the significance of this shortcoming. The limited data suggest that QFD requires an inordinate amount of time for the benefits achieved.

The 7JDT are highly intuitive tools, used without adequate quality controls on entries or discussion. Experience suggests that these tools have brought considerably improved performance in practice, largely because they help avoid errors that previously were made by designers and manufacturing people alike. By providing greater breadth to considerations, and more depth to potential error-correcting practices, improvements occur.

IM is a heavily disciplined approach that maintains strict quality controls on the process at all times. In this respect it is very different from QFD and 7JDT. The price paid for this discipline is that a special facility is required in which to do the work, specially trained process facilitators are needed, and careful planning of meetings is vital. In some organizations, it is not possible to establish and maintain the necessary quality controls.

14.6 USER ACCESS TO GENERIC DESIGN SCIENCE: INFRASTRUCTURE AND DECISION REQUIREMENTS.

A central concern in this chapter is to discuss how to provide user access to the generic design science. This implies a precondition that much or perhaps most of what is contained in Interactive Management will be devoted to that user access. (It does not imply, however, that Interactive Management will be used exclusively.)

What is the outline of the central concepts that are involved in making the generic design science accessible to users? The following are the four central points:

1) ***Infrastructure.*** Because (a) this science is broad in scope, (b) it involves the use of non-conventional facilities as a specially-designed working space, (c) it uses sophisticated software in some of its activity, (d) it relies on facilitated groups working together, and (e) there are not many people who are educated in this science; **if it is to be applied significantly in any large organization, it is necessary to provide a supporting infrastructure.**

2) ***Top Management Insight.*** Because this science anticipates and supports a significant change in organizational culture, and therefore requires that individual actors put forth considerable effort involving unfamiliar behavioral patterns; and because experience has shown that such changes cannot be implemented in the long term without visible top management backing from the beginning, certain **highly visible decisions must be taken before the science is applied in the organization's internal programs.**

3) ***No Discontinuities.*** Because the kind of changes that are needed involve a transition to a new mode of operation that will require quite a few months, access to the generic design science will keep changing in extent, style, and scope over time. This means

202

that the supporting infrastructure and the highly visible decisions must be perceived through a time interval, as opposed to being seen as a time point, **to avoid dysfunctional discontinuities in the progress sought.**

4) Fast Credibility. Most organizations are inclined to approach such changes very gingerly, and want to incur a protracted period during which miniscule efforts are used to test the water, and numerous small go-no-go decision points are attained. While this approach was wise in the early days when work started on generic design science, and in the early applications of its initial manifestations; this approach is no longer reasonable. In the changes that are sought, time is of the essence; competitors are a moving target. **Fast credibility should be consciously sought, and can be attained.** There have been hundreds of applications of this science in many locations around the globe, and the personnel who have provided leadership can be consulted (preferably as a group at a single conference, to save time), and they can provide a collective, compelling, and unique perspective on hundreds of applications and on the challenges of implementation. The same individuals who can provide the perspective will be among those chosen to provide assistance in providing initial access to the generic design science in the host organization. *{Note: Individuals who can provide the perspective are identified in Appendix 5.}*

14.6.1 Infrastructure Requirements. The principal infrastructure requirements for providing access to the science of generic design are:

- A specially-designed working facility, estimated to cost $120,000 per copy (if installed in the U. S. A.). Initially a single facility will suffice.
- Equipment, including computers with ISM software, properly located in the facility, whose cost is included in the facility cost estimate.
- Staff who are trained in the planning, facilitation, interpretation, and reporting of the work.

In the early days of the work, the staff should be a mix of in-house personnel and outside contractors. These people will work collaboratively to plan, organize, conduct, interpret, report on, and facilitate implementation of results. For the first year of the work, most of the training will be on-the-job training, with the bulk of the workshop activity being directed by outside contractors. In the second year, in-house education and training will be provided, and in-house interns will assist in the conduct of workshops. In the third year, all of the work will be turned over to company staff, with outside contractors used only in unusual circumstances.

14.6.2 Decision Requirements Top management of the organization must make the key decisions to move forward to provide the funds necessary to create the infrastructure, identify the in-house people who will be involved in the work and whose time will be made available, and provide the funds to support the work of outside contractors who will assist in planning workshops and who will conduct them and help interpret the results.

Before this can be done, top management and staff could plan to take part in a "Credibility Conference" that brings together those key practitioners and scholars who are thoroughly familiar with the science and the hundreds of applications of it, for the purpose of providing the knowledge, insights, and confidence needed to warrant top management to say "go ahead with this with our blessings, and do it is expeditiously as possible".

14.6.3 Implementation: A Hypothetical Scenario. Any decision to move ahead with such changes in an organization must necessarily involve these considerations: (a) the feasibility of introducing the changes without incurring any significant disruption in ongoing company programs; (b) the virtual certainty that the changes will be acceptable to company employees; (c) the likelihood that the changes will enable the singular goal of "catch up and pass the competition" to be achieved within a reasonable period of time; and (d) the assurance that the benefits to be achieved will be vastly larger than the costs incurred. Past experience in introducing such changes shows that the feasibility of introducing the changes without incurring any significant disruption in ongoing company programs is virtually assured by cooperative planning that follows the prescriptions given in earlier chapters of this book..
The likely acceptability of the changes is a conclusion based on extensive previous experience with IM in organizations.

All change processes can be studied by looking at the beginning situation, the desired end situation, and the transition from the beginning situation to the desired end situation.
If the end conditions are well defined, the IM processes can readily be used to design the transition conditions.

14.6.4 Transition Beginning and End Points. Strictly speaking, there should never be an end to the transition, because continuous improvement should be both part of the process design as well as the product design. However, for initial planning purposes, the end of the transition can be marked as that point in time when all of the improvements that can presently be envisioned will have found their way into the existing system, which has become the base for the beginning of change.

14.6.5 Moving from Beginning to End. Movement from the beginning to the end of the transition will require making the decisions identified in Section 14.6.2, developing the infrastructure identified in Section 14.6.1, constructing a transition scenario in detail, and prioritizing the change sequence.

14.6.6 Transition Program Scenario. The development of the transition program scenario is the primary next step. It will involve a cooperative effort between the organization seeking change and those who are knowledgeable of the generic design science. It will especially require corporate management attention at the highest levels, and the availability of talented corporate staff, who will begin to understand the new system and the ways to ease its changes into existing processes.

14.7 ENHANCED INTERACTIVE MANAGEMENT.

A primary goal of the work reported here is to present a process that embodies the best features of QFD, 7JDT and IM. This process will be referred to as "Enhanced Interactive Management", for reasons to be explained later in this section. To pursue this purpose, it is important to identify the unique strengths of QFD, 7JDT, and IM.

The strengths of these several processes can be assessed from two points of view. One is the *broad point of view* that takes into account such factors as sunk investment, personnel familiarity with processes already in use, and cost of conversion to a new system of action. The *narrow point of view* considers only the process features themselves. In the following, elements of both points of view will be considered.

The second issue has to do with uniqueness in a feature. In making this judgment, one may distinguish between *essential uniqueness* and *marginal uniqueness*. If a process is marginally unique, the meaning is that while it has enjoyed uniqueness in practice, it is almost a trivial matter to incorporate that marginal uniqueness in one of the other two process groups. If a process is essentially unique, it has at least one feature that would produce a major change by incorporating it into the other two process groups.

14.7.1 QFD: Unique Strengths. From the broad point of view Quality Function Deployment has the strength that there is already a considerable sunk investment and a familiarity among relevant personnel. Also, because some other organizations are using it, it becomes possible to learn from time to time how to improve it by observing its use in other organizations. Furthermore, the colloquial language used (i.e., the image of a house with a roof, etc.) may make this sophisticated approach less fearsome or more friendly to users, as well as easier to discuss and to conceive. From the narrow point of view, QFD has no unique strengths as a methodology.
However, QFD has an essential uniqueness in that it assigns to each cell of the various matrices quantitative values that are unique to that cell.

14.7.2 7JDT: Unique Strengths. From the broad point of view, the 7 Japanese Design Tools have established a foothold in the U. S. technical community, because of the widespread entrepreneurial dissemination of venture literature describing these tools. The names given to the tools may be fairly well established, so that the possibility of communicating about them may be rather high. The informal way in which these tools are used precludes the need for a well-trained and experienced staff to provide leadership and quality control in the use of the tools. From the narrow point of view, these tools have no unique strengths.

The 7JDT group has no essential uniqueness.

14.7.3 IM: Unique Strengths. From the broad point of view, IM has the unique strength that it is thoroughly grounded in science, and heavily documented. This means that the basis for continuous process improvement is already present. IM has been used in numerous different kinds of agencies and companies, as shown in Table 1.1, so it has a unique and documented history of application. From the narrow point of view, IM meets the requirements for carefully studied and reasoned criteria for choice of methodology.

Accompanying the description of IM are descriptions of a specially-designed facility that has been proved to be excellent for conducting design activity; as well as a carefully-specified set of roles, so that the staffing situation for providing IM services is well-defined.

A single software package is appropriate for constructing any member of the 7JDT group, and can be effective in constructing QFD relationships of a qualitative nature. From the available data, it appears that IM has the capacity to diminish substantially the amount of time required to construct the QFD matrices and the 7JDT structures, while upgrading the quality of their content and the readibility and usability of the documentation.

14.7.4 A Composite Process. In light of the foregoing, it appears that the construction of a composite process that represents an enhanced version of Interactive Management can disregard completely the 7JDT group in deference to IM, because IM produces all of the products that the 7JDT group produces, and does so in a superior way.

The construction of Enhanced IM must recognize the content categories and quantitative information collected in QFD, and incorporate them into it. The alternative of developing what might be called "Enhanced QFD" would involve changing almost totally the way information is gathered, structured, displayed, and interpreted, using the methods of IM. After the bulk of the information has been gathered, structured, displayed, and interpreted; it would then be appropriate to incorporate the quantitative information into QFD matrices, taking advantage of numerous efficiencies that would derive from the use of IM. An amended interpretation could then be made, in the light of any changes introduced by the quantitative information. Application could then benefit from both the IM products and the newly-formed QFD matrices. It is conceivable that ultimately the QFD matrices could be dispensed with altogether for purposes of visual representation for interpretation, being replaced by new presentations of the information in forms more readily interpreted.

The new composite process, a system of action, would also rely on a special-purpose facility of the DEMOSOPHIA type, as well as a set of staff roles experienced in the conduct of IM work. Initially these roles could be contractor roles, but over time all contractors would be phased out, and internal staff would take over the support provisions.

14.8 DETAILED TOOL COMPARISONS

Many scholars are well aware of the benefits brought to Japan by the Western Electric Company Engineers, including Deming, whom the Japanese continue to credit for their industrial successes. Top managers in the US, on the other hand, for the most part still don't seem to understand in any depth the impact of Deming in Japan.

Not long ago, for example, a top executive of a large American firm gave a speech in which he described his surprise and that of his company when they invited Deming to give a talk to his company. The company people didn't anticipate what he would say, even though Deming has been saying the things he said there for decades.

Also not long ago a top executive of another large American firm was featured in the Sunday edition of the Business Section of the Washington Post. In this article, the executive was credited with inventing and implementing a process called "Workout". This process was one of the many advocated by Deming decades earlier, yet the tone of the article was that a totally new idea had been discovered by this executive after thinking about the mental analog of the physical workouts that are so prominent in American television. The great discovery was to bring groups of managers together to discuss openly the problems they were having, so that each might help the other think through possible solutions.

While Deming, Juran, and others helped get statistical process control into Japan; and thereby helped Japanese companies learn how to produce quality products; other American innovations have entered Japanese activity with much less fanfare.

It is notable that Deming dealt directly with top management in Japan, and having started at the top, the flow of information downward in the organization was the key to getting statistical quality control started and keeping it going. Also this approach assured that continuing visibility over the years would accrue to Deming, because the top management understood the source of the ideas and achievements. Clearly such an approach depended for its success upon the willingness of top management (a) to listen, (b) to ask the requisite questions for understanding, (c) to accept something that they did not invent, (d) to provide for the education of subordinates, (e) to implement the ideas in their own organization and (f) to sustain the innovation through time. An environment of "not invented here" cannot be host to such an innovation. Top management's ability to absorb new ideas and their willingness to take action on good ideas is vital.

Other ideas to be discussed in this chapter did **not** enter through the top management route, and their entry was much less visible to top management. In fact the only clear evidence of entry lies in papers published by Japanese engineers in which they refer to the American developments. Even this form of acknowledgment tends to evaporate over time as the innovations diffuse away from the engineers who first noted the American material and first introduced it into Japanese companies. Failure to maintain a clear literature audit trail pollutes the literature and defeats a central purpose of scientists, which is to sustain the capacity of the scientific community to represent properly the sequence of development, and to provide relevant criticism and amendment to previous developments. Moreover a kind of Gresham's law of literature is supported: bad literature drives out good literature, and thereby obscures relevant contributions.

Frequently engineers, when introduced to a new development, will make a very minor alteration in it and present it as their own work in which they may or may not refer to the origins. One one can take that as a mark of non-scientific behavior on the part of people whose primary livelihood may depend, in the long run, on sustaining the credibility of the scientific literature.

14.8.1 The Japanese Tool Box. In June of 1986, the Union of Japanese Scientists and Engineers published a journal issue, [Ishikawa, Editor, DP-6], in which they identified "7-QC-Tools" and "7-M-Tools" (the Quality-Control Tools and Management Tools). The former had been in use for quite a few years in Japan possibly, for some of the tools, going all the way back to Deming's initial recommendations to Japan top management. The latter are described in the referenced journal in these terms: "After a long period of studies by the committee, the 7 Management Tools for QC were proposed in 1977." The two sets of "tools", taken collectively, are referred to here as the **Japanese Tool Box.**

■ **Older 7-QC-Tools.** Table 14.3 identifies the older subset consisting of the 7-QC-Tools.

TABLE 14.3
OLDER 7-QC-TOOLS [1]

■ Pareto Diagram (#1) [Pareto Chart, p. 271/17]
■ Cause and Effect Diagram (#2) [Fishbone Diagram, p. 275/24]
■ Stratification (#3) [Stratification, p.301/76]
■ Check Sheet (#4) [Check Sheet, p. 270/14]
■ Histogram (#5) [Histogram, p. 281/36]
■ Scatter Diagram (#6) [Scatter Diagram, p. 285/44]
■ Graphs and Control Charts (#7) [Control Chart, p. 288/51]

[1] The first listing refers to the nomenclature used in Ishikawa [DP-6, 1986]. The nomenclature in brackets is that used in Brassard [DP-2, 1989]. The first page number in the bracket refers to the actual page number in DP-2. The second number (after the slash) refers to a page number within a page number in DP-2.

■ **Newer 7-M-Tools.** Table 14.4 identifies the newer set consisting of the 7-M-Tools.

TABLE 14.4
NEWER 7-M-TOOLS [7MP TOOLS] [2]

■ Affinity Diagram (#8) [Affinity Diagram, p. 17]
■ Relations Diagram (#9) [Interrelationship Digraph, p. 41]
■ Tree Diagram (#10) [Tree Diagram, p. 73]
■ Matrix Diagram (#11) [Matrix Diagram, p. 135]
■ Matrix-Data Analysis (#12) [Prioritization Matrices [3], p. 99]
■ Process Decision Program Chart (#13) [Process Decision Program Chart, p. 171]
■ Arrow Diagram (#14) [Activity Network Diagram, p. 201]

[2] The first listing refers to the nomenclature used in Ishikawa [DP-6, 1986]. The nomenclature in brackets is that used in Brassard [DP-2, 1989]. The number in brackets is the actual page number in DP-2.
[3] In dealing with the 7MP Tools, Brassard [DP-2] has discarded the Matrix-Data Analysis from the list, and replaced it with Prioritization Matrices.

■ **Combined Use of Tools.** The Japanese strongly urge the combined use of the tools, as opposed to separate use of each one. Also they say that the 7-M-Tools "should <u>not</u> be used for solving simple problems". They point out that it usually takes a long time to solve a problem using the 7-M tools for QC. Also they recommend "parallel use of numerical data" [Ishikawa, DP-6, 1986].

■ **Reorganization of the Japanese Tool Box.** The organization of the Japanese Tool Box according to Tables 14.3 and 14.4 is **historical in terms of their acceptance.** A different way of organizing these tools is required in order to provide an organized discussion of them effectively. Of these 14 tools, seven may be called "qualitative relational diagrams". Underlying their structure is the basic theory of relations going back in history to the 1847 publication by Augustus De Morgan, and subsequent elaboration by other scholars. The importance of recognizing this is as follows: because these seven stem from the same underlying mathematics of relations, it is possible to apply the same computerized scheme to work with any of the seven. In turn, this makes possible a very efficient scheme for generating, organizing, and displaying any of the seven qualitative relational diagrams (QRD's). It is also true that there are a good many other qualitative relational diagrams that can be incorporated into the same software scheme. From this perspective, these seven can be seen as members of a very large family of qualitative relational diagrams, some of which will be more useful in some design situations than the seven found in the Japanese Tool Box. Failure to recognize this common root introduces a confusion of nomenclature into the names of the members of the Japanese Tool Box, as will be explained shortly. Table 14.5 lists those items from the Japanese Tool Box that are QRD's.

TABLE 14.5
QUALITATIVE RELATIONAL DIAGRAMS
FROM THE JAPANESE TOOL BOX

■ Cause and Effect Diagram (#2)
■ Affinity Diagram (#8)
■ Relations Diagram (or Relationship Digraph) (#9)
■ Tree Diagram (#10)
■ Matrix Diagram (#11)
■ Process Decision Program Chart (#13)
■ Arrow Diagram (#14)

Once more, **all seven of the Qualitative Relational Diagrams can be developed through the same process with only minor variations! There is no hint of this possibility in the journal issue published by the Union of Japanese Engineers and Scientists, (even though other Japanese have published research papers that relate directly to the theory of relations, as implemented in Interpretive Structural Modeling).**

The theory and process for the development of the QRD's (based in the theory of relations) was developed at the Battelle Memorial Institute in Columbus, Ohio, in the period 1970-1973, largely by Warfield, with some help also from colleagues at Battelle. Moreover, specialized diagrams that are members of this family were also largely developed as a part of or as a direct consequence of the Battelle work [Warfield, DP-20, 1974 and DP-21, 1976].

14.8.2 Quality Function Deployment. In 1971, at Battelle Columbus Laboratories, J. D. Hill and J. N. Warfield developed a concept called "Unified Program Planning", then applied it to complex system design, and then published an illustration of how it could be used in contemplating the design of a V-STOL aircraft [Hill and Warfield, DP-5, 1972]. This publication was preceded by an earlier one whose contents were delivered at an international conference at Purdue University (arranged by the School of Industrial Engineering) and published by Purdue, with a later publication in a refereed journal [Warfield, DP-18, 1972, 1973]. Seventeen years later, the <u>Harvard Business Review</u> [Hauser and Clausing, DP-4, 1988] published an article stating that this method had been invented in Japan and was brought to the U. S. by some New Englanders and introduced to Ford Motor Company, which started using it in 1987. This "Japanese development" was called by either of two names, the one being "The House of Quality" and the other being "Quality Function Deployment" (QFD). A detailed letter to the Editor of the <u>Harvard Business Review</u> (one of the more high-class parts of the venture literature) produced a short, friendly response, but absolutely no indication in the later issues of that publication that any mistake or misimpression had been introduced, in spite of the highly documented nature of what was presented to that publication.

A publication from the U. S. venture literature [King, DP-8, 1989 (3rd Ed.)] includes a Foreword by Professor Yoji Akao (an industrial engineer) that gives a somewhat different history of the evolution of QFD. In the Foreword, these events are mentioned:

1966--Professor Akao "first proposed the concept of QFD".

1972--Professor Akao "introduced the idea of 'quality deployment' and how to go about it, based on the efforts to try it out in several companies". He "could not, however, come up with the best way to set up quality control in planning until I hit upon the idea of the quality control chart introduced subsequently at the Kobe Shipyard of Mitsubishi Heavy Industries".

1978--A book was published under the co-editorship of Mizuno and Akao: "After years of development, we could finally put together a book on 'Quality Function Deployment'". The citation appearing in [DP-8] is: Shigeru Mizuno and Yoji Akao (1978): "Quality Function Deployment - An Approach to CWQC", J. U. S. E.

1983--Professor Akao conducted the first seminar on the subject of QFD in the United States in Chicago.

1985--Professor Akao met Bob King.

1987--The first publication of <u>Better Designs in Half the Time</u> by Bob King appeared. It includes this citation: Yoji Akao (1987): "Quality Function Deployment", JSA.

1989--A revised version of <u>Better Designs in Half the Time</u> appeared. In addition to the Akao approach, the book also "includes the New Concept Selection Methods of Stuart Pugh of Scotland".

Meanwhile Ford Motor Company has supported the development and use of extensive software called TIES to make possible the continuing use of QFD in their company [Staley and Vora, DP-10, 1990; Vora et al, DP-14, 1989, Vora et al, DP-15, 1990].

14.8.3 Producing the Qualitative Relational Diagrams. The system available for producing the QRD'S listed in Table 14.3 is referred to as Interactive Management [Warfield, DP-25, 1983, DP-26, 1984; Warfield and Cárdenas, DP-32, 1994]. Interactive Management makes use of the Science of Generic Design [Warfield, DP-30, 1990 and DP-31, 1994], and especially it uses a process called Interpretive Structural Modeling invented at Battelle and heavily documented and tested [Warfield, DP-20, 1974, DP-21, 1976, DP-29, 1990] . [The library of the Defense Systems Management College, Fort Belvoir, Virginia, contains a five-drawer filing cabinet (the "IASIS File") filled with documentation and heavily indexed.]. The same process can be applied to develop a significant part (but not all) of the QFD linked matrices.

One problem faced by the system designer is how to choose which QRD(s) to produce in a specific design situation. The rationale for making such choices has been explained [Warfield and Cárdenas, DP-32, 1994] in the light of the variety of situations that a system designer may encounter.

14.8.4 Exploring The Qualitative Relational Diagrams. In this section, the 7JDT's will be discussed and compared to the QRD's.

■ **Cause and Effect Diagram (#2).**

The "Cause and Effect Diagram" (also called a "Fishbone Diagram", because it has been drawn to look like the skeleton of a fish, and sometimes is shown within the outline of a fish) is a graphical structure wherein a given event is perceived and so designated as a cause of another event (the effect). But this caused event (the effect) may then itself become a cause of still another event and so on. The benefit of such a diagram is to help the individual understand a complex interplay of events wherein many are both cause and effect; in effect to understand a complex process. [Lester Thurow, Dean of the Sloan School, has pointed out that perhaps the greatest distinction between the Japanese industry and the American is that the former is much more competent in the process area.]

Two types of diagrams that compare directly to the cause and effect diagram have been a part of the Battelle-initiated activity since its inception. One is called the "Problematique", and the other is called an "Enhancement Structure". In the Problematique, the elements of the structure are related through an "aggravation relation"--i.e., "element A aggravates element B". We can readily change the language to read that "element A is a cause of an increase in the intensity of element B". In the Enhancement Structure, the relationship is changed to "element A enhances element B".

The Problematique became part of the Battelle interest in the early 1970's, when it was used as the core of the project at the Battelle Geneva Laboratories to understand the "World Problematique". Many publications were distributed all over the world in the period around 1973 to help people understand (a) how problems were linked, and (b) that many of them couldn't be resolved without international cooperation. The long and difficult questionnaire that was used at that time to gain the necessary data was seen as a major problem, and that is one of the several reasons that the Interpretive Structural Modeling process was invented--to cut down on the difficulty of creating Problematiques as well as Enhancement Structures. Large numbers of examples of such structures are contained in the IASIS file in the libraries mentioned.

The problematique reflects a somewhat different philosophy than that exemplified by the Cause and Effect Diagram. As pointed out earlier [Warfield, DP-18, 1972], Pascal said that "everything is both cause and effect, working and worked upon, mediate and immediate, all things mutually dependent"; and Goethe said "The thinker makes a great mistake when he asks after cause and effect. They both together make up the indivisible phenomenon". The problematique shows, for the selected relationship, the mutuality of relationship that can be perceived by the participants in its development, expressed as structural cycles. Where a one-way relationship is all that can be perceived that, too, is shown as such.

■ **The Affinity Diagram (#8).**

The Affinity Diagram is one graphical transformation away from what is called the Field or the Options Field. The concept of a Field for organizing complex information into related groups with the help of the Interpretive Structural Modeling Process was developed in the period 1976-1979, and was published in connection with an environmental education project [Warfield, DP-22, 1979]. It does not predate the Affinity Diagram. On the other hand, it is superior to the Affinity Diagram in its visual significance and utility in design for numerous reasons, one of which is that it is "open at scale" and can readily be extended to produce a "tapestry" of fields. The latter may be used to represent all perceived design options for a very complex system, organized into design dimensions which are sequenced for design decision making.

■ **The Relations Diagram (#9).**

In designating a "relations diagram", the Japanese have given what ought to be a generic name to a specific kind of application. Once again, this is essentially the same as the Problematique described above. What hasn't been clearly understood is that distinctions among these types depend solely on the type of elements and the kind of relationship that is being used, as many applications in the IASIS File illustrate.

■ **The Tree Diagram (#10).**

As described in the Japanese literature, the Tree Diagram is closest to the Intent Structure [Warfield, DP-19, 1973]. However the presupposition of a tree structure is no longer required in any of the applications because the Interpretive Structural Modeling process yields the structure that is appropriate to the information furnished. So if the structure is a tree, a tree will appear as the product of the process; but if the structure is some other kind, the other kind will appear as a consequence of the process used.

■ **The Matrix Diagram (#11).**

The matrix diagram is presented by the Japanese as a matrix showing a connection between objectives and means. The connection is first developed in qualitative form simply to show its existence; then it is modified to show the strength of the connection. However this is only one type of matrix that is important in system design. The Unified Program Planning Process recognized the value of interconnecting matrix diagrams [Warfield, DP-18, 1972, and Hill and Warfield, DP-17, 1972] and, more importantly, recognized that the matrix itself is often not the best form of representation of the information. Any information that can be represented in a matrix diagram can also be represented in a "digraph-like" structure. The latter is often much easier to read and interpret, largely because it makes the structure visible, while the structure is obscured in the matrix. The specific type of structure corresponding to the qualitative portion of the Matrix Diagram is called a Resolution Structure in Interactive Management literature, and can be produced using the George Mason University PC ISM software [Warfield and Cárdenas, DP-32, 1994].

■ **The Process Decision Program Chart (#13).**

The Process Decision Program Chart is functionally like a DELTA Chart [Warfield and Hill, DP-16, 1971] introduced as a proposed successor to PERT. The reasons why a successor to PERT was warranted were given, and have since been elaborated along with presentation of an improved version of the DELTA Chart [Warfield, DP-31, 1994].

■ **The Arrow Diagram (#14).**

Again the Japanese have taken a potentially generic term and applied it to a specific case. The Arrow Diagram is the same as a PERT diagram. The difference between #13 and #14 is that #13 includes more information and is drawn differently. However both #13 and #14 can be replaced by the DELTA Chart.

14.9 SUMMARY AND CONCLUSIONS

Three sets of processes can be thought of initially as competitors for use in applications involving the relationship between design and manufacturing. These are: (a) Quality Function Deployment (QFD), (b) the 7 Japanese Design Tools (7JDT), and (c) Interactive Management (IM).

These three sets of processes have been assessed on the basis of five criteria related to producing and using information or, in a finer grained set of criteria: *generating, organizing, displaying, interpreting, and applying information*. Depending on current organizational practices, any one of the three competitors could initially be in a favored position by virtue of familiarity and past usage. For example, QFD would be in a favored position in the American domestic auto industry. However, upon applying the criteria to the three competitors, it can be seen that a composite process which can be called "enhanced IM" holds the possibility of becoming significantly superior to QFD. Enhanced IM would take most of the current aspects of IM, and incorporate the quantitative aspects of QFD. The use of Enhanced IM would also involve a specially-constructed facility for carrying out the process, and would be supported by a staff trained primarily in IM.

Two of the main consequences of a transition to Enhanced IM would be ***greatly increased efficiency in design activity***, thereby cutting significant amounts of time and cost out of the design process; and ***greatly upgraded documentation*** which would diminish errors stemming from poor graphical communication among designers and manufacturing personnel.

Because of the current international competitive situation, there is no time to lose in introducing processes that have clear benefits in time and cost. IM has been applied successfully in many organizations, and there is ample evidence available from past applications to provide firm credibility concerning the efficacy of the process. Therefore it is ***not*** recommended that a gradual approach be taken over a period of years to introduce the changes. Instead, it is recommended that a "credibility conference" be convened, where overwhelming evidence can be produced from a variety of sources, to establish the adequacy of the rationale for moving into Enhanced IM.

A joint plan would then be formulated to proceed with all due haste on the basis of "speed with quality" to institute the new system. This would involve the use of experienced contractors who have good track records in industry work. The sponsoring organization would construct and equip a DEMOSOPHIA facility (see DP-31 for photographs of one such facility) to carry out the work. After sufficient experience has been gained by internal personnel, the contractor staff would be phased out, and corporate staff would take over the provision of the support services required. A training program would be carried out to assist these personnel in the transition. This could include brief internships at locations where IM is now being practiced.

REFERENCES

[The following prefixes are used to designate the nature of a reference: **SF**, system failure; **JG**, a Japanese or German publication relating to structural modeling (ISM); **OC**, organizational cultures; **DP**, design processes; and **P**, prescriptions.]

A. REFERENCES TO SYSTEM FAILURE

SF-1. W. L. Alpert, "A $230 Million Turkey: The Sad Saga of Trilogy", <u>Barrons</u>, New York: Dow-Jones, Aug. 27, **1984**.

SF-2. F. Brooks (Chair), Report of the Defense Science Board on Military Software, Office of the Under Secretary of Defense for Acquisition, Washington, D. C., 20301, September, **1987.**

SF-3. J. R. Fisher, <u>Work Without Managers: A View from the Trenches,</u> Tampa, FL: The DELTA Group, **1991.**

SF-4. John Kemeny, "Chairing a Presidential Commission: Reflections", transcript of a talk delivered at MIT, April 11, **1980**.

SF-5. John N. Warfield, "What Disciplines Large-Scale Systems Design?", <u>Proceedings of the 1987 Conference on Planning and Design in the Management of Business and Organizations</u> (P. C. Nutt, Editor), New York: American Society of Mechanical Engineers, 1987, 1-8.

B. REFERENCES TO JAPANESE/GERMAN PUBLICATIONS RELEVANT TO STRUCTURAL MODELING

JG-1. M. Arai, S. Tamura, and H. Mizutani, "A Method for Structured Modeling of Complex Systems," Toshiba R&D Center, Kanagwa, Japan, **1981**.

JG-2. K. Haruna and N. Komoda, "An Algorithm for Structural Sensitivity Analysis in Structural Modeling", <u>Proc. **1978** International IEEE Conference on Cybernetics and Society,</u> IEEE: New York, 989-994.

JG-3. N. Komoda and K. Haruna, "Accessibility and Maintainability in Man-Machine Interactive Structural Modeling", <u>Proc. **1978** International Conference on Cybernetics and Society,</u> IEEE: New York, 1978, 1231-1246.

JG-4. K. Kawamura, "Interpretive Structural Modeling", <u>Journal of the Society of Instrument and Control Engineers,</u> Special Issue on Society and Control 16(1), **1977**, 157-161 (in Japanese).

JG-5. K. Komaya and T. Fukuda, "A Method of Analysis and Synthesis of Complex System", <u>IEEE Proc. of the International Conference on Cybernetics and Society,</u> IEEE: New York, **1980**, 816-820.

JG-6. F. Mizoguchi, K. Tahara, and M. Saito, "Use of ISM to an Analysis of Expert Role in Simulation Modeling Process", <u>Proc. **1978** International IEEE Conference on Cybernetics and Society,</u> IEEE: New York, 983-988.

JG-7. K. Nakao, M. Funabashi, H. Maezawa and M. Ohnari, "Successive Hierarchical Structuring Method: A New Tool for Constructing Objectives Trees", <u>Proc. **1978** International IEEE Conference on Cybernetics and Society,</u> IEEE: New York, 1272-1277.

JG-8. Y. Nishikawa and A. Udo, "Methods of Interpretive Structural Modeling Considering Intransitivity in Human Judgments", <u>Proc. 1978 International Conference on Cybernetics and Society,</u> IEEE: New York, **1978**, 1266-1271.

JG-9. A. Ohuchi, I. Kaji, and J. N. Warfield, "Structural Analysis and a Complexity Metric for High-Level Software Languages", <u>Proceedings of the Conference of the Japan Information Processing Society</u> (in Japanese), **1988**, 646-647.

JG-10. T. Sato, "Hierarchical Display of Networks of Teaching Elements Using the Interpretive Structural Modeling Method", <u>IECE Transactions on Educational Technology</u> ET78-4, **1978,** 23-28 (in Japanese).

JG-11. T. Sato, "Determination of Hierarchical Networks of Instructional Units Using the ISM Method", <u>Education Technology Research</u> 3, 67-75, **1979.**

JG-12. Y. Sawaragi and K. Kawamura, <u>Participatory Systems Approach: Methods and Applications,</u> Tokyo: Daily Industrial Newspaper Company, **1982** (in Japanese)

JG-13. K. Sugiyama, S. Tagawa, and M. Toda, "Methods for Visual Understanding of Hierarchical System Structures", <u>IEEE Transactions on Systems, Man, and Cybernetics</u> 11(2), 109-125, **1981**.

JG-14. M. Szyperski and M. Eul-Bischoff, <u>Interpretative Strukturmodellierung (ISM)</u> Braunschweig: Vieweg, **1983** (in German)

C. REFERENCES ON ORGANIZATIONAL CULTURES

OC-1. Chris Argyris, <u>Reasoning, Learning, and Action</u>, San Francisco: Jossey-Bass, **1982.**

OC-2. Warren Bennis, "The Four Components of Leadership", <u>Training and Development Journal</u> 38(8), Aug., **1984**, 15-19.

OC-3. Kenneth Boulding, "Towards a Theory of Vulnerability", <u>J. Appl. Syst. Anal</u>. 16, **1989**, 11-17.

OC-4. Taft H. Broome, Jr., "The Slippery Ethics of Engineering", <u>The Washington Post,</u> .(Outposts Section), December 28, **1986.**

OC-5. G. R. Bushe, "Cultural Contradictions of Statistical Process Control in American Manufacturing Organizations", <u>Journal of Management</u> 14(1), **1988**, 19-31.

OC-6. J. B. Conant, <u>Two Modes of Thought</u>, New York: Trident, **1964**.

OC-7. Anthony Downs, <u>Inside Bureaucracy,</u> Boston: Little, Brown, **1967.**

OC-8. Duane S. Elgin, "Limits to the Management of Large, Complex Systems," Stanford Research Institute Report, February, **1977**.

OC-9. Amatai Etzioni, "Societal Overload: Sources, Components, and Corrections", <u>Political Science Quarterly</u> 92(4), **1977-78**, 607-631.

OC-10. U. Fidelman, "Experimental Testing of Constructivism and Related Theories", <u>Behavioral Science</u> 36(4), 1991, 274-297.

OC-11. Honeywell Lectures (a series of lectures presented at the University of Minnesota in connection with a new center for development of technical leadership sponsored by Honeywell Corporation)

OC-12. I. L. Janis, <u>Stress, Attitudes, and Decisions,</u> New York: Praeger, **1982**.

OC-13. A. L. Kroeber and C. Kluckhohn, "Culture: A Critical Review of Concepts and Definitions", <u>Papers of the Peabody Museum of American Archaeology and Ethnology</u> 47(1), Cambridge: Harvard University Press, **1952**.

OC-14. J. L. LeMoigne, "The Paradoxes of the Contemporary Engineer", <u>European Journal of Engineering Education</u> 6, **1981**, 105-115.

OC-15. Thomas H. Lee, Keynote address on models and modeling, a talk given at the annual meeting of the International Society for General Systems Research, Budapest, Hungary, June, **1987.**

OC-16. J. Lukasiewicz, "The Ignorance Explosion", <u>International Journal of the Contemporary Artist</u> 7(2), **1974**, 159-163.

OC-17. C. Margerison and A. Kakabadse, <u>How American Chief Executives Succeed</u>, New York: American Management Associations, **1984**.

OC-18. James Martin and Carma McClure, <u>Diagramming Techniques for Analysts and Programmers</u>, Englewood Cliffs: Prentice-Hall, **1985.**

OC-19. H. Mintzberg, "Why America Needs, But Cannot Have, Corporate Democracy", <u>Organization Dynamics,</u> Spring, **1983**, 5-20.

OC-20. M. Moriconi and A. L. Lansky, "Representation and Refinement of Software Specifications", <u>Software Validation</u> (H. L. Hauser, Ed.), Elsevier, **1984**.

OC-21. D. Muster and W. H. Weekes, "System Duality and Equilibrium States in Organization Design", <u>Proceedings of the International Society for General Systems Research,</u> Budapest, June, **1987**.

OC-22. Charles Perrow, Normal Accidents: <u>Living With High-Risk Technologies,</u> New York: Basic Books, **1984**.

OC-23. R. B. Reich, "The Next American Frontier", <u>The Atlantic Monthly,</u> March, 1983, 43-58 and April, **1983**, 97-108.

OC-24. G. Vickers, <u>Human Systems are Different</u>, London: Harper and Row, **1983**.

OC-25. R. J. Waller, "Traps That Lurk in Your Decisions", <u>The Des Moines Sunday Register,</u> circa **1986.**

OC-26. T. J. Watson, "A Business and Its Beliefs", <u>Computerworld,</u> Dec. 14, **1985**.

OC-27. A. L. Wilkins, "The Culture Audit: A Tool for Understanding Organizations", <u>Organization Dynamics,</u> Autumn, **1983**, 24-38.

OC-28. G. Zaltman, "Knowledge Disavowal in Organizations", in <u>Producing Useful Knowledge for Organizations</u> (R. H. Killman, et al, Eds.), New York: Praeger, **1983**.

D. REFERENCES ON DESIGN PROCESSES

DP-1. American Supplier Institute, "Quality Function Deployment: 3-day Workshop Implementation Manual", Dearborn, MI: 1987.

DP-2. Michael Brassard, The Memory Jogger Plus +, Methuen, MA: Goal/QPC, **1989**.

DP-3. A. L. Delbecq, A. H. Van de Ven, and D. H. Gustafson, Group Techniques for Program Planning: A Guide to Nominal Group and DELPHI Processes, Glenview, IL: Scott-Foresman, **1975**

DP-4. J. R. Hauser and D. Clausing, "The House of Quality", Harvard Business Review, May-June, **1988**, 63-73.

DP-5. J. D. Hill and J. N. Warfield, "Unified Program Planning", IEEE Transactions on Systems, Man, and Cybernetics SMC-2(5), November, **1972**, 610-621.

DP-6. Kaoru Ishikawa, Editor, Reports of Statistical Application Research, Union of Japanese Scientists and Engineers, Special Issue: "Seven Management Tools for QC", Vol. 33, No. 2, June, **1986** (60 pages).

DP-7. K. Kawamura and D. W. Malone, "Structuring Objectives in a Systematic Decision-Making Methodology", Proc. **1975** Pittsburgh Conf. on Modeling and Simulation, Instrument Society of America, Pittsburgh, 779-784.

DP-8. Bob King, Better Designs in Half the Time: Implementing QFD Quality Function Deployment in America (with a Foreword by Professor Yoji Akao, Tamagawa University, Tokyo, Japan), Methuen, MA: Goal/QPC, Third Edition, 1989.

DP-9. S. M. Staley, "Topics in Design Theory and Methodology", Proceedings of the IPC-91 Conference, Detroit, MI, April, **1991**.

DP-10. S. M. Staley and L. S. Vora, "Reconciling Design Theory and Methodology: QFD/TIES and its Place in the Domain of Science Model", Internal Research Report (SR-90-41), Ford Motor Company, February, **1990.**

DP-11. L. C. Thurow, "A Weakness in Process Technology", Science 238, 18 Dec., **1987**, 1659-1663.

DP-12. L. P. Sullivan, "Quality Function Deployment", Quality Progress 19(6), June, **1986,** 39-50.

DP-13. E. H. Vannoy and J. A. Davis, "Test Development Using the QFD Approach", SAE Technical Paper 890807, Warrendale, PA: Society of Automotive Engineers, **1989**.

DP-14. L. S. Vora, et al, "Technical Information Engineering System (TIES)", Proceedings AUTOFACT-89, pages 26:37 to 26:44, Detroit, MI, October, **1989**.

DP-15. L. S. Vora, et al, "TIES: An Engineering Design Methodology and System", Proceedings IAAI-90, Washington, D. C., May, **1990.**

DP-16. J. N. Warfield and J. D. Hill, "The DELTA Chart: A Method for R&D Project Portrayal", IEEE Transactions on Engineering Management EM-18(4), November, **1971**, 132-139.

DP-17. J. N. Warfield and J. D. Hill, A Unified Systems Engineering Concept, Columbus, OH: Battelle, **1972**.

DP-18. J. N. Warfield, "Participative Methodology for Public Systems Planning", Proceedings of an International Symposium on Systems Engineering and Analysis, West Lafayette, IN: Purdue University, October, **1972**, 23-40 [reprinted in Computers and Electrical Engineering 1(1), 1973, 187-210 by invitation of the Editor].

DP-19. J. N. Warfield, "Intent Structures", IEEE Transactions on Systems, Man, and Cybernetics, March, **1973,** 133-140.

DP-20. J. N. Warfield, Structuring Complex Systems, Columbus, OH: Battelle Memorial Institute, Monograph No. 4, April, **1974**.

DP-21. J. N. Warfield, Societal Systems: Planning, Policy, and Complexity, New York: Wiley, **1976** (reprinted, Salinas, CA: Intersystems, 1989; Chinese translation, Zhang Bihui and Li Da Xu, Editors, Wuhan, China, 1992).

DP-22. J. N. Warfield, Systems Planning for Environmental Education", IEEE Transactions on Systems, Man, and Cybernetics, December, **1979**, 816-823.

DP-23. J. N. Warfield, "Priority Structures", IEEE Transactions on Systems, Man, and Cybernetics, October, **1980,** 642-645.

DP-24. J. N. Warfield, "Selecting Participation Methodologies for Systems Design", Proceedings of an International Conference on Cybernetics and Society, New York: IEEE, January, **1983**, 762-764.

DP-25. J. N. Warfield, "Principles of Interactive Management", <u>Proceedings of an International Conference on Cybernetics and Society,</u> New York: IEEE, January, **1983**, 746-750.

DP-26. J. N. Warfield, "Progress in Interactive Management", <u>Proceedings of the 6th International Congress of the World Organization of General Systems and Cybernetics,</u> Paris: AFCET, **1984, XXIX-XXXV.**

DP-27. J. N. Warfield, "Dimensionality", <u>Proceedings of the 1986 International Conference on Systems, Man, and Cybernetics,</u> Vol. 2, New York: IEEE, **1986**, 1118-1121.

DP-28. J. N. Warfield, "What Disciplines Large-Scale System Design?", <u>Proceedings of the 1987 Conference on Planning and Design in the Management of Business and Organizations</u> (P. C. Nutt, Editor), New York: American Society of Mechanical Engineers, **1987**, 1-8.

DP-29. J. N. Warfield, <u>Annotated Bibliography: Interpretive Structural Modeling and Related Work,</u> Fairfax, VA: IASIS, **1990**, 131 pages, 2nd Edition (first edition was made available by the Department of Electrical Engineering, University of Virginia, 1980.)

DP-30. J. N. Warfield, <u>Annotated Bibliography: Generic Systems Design and Interactive Management,</u> Fairfax, VA: IASIS, **1990**, 141 pp.

DP-31. J. N. Warfield, <u>A Science of Generic Design: Managing Complexity Through Systems Design,</u> First Edition, Salinas, CA: Intersystems, **1990** (two volumes); Second Edition, Ames, IA: Iowa State University Press, **1994**.

DP-32. J. N. Warfield and Roxana Cárdenas, <u>A Handbook of Interactive Management</u>, Ames, IA: Iowa State University Press, **1994** (the book you are reading).

DP-33. E. Zameirowski, D. Hornbach, and R. Fitz, "Ecological Components of Climax Agriculture: An Example of Structuring Complex Feedback Systems", <u>Proc. Intl. Conf. on Cybernetics and Society,</u> New York: IEEE, **1976**, 667-673.

DP-34. R. E. Zultner, "Software Quality [Function] Deployment: Applying QFD to Software", Princeton, NJ: Zultner & Company, **1989.**

E. REFERENCES ON PRESCRIPTIONS

P-1. Peter F. Drucker, "The Emerging Theory of Manufacturing", Harvard Business Review, May-June, **1990,** 94-102.

P-2. E. M. Goldratt and J. Cox, The Goal: A Process of Ongoing Improvement, Croton-on-Hudson, NY: North River Press, Revised Edition, **1986.**

P-3. Charles Handy, The Age of Unreason, Boston: Harvard Business School Press, **1990**.

P-4. S. Marsland and M. Beer, "The Evolution of Japanese Management: Lessons for U. S. Managers", Organization Dynamics, Winter, **1983**, 49-67.

P-5. F. D. Peschanel, "System Design With the Right Brain,", Proc. 6th Intl. Congress of the WOGSC 2, Paris: AFCET, **1984**, 725-730.

P-6. G. A. Rummler and A. P. Brache, "Managing the White Space", Training, January, **1991**, 55-70.

P-7. Peter Senge, The Fifth Discipline: The Art and Practice of the Learning Organization, New York: Doubleday, **1990**.

P-8. J. N. Warfield, "Some Principles of Knowledge Organization", IEEE Transactions on Systems, Man, and Cybernetics 9(6), June, **1979**, 317-325].

P-9. Y. E. Zussman, "Learning from the Japanese: Management in a Resource-Scarce World", Organization Dynamics, Winter, **1983**, 68-80.

STUDY QUESTIONS
CHAPTER 14. COMPARING IM WITH METHODS WIDELY USED IN JAPAN

1. What two major types of literature deal with comparisons of methods or processes?

2. What attributes characterize venture literature?

3. What three systems of methods are compared in this Chapter?

4. What categories of reference materials are presented?

5. What sources are used for technical nomenclature?

6. What do these acroynms represent: (a) QFD, (b) 7-QC, (c) 7-M, (d) JTB, (e) 7JDT?

7. What is meant by competitive benchmarking?

8. What do companies usually do and what do they usually not do with respect to competitive benchmarking; if they do anything at all?

9. What singular goal might be applied to implement a "catch up and pass strategy"?

10. What five factors are applied in making process comparisons?

11. What are the conclusions of comparisons on *Generating* Information?

12. What are the conclusions of comparisons on *Organizing* Information?

13. What are the conclusions of comparisons on *Displaying* Information?

14. What are the conclusions of comparisons on *Interpreting* Information?

15. What are the conclusions of comparisons on *Applying* Information?

16. What central concepts are involved in making the generic design science accessible to users?

17. What are the unique strengths of (a) QFD? (b) 7JDT? (c) IM?

18. What are the seven older Q-C tools?

19. What are the newer 7-M tools?

20. What do the Japanese recommend concerning the combined use of the tools?

21. What are the qualitative relations in the Japanese Tool Box?

22. What process can be used to produce all seven of the qualitative relational diagrams?

APPENDIX 1

EXECUTIVE OVERVIEW OF INTERACTIVE MANAGEMENT

This overview of Interactive Management (IM) is meant to serve executives who will oversee installations of IM in their organizations. Installation of IM will be part of a strategy for systematically attacking complex issues involving their organizations, or to enable the organizations to provide services to other client organizations in which IM plays a key role.

No prior detailed knowledge of IM is presumed, nor is it presumed that the reader intends to gain such detailed knowledge. Instead it deals only with the major factors that high-level executives need to know in order to supervise or direct the work of subordinates to help ensure that they are pursuing a wise course in their work to introduce and install IM in the organization. This information will help the executive know what to ask and what kinds of directions or suggestions to provide to those who report to the executive.

The executive should understand that IM is a participative process for helping groups work together on complex issues. Because the issues are complex, the process and its theory is complex and requires substantial study and experience for expertise. It is possible to state eleven rules which, if followed, will go a long ways to ensure that high-quality work can be done and good results achieved while those involved with IM are still learning about it. To understand them, additional explanation is needed, which follows the statements of the rules.

A1.1 RULES FOR SOUND INTRODUCTION AND USE OF INTERACTIVE MANAGEMENT

Rule 1. SUCCESS AND FAILURE. Check Lists reveal the success factors and failure factors for each of the Three Phases of IM. Learn them and apply them.

Rule 2. SUCCESS LEVELS. Possible Outcomes from the application of IM are enumerated. These Outcomes may promote success at any of five stated levels. For any given application of IM, be sure to assess the expected Outcomes against the five Success Levels, and decide on what minimum level of success is required in order to warrant the application of IM.

Rule 3. STANDARDIZATION. Standardization is essential for quality control of IM in applications. Standardization comes from well-defined modular concepts treated as inviolable for: (a) Roles, (b) Processes (methodologies), and (c) IM Products (pattern types).

227

Rule 4. FLEXIBILITY. Flexibility is also essential for quality control of IM in applications. Flexibility comes from the way the Process and Product modules are chosen, sequenced, and packaged for each particular application, and in the choice of actors to fill Roles in each application. Study the packaging applied in previous applications to gain an understanding of the flexibility that is available, and how it has been used.

Rule 5. PROACTIVE AND AVOIDANCE BEHAVIOR. Behavioral components of the Success, Failure, and Outcome Check Lists should be understood, observed, and assessed for both proactive and avoidance behavior by all actors for all three Phases of Interactive Management, and for each type of Outcome sought.

Rule 6. WORKING FACILITY. The facility in which Phase 2 (the Workshop Phase) of IM is conducted should be designed to provide quality working conditions for human beings. Human requirements should dominate all other aspects of facility design, including the way in which machinery is introduced and applied. Facility designers must be thoroughly familiar with what is known about human beings that has a bearing on their performance in groups.

Rule 7. CONTINUITY AT HIGH AUTHORITY LEVEL. Continuity of oversight of IM activity at high authority levels is required across all three Phases of IM, if the highest of the five Success Levels is sought. The lower the Success Level sought, the less significant this continuity becomes.

Rule 8. SEPARATION OF PHASE 2 OUTCOMES. Phase 2 of IM work will normally be done in such a way that the three prototypical Outcomes are the result of three distinct plans and three distinct sets of activities. Definition should be done separately from the Design of Alternatives, and both should be done separately from Choice of an Alternative. Nonetheless, continuity of participation is essential.

Rule 9. RELATIVE IMPORTANCE OF THE THREE PHASES. Because each of the three Phases can readily induce failure and, thereby, annul any success that might be had in the other two, the three Phases should be regarded as equally important. Resources and energy should be allocated with this in mind.

Rule 10. NO COMPROMISE OF QUALITY. As Deming has stated, quality is not your problem. Quality is the solution to your problem. Do not compromise with quality. The meaning of Quality must be incorporated in applying RULE 1 in each Phase of IM activity.

Rule 11. PARTICIPANT COMPREHENSION. Participants will only partly comprehend the patterns that are developed in Phase 2 activity. Staff must fill the interpretation gap as part of their Phase 3 involvement.

A1.2 INTERACTIVE MANAGEMENT: PART OF A MULTILEVEL SCHEME

Interactive Management (IM) is part of a multi-level scheme devised over two decades for coming to grips with large-scale complexity, especially in organizations. An understanding of IM alone is not sufficient for its consistent successful application. Instead it needs to be seen in the context of the larger scheme.

Level 1. The Science of Generic Design. The most basic level in the multi-level scheme is a new science called "the science of generic design". This science is to IM as biology is to the development of pharmaceuticals. The science has been developed, tested, and documented in an attempt to apply the highest standards of scientific investigation and reporting. It provides the foundations, theory, and methodology needed to show what kind of management practice is required to attack and to solve, resolve, ameliorate, or dissolve complex situations and issues that tend to survive in dysfunctional forms long beyond the time they should have been systematically managed.

Level 2. Interactive Management. Interactive Management consists of a multi-faceted scheme for designing and choosing alternative resolutions or solutions to complex situations and issues when such is possible. If alternative designs are found not to be feasible, IM can illuminate this situation and provide guidance for policies and decisions.

IM is designed to support a three-phase activity sequence through one or more passes. If the initial pass through the three-phase sequence proves productive, a second and more involved pass will often be seen as justifiable and necessary.

The three Phases are: (a) Planning, in which the basis is laid and the plan developed for the following two Phases; (b) Workshop, in which the selected participants work together with the aid of a highly-skilled IM Facilitator ("Pilotos", to distinguish this Role from the normal role of "facilitator"); and (c) Followup, in which the results are implemented or another iteration through the Phases is considered.

IM is characterized by the following Portfolios, which involve various sets, with one descriptive Module for each member of one of the component sets:

- A set of "Success Factors" for each of the 3 Phases
- A set of "Failure Modes" for each of the 3 Phases
- A set of five Success Levels
- A set of well-defined product types
- A set of well-defined processes
- A set of well-defined Roles

Level 3. Group Work. IM involves formal group work in the second (Workshop) Phase of activity. The generic design science provides IM with the integrated results of scholarly studies about people in general, as well as what has been learned about people from the past practice of IM.

Outstanding research about human behavior is rare. But it does exist. Much of what exists has already been incorporated in IM. One conclusion from the extensive study in this area is that social scientists in such fields as anthropology, sociology, and psychology, can generally be classified as falling into either (a) "top-tier" or (b) "second-tier". The vast majority fall into the second tier. The distinctions between tiers are as follows. Top-tier scientists understand the importance of integrated theory and experience, and their work is at one and the same time the most theoretical and the most practical. Moreover the top-tier people write clearly and their writings are mostly ignored by professional schools in the universities. The second-tier people are highly critical of the top-tier people, and do not generally strive to match and integrate theory and experiment or practice. Instead their work is largely metaphysical or just experimental without broad interpretation or significance. IM strives to draw only on top-tier people.

Since most practitioners of IM will not be strongly interested in social science, and may well listen to second-tier consultants, the generic design science and IM have anticipated these conditions and have incorporated top-tier thinking in theory and practice. When practitioners deviate from the established science and IM practice, they are very likely violating the results of top-tier social science thinking.

Level 4. Documentation. The quality of documentation of most work involving complex systems or issues almost never meets standards required for effective communication. Accordingly a most painstaking effort has been made in specifying the documentation to be developed in IM practice. The attributes that such documentation must satisfy to be of acceptable quality are spelled out and incorporated in the designs of the products.

Patterns form the core of each of the outcomes.

Level 5. Relational Software. The core of the documentation consists of relational patterns developed by groups through a process of questioning and dialog. This work is strongly supported by relational software founded in the most fundamental scientific and philosophical thought.

A1.3 OUTCOMES

There are three prototypical Outcomes from IM activity. They are: (a) Detailed *Definitions* (of a Situation, Issue, or Problem); (b) *Alternative Designs* (for solving, resolving, or dissolving the Situation, Issue, or Problem); and (c) *Choice* (of a preferred alternative). Normally these Outcomes will arise in the sequence just stated. There will be an intervening time between the development of each to allow for digestion, interpretation, evaluation, refinement of plans, and preparation for the next activity. Each Outcome would itself be the consequence of one Three-Phase activity of the type described previously.

Generally speaking, any one application of IM will deal with just one of these Outcomes. If the expected Outcome is a Definition, it is normally anticipated that the results will be reviewed to see whether the situation is sufficiently well-defined to warrant proceeding to Design Alternatives. If the latter is achieved and is promising, again a period of assessment would normally occur before proceeding to Choice.

Levels of Outcomes. Outcomes can be further distinguished as: (a) Qualitative (in-depth logic patterns that reveal rationale and qualitative relationships), (b) Quantitative (numerical assessments that may deal with statics or dynamics of situations as well as with measures of parameters or variables), and (c) QQ (Qualitative-Quantitative Integrated) results.

Considerable efficiency is gained by doing the qualitative aspects first to reveal and comprehend the logical, relational aspects of the situation or issue. If this kind of in-depth study is bypassed, numerical considerations will be misdirected and results will be incorrect. It is only through the careful and high-quality integration of qualitative reasoning and quantitative measures (guided by strong intuition based on experience) that a mature approach to final choice is achieved, in most instances.

A1.4 TRADEOFFS: THE IMPORTANCE OF QUALITY

Experience shows that high quality of performance and outcomes is something that most individuals are willing to trade away or erode for something that is commonly thought to be of immediate importance. People will debase quality (a) to save time, (b) to follow a schedule (which they themselves feel they must impose), (c) to satisfy authority (which almost always does not understand the tradeoffs involved) and/or (d) to give an outward appearance of orderly control.

Repeated compromise of quality in many small ways when making tradeoffs often allows lots of little compromises to add up to a large failure.

A1.5 WORKING FACILITY

Experience shows that superior work is done when informed people are allowed to work together in a superior working facility designed to enhance their capacity to interact.

A1.6 BEHAVIOR

Two forms of behavior must be distinguished in doing IM work. These are: (a) knowing what to avoid doing and (b) knowing what to do. These two forms are relevant for all three Phases of IM, and for the production of all three types of Outcomes.

A1.7 PLANNING

In planning IM activity, one needs both standardization and flexibility. Standardization is needed primarily for quality control of actor performance in roles, in order to support the production of successul Outcomes. It is also vital to enable cumulative experience to be sufficiently reliable for drawing scientific conclusions. It is achieved at the module level.

Flexibility is needed to allow tailoring of activity to the needs of each individual application. Flexibility is attained by how modules are put together in sequences, and by choice of actors to fill roles.

A1.8 SUCCESS ORIENTATION

A success orientation toward all aspects of IM activity is urged. This means that one must understand what success can mean in the application, what factors are involved in each of the three Phases, and what also is involved in producing failure.

Layers of Success. Success can be had at five layers or levels. Complex issues are never well understood at the beginning, so one cannot initially predict which level will be attained. Ability to predict generally improves significantly after one pass through the three Phases and thereafter. The following are distinguishable layers of success:

• Learning more about what is involved in approaching the issue (the lowest level of success)
• Learning more about the issue itself
• Achieving a good definition of the issue

- Finding good alternative designs for resolving the issue
- Arriving at a good action choice to resolve the issue

It is good practice to be conservative in predicting which layer can be attained, because unnecessarily raised (and then unmet) expectations may lead to unwarranted negative reactions.

STUDY QUESTIONS
APPENDIX 1. EXECUTIVE OVERVIEW OF INTERACTIVE MANAGEMENT

1. How is success treated in applying IM?

2. Can standardization and flexibility both be accomodated in IM?

3. What two types of behavior are both needed in IM?

4. Can continuity and separation both be accomodated in IM?

5. Are the three Phases of IM significantly different in importance?

6. How does quality relate to problems, according to Deming?

7. Who is responsible for providing an interpretation of patterns developed using IM?

8. What is the most basic level in understanding IM?

9. What are the "portfolios of IM"?

10. How do universities deal with "top-tier" versus "second-tier" research?

11. What form the core of each of the outcomes in IM?

12. What are the three prototypical outcomes from IM activity?

13. What are the levels of outcomes?

14. Why should high-quality qualitative work precede quantitative work?

APPENDIX 2

GMU ISM SOFTWARE

Chapter 9 gives an IM Software overview. Only one software package is described here.

A2.1 GETTING STARTED.

The GMU ISM PC software is expected to run on an IBM-compatible machine, *provided* the machine also contains a math coprocessor. Attempts to run the programs without the coprocessor will cause an error message to occur that mentions floating point. The IBM-compatible PC must have at least 640K of RAM. Old machines sometimes have only 512 K, and the software will "hang up" at the point where querying begins. The machine must have a graphics capability, because the querying may use more than one font, depending on the length of the query.

Three software commands are featured, one of which will be chosen in a specific structuring application. These commands are: DOMODEL, DOCLUS, and DOPRIOR.

DOMODEL. DOMODEL is the most general command, and it can be used in any ISM structuring application. As programmed in this software, it will not be as efficient as the other two commands for those applications where the other two are appropriate. The user should learn when to use DOCLUS and DOPRIOR and choose one of them when appropriate. For all other applications, the user should use DOMODEL.

DOCLUS. The DOCLUS command is to be used when and only when the user knows at the beginning that the structure to be produced will consist only of one or more cycles. (This knowledge allows the machine to use the following inference rule: If ARB, then BRA for all A&B. Conversely, if A is not related to B, then B is not related to A.)

DOPRIOR. The DOPRIOR command is to be used when and only when the user knows at the beginning that the structure to be produced will consist of a priority structure (or a structure that meets all the requirements of a priority structure). Such a structure will have a single path from one end of the structure to the other. It may have cycles on this path.[1]

These notes have been prepared to help the user apply the software, once it has been installed in the C Drive. After the software has been installed, the ISM programs are held in the ISM Directory. This directory will also hold user-produced files, which will be explained in the next section. To see the program files in the ISM Directory, after installation of the software, you transfer to the ISM directory as shown later in these notes, and then you enter this command: C:\ISM>>DIR /p

and press the ENTER or RETURN key. You should then see the following on your screen:

```
C:\ISM.dir

Volume in drive C is DISK1_VOL2

Directory of C:\ISM

PRIOR       EXE   301456  8-13-88     1:59 p
MODLDK      EXE   299520  8-13-88    11:36a
MYFLAG      DAT   128     8-12-88    10:05a
OLDNEW      DAT   128     8-12-88    10:04a
OLDOLD      DAT   128     8-12-88    10:05a
CLUSDK      EXE   251344  8-13-88    10:18a
NEWNEW      DAT   128     8-12-88    10:04a
NEWOLD      DAT   128     8-12-88    10:05a
HALOIBMG    DEV   9862    4-02-88     6:50p
RUNISM      BAT   25      11-08-90    2:03p
DOCLUS      BAT   339     11-08-90    2:02p
DOMODEL     BAT   339     11-08-90    2:02p
DOPRIOR     BAT   339     11-08-90    2:03p

     15 File(s)      8734720 bytes free
```

Each time you use the ISM software, you will create a matrix file ("mat") and a text file ("txt") . After you have created matrix and text files, they will also appear in the ISM directory listing. Instead of the listing shown above, the screen will then present a display like the following (showing just one illustrative matrix file and one illustrative text file):

```
Same contents as in the above files listing, followed by:

TEST1       MAT   10741   11-13-90    11:34a
TEST1       TXT   57792   11-13-90    11:34a

     17 File(s)      8663040 bytes free
```

In the above, TEST1.MAT is a name that a user has arbitrarily assigned to a <u>matrix</u> file; while TEST1.TXT is a name that a user has arbitrarily assigned to a <u>text</u> file. Many other names could have been used, such as JOE, SALLY, PRINCETON or YALE.

This ISM software operates with two kinds of user-produced files. One is a file to hold a matrix that is developed in an ISM session. The other is a file to hold relevant textual information. ***It is suggested that you use your word processor to create an ISM Files Log.*** It is optional whether you do this, since this Log does not involve the ISM software, and is only for the convenience of the user in having a separate location for important information. The files held in this log might be retrieved by using a number, and should be assigned distinctive textual names to identify what they represent, as well as what ISM Project they relate to. The main purpose of this file is to enable past information to be retrieved for future use.

The suggested format is as follows:

ISM MATRIX FILE
<u>Entry#1</u>.

File Designation:	NAME1.mat
Pertains to ISM Project:	(describe the project)
Involves the Application Structural Type:	(describe the type)
Involves the following elements:	(describe the element set)
Involves the following generic question:	(type the generic question)
Information prepared by:	(type the name of the file creator)
Date of entry:	(type the current date when creating or amending the file)

<u>Entry #2.</u>

File Designation:	NAME2.mat

Fill in similarly as for NAME1, and so on.

ISM TEXT FILE
<u>Entry#1</u>.

File Designation:	NAME1.txt
Pertains to ISM Project:	(describe the project)
Involves the Application Structural Type:	(describe the type)
Involves the following elements:	(describe the element set)
Involves the following generic question:	(type the generic question)
Information prepared by:	(type the name of the file creator)
Date of entry:	(Type the current date when creating or amending the file)

Entry #2.

File Designation: NAME2.txt
Fill in similarly as for NAME1, and so on.

Of course you may choose not to bother with this, preferring to use some other means to keep track of your files.

If the software has been loaded successfully into the C drive, the user may then go into the DOS system prepared to enter a command. The command that is recommended is:

      chdir ISM

This command should put the user in touch with the C drive and the ISM directory, as the following material indicates.

Assumption 1	Assume that the GMU Software has been loaded into the C Drive. Then you will have a situation where you go to DOS to get into the ISM program.
Assumption 2	You are in the DOS program on C Drive
Assumption 3	You are looking at C:\>>

■   TYPE IN MATERIAL SO THAT THE COMMAND READS AS FOLLOWS:

C:\>>chdir ism

■   PRESS "ENTER" OR "RETURN". The DOS display should then read:

C:\ISM>>

You are now operating in the ISM directory.

■   STARTING TO MODEL. Decide which of the three major commands you want to use; i.e., **(A)** DOMODEL, **(B)** DOCLUS, or **(C)** DOPRIOR. These commands are discussed, respectively, in Secs. A2.2, A2.3, and A2.4.

A2.2 THE DOMODEL COMMAND. The description of the DOMODEL Command begins with assumptions.

Assumption 1	You have decided to use the DOMODEL Command.
Assumption 2	Your ISM Files Log does *not* contain any old files that you wish to use. If this assumption is correct, (optional) choose a name for your matrix file and a name for your text file and enter these names in your ISM Files Log, then proceed with the instructions below. Otherwise, go to A2.2.2.

■   NOW TYPE IN MATERIAL SO THAT THE COMMAND READS AS FOLLOWS:

C:\ISM>>DOMODEL XXX.MAT XXX.TXT

where instead of **XXX** you use the new file name that you have entered in your ISM Log.

Now hit the Enter or Return Key. As a result of this step, you should now see a screen display like this:

```
C:\ISM>>echo off
1 File(s) copied
TEXT FILE EMPTY - PLEASE CREATE ONE!
BLANKING OUT NEW TEXT DATA FILE.
PLEASE WAIT.......

--------------------BEGINNING OPTIONS----------------------
1.  CREATE RELATIONAL STATEMENTS
2.  CREATE TEXT ELEMENTS
?
```

■   Now set the caps lock so that any letter that you type in response to computer questioning will be a capital letter.

You have reached this point by starting to use the DOMODEL command, and because you are going to start with new file material. The screen display gives you two options:

239

1. Create relational statements
2. Create text elements

You must do both of these because you have begun with a blank text file.

Assumption 1	You have already constructed a generic question and are ready to fit it into the format that is required in this Case. The format is seen by pursuing option 1 above. If you have not constructed such a question, you will need to do so before continuing. Then select option 1. You will note that this option requires that you enter three distinct parts of your generic question in a prescribed format.

At this point, an example is introduced that takes the user through the entire process of using the DOMODEL command to develop a structure.

After you have worked through the example, you should be in a position to do a more complex example using your own information[2].

A2.2.1 Illustrating the Use of ISM Through an Example (The DOMODEL Command). This example illustrates the DOMODEL command.

1. Goal. I want to structure the following element set:

{1. feather, 2. Mack Truck, 3. beer can, 4. Volkswagen, 5. small boy, 6. professional wrestler, 7. universe}

using the following generic question:

Is
Element A
heavier than
Element B
?

2. Flow of Activity Style. I will write this example in the flow of activity style, i.e., I will present each step in the sequence that I do the step on the computer.

3. Starting Conditions. My ISM Files Log is empty. I have no prior matrix file and no prior text file. The ISM software is installed in my PC, which has the required math coprocessor, at least 640K of RAM, and graphics capability.

I have decided to use the DOMODEL program. (I could also use the DOPRIOR program because the structure I expect meets the conditions of a priority structure.

However I will **not** use the DOCLUS program, which is only used when it is known that the structure to be developed consists entirely of cycles.)

4. Start the ISM Files Log (optional). I will use my word processor to start my ISM Files Log. The entry I will make is as follows:

ISM Files Log

ISM MATRIX FILE
Entry #1.

File Designation:	JEFF.MAT
Pertains to ISM Project:	creating an example to illustrate the use of the ISM PC Software
Involves the Application Structural Type:	None
Involves the Graphics Structural Type:	Linear hierarchy
Involves the following elements:	{feather, Mack Truck, beer can,Volkswagen, small boy, professional wrestler, universe}
Involves the generic question:	Is Element A heavier than Element B?
Information prepared by:	John N. Warfield
Date of Entry:	November 23, 1990

ISM TEXT FILE
Entry #1.

File Designation:	JEFF.TXT

Other entries are the same as for Matrix File JEFF.MAT

5. Entering the ISM Directory. I turn on my computer and enter the ISM Directory.

6. Entering the DOMODEL Command. I create this screen display (entering the DOMODEL command)

```
C:\ISM>>DOMODEL   JEFF.MAT   JEFF.TXT
```

and then hit the Enter key.

7. Choosing an Option from a Menu. The machine asks me which of two options to choose, and I choose the option 1--"Create relational statements".

When it asks for R1, I enter   IS
When it asks for R2, I enter HEAVIER THAN
When it asks for R3, I enter   ?

NOTE : While entering this information, the screen asks me whether I want more lines, and whether I want to keep the displayed entry. The user should appreciate that the ISM program is written in such a way that when the user is asked to type in text information, the user should type only one line, and wait until the program asks you if you need more lines. Then you should type in the next line, and so on. If you don't fill up the line that's okay. The machine will later put all your lines together into an integrated text presentation. When the machine asks if you want to keep the entry you have just finished, it is giving you the opportunity to edit it further immediately before putting it in the text file.

Also note that unless you use only capital letters in response to queries, the machine will ignore your responses. So use the Caps Lock before continuing.

---

8. *Limited Set Size*. The screen then reveals that I am allowed up to 85 elements in the element file. (The program has automatically put me in the position of starting to carry out the second option (see 7 above)).

9. *Responding to Queries*. Several questions appear in sequence on the screen and I respond Y to each of them and hit the Enter or Return key.

10. *Typing in the First Element*. The machine now asks for element #1. I type :

FEATHER

11. *More of Those Thrilling Queries*. Once again the machine asks if I need more lines and I reply NO, then it asks if I want to keep the element I entered and I reply YES, and then it asks if I want to continue with another element, and I reply YES. [I reply by typing Y or N as prompted by the screen.]

12. *Recycling*. I then recycle steps 10 and 11, entering a new element each time, until I have entered the whole element set that I began with as given in Item 1 above. After I have entered element #7, and the machine asks if I want to enter another element, I type in NO.

13. ***Entering File Reference Information.*** The screen now asks me to type in file information. I then enter the following:

ISM FILES LOG ENTRY #1 dated Nov. 23, 1990.

14. ***Main Editor Options.*** Next the screen shows me the Main Editor Options. The list is as follows:

```
--------------------- MAIN EDITOR OPTIONS ᵃ ---------------------
0 - EXIT THE EDITOR
3 - EDIT AN ELEMENT
4 - EDIT A RELATIONAL STATEMENT
5 - ADD AN ELEMENT
6 - LIST TEXT ELEMENTS IN THE FILE
7 - EDIT AN ELEMENT LABEL
8 - DELETE THE CONTENT OF AN ELEMENT
9 - MODIFY THE FILE INFORMATIONAL STATEMENT
```

15. ***Review or Exit the Editor ?*** If I have done everything correctly to this point, I do not need to do any editing, so I will press 0 to Exit the Editor. However if I did need to review, I would choose Option 6 followed by Sub Option 2 in order to change any element statements. If I needed to revise the generic question, I would choose Option 4 followed by the appropriate sub-option chosen from those shown on the screen following my choice of option 4.

16. ***Exit Editor.*** Next I would exit the Editor by pressing 0.

17. ***Entering an ISM Command.*** The screen then shows me the following:

>>>> TYPE AN I S M COMMAND (OR "HELP")

If you type "HELP", the screen will display the ISM Commands.

18. ***Border.*** I now choose the command BO to initate the ISM structuring activity.

ᵃ The word "label" normally refers to the number assigned to an element. The word "content" refers to the written statement of the element. A generic question typically is formed from three statements. The term "relational statement", as used here, is a misnomer, but that is what the programmer chose to use. The symbols chosen for the three statements are R1, R2, and R3 respectively.

19. *Responses the Machine Accepts*. The machine tells me I must choose one of the four responses to each displayed question:

> Y   yes, the relationship is true
> N   no, the relationship is false[b]
> AB, abort
> ED, suspend comparisons to edit and then continue

20. *Subordination Relation?* After I hit the Return key, the machine asks if I am using a subordination relation (i.e., one that necessary yields a hierarchical structure--a structure without any cycles). Since I am doing so in this particular example, I type Y and hit the Return or Enter key.

21. *Problem - Options Structure*. Next the screen asks if I am using a particular type of modeling plan--one in which I am connecting a set of proposed solution options to a structure comprised of interrelated problems (a "problematique"). Since I am not doing so, I type N. (This plan will be explained in A2.5.)

22. *Element Numbers to Start Structuring*. Now the screen asks for element numbers. First I type 1 and hit the Return key. Then I type 2 and hit the return key.

23. *Question Sequence*. The following is the sequence of steps that represents the questions, answers, and new element entries (I will now use the shorthand symbol "R" to represent the relationship "heavier than".) :

Is 1R2?	N	Return		5						
Is 2R1?	Y	Return		Is 4R5?	Y	Return				
3				Is 3R5?	N	Return				
Is 2R3?	Y	Return		Is 5R1?	Y	Return		7		
Is 1R3?	N	Return		Is 5R3?	Y	Return		Is 6R7?	N	Return
Is 3R1?	Y	Return		6				Is 7R5?	Y	Return
4				Is 4R6?	Y	Return		Is 7R4?	Y	Return
Is 3R4?	N	Return		Is 3R6?	N	Return		Is 2R7?	N	Return
Is 4R3?	Y	Return		Is 6R3?	Y	Return		Is 7R2?	Y	Return
Is 2R4?	Y	Return		Is 5R6?	N	Return				
				Is 6R5?	Y	Return				

(handwritten note: missing opposite statement? Is 7R6?)

---

[b]   In the above the correct statement should read as follows:
No, the relationship is false OR I don't know enough to believe that the relationship is true.

24. *Request for Next Command.* The machine now asks for an ISM C~~ommand.~~

25. *Display.* I type DI and hit return to ask for a display of the structural information.

26. *Getting a Printout of the Structural Information.* On my machine I hit the SHIFT - "Print Screen" keys repeatedly to get a printout of the structural information. The following is what the printout shows for this example:

```
LEVEL NO.      1
  1
LEVEL NO.      2
   3 =>> 1   ,
LEVEL NO.      3
   5 =>> 3   ,
<<RETURN>>  TO CONTINUE
LEVEL NO.      4
   6 =>> 5   ,
LEVEL NO.      5
   4 =>> 6   ,
LEVEL NO.      6
   2 =>> 4   ,
 <<RETURN>> TO CONTINUE
LEVEL NO.      7
   7 =>> 2   ,
TYPE AN I S M COMMAND (OR "HELP")
```

27. *Interpretation.* For example, LEVEL NO. 4 contains the element number 6, and the statement 6 =>> 5 means that an arrow should be drawn from element 6 lying at Level 4 to element 5 lying at Level 3. The following figure shows the drawing that is constructed from the printout.

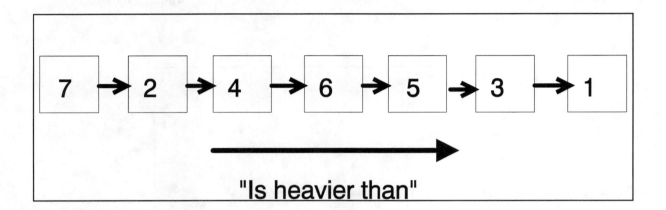

28. *Terminating the Session.* Having completed the development of the structure, I type the command TE to terminate the session. The machine then transfers back to the screen entry C:\ISM>>.

This example illustrates the use of the DOMODEL command.

A2.2.2 Using the DOMODEL Program With a Set of Old Files. There are many cases in which it is important to start using the DOMODEL option of the GMU ISM Software with a set of already existing files (as for example when an IM session has been interrupted because the end of the day, or maybe because for some reason it is important to create a new structure with the same set that has already been generated). For those cases, assuming that you are ready to start using the software, the assumption and steps are the following:

Assumption 1	Your ISM Files Log ***contains old files*** that you wish to use. If this assumption is correct, identify the names of the files and write them down to be used in carrying the steps below. Otherwise, go to A2.2

■   NOW TYPE IN MATERIAL SO THAT THE COMMAND READS AS FOLLOWS:

C:\>>ISMDOMODEL www.MAT www.TXT

except that instead of www you enter the name of the old file that you will be using.

Now hit the Enter or Return Key to activate the command.

As a result of this step you may now see a screen display like this, beginning with the command entered above:

```
C:\ISM>>DOMODEL  www.MAT www.TXT
C:\ISM>>echo off
1 File(s) copied
NEW STRUCTURE (Y/N)?
```

■ Set the CapsLock key so that any letter you type in response to a screen query will be a capital letter.

■ Answer the query NEW STRUCTURE (Y/N)?
a) If you plan to create a **new structure** using the elements contained in the text file given in the above command, type Y and press the Enter or Return key.
b) If you are **not** planning to create a new structure using the old file material, type N and press Enter or Return.

You will see the following screen display:

>>>> TYPE AN ISM COMMAND (OR "HELP")
?

■ In this case you have two options :

a. If you are familiar with the ISM Commands, enter the appropriate one and continue. Otherwise go to Step b.
b. Type HELP after the question mark, creating the following screen display:

?HELP

and press Return or Enter. You will then see the display of the ISM COMMANDS (which is shown on the following page).

Enter the appropriate command and continue. Use the examples given before to understand the most important ISM Commands.

```
------------------------ I S M   COMMANDS --------------------
=== EMBEDDING ELEMENTS[c]
BO - Transitive Bordering
BOQ - Transitive Bordering with Selectable Queries
=== DISPLAYING STRUCTURES
DI - Display Minimum Edge Digraph in a Levels Format
DIS - Display Minimum Edge Digraph in a Stages Format
PRM - Print (portray on screen) the Reachability Matrix
=== SUBSTANTIVE AMENDING
ADD - Add Elements
ELIM - Eliminate Elements
AE - Add Edges (Relationships between elements of the
minimum edge digraph)
EE - Erase Edges (on the minimum edge digraph)
=== FORMAT AMENDING
PO - Pool Elements
EC - Elementary Contraction
=== TEXT EDITING
ED - Edit an Element or Relationship
=== END STRUCTURING
TE - Terminate

NOTE:  ENTER  <<RETURN>> TO CONTINUE
```

[NOTE ENTERED BY THE WRITER OF THIS CHAPTER: I have had better success using the "MAIN EDITOR OPTIONS" directly than I have had with the editing commands in the above list. If you choose the command ED from the above list, it takes you into the MAIN EDITOR OPTIONS menu, from which you can proceed.]

A2.2.3 Descriptions of ISM Commands for DOMODEL Program.[d] Each of the ISM Commands described below is initiated by typing the symbol for the command (following a prompt) and then pressing the Enter or Return key.

---

[c] The ISM commands for "EMBEDDING ELEMENTS" will be different if you are using the DOPRIOR or DOCLUS commands.

[d] Commands will be slightly different for DOPRIOR and DOCLUS programs.

A. *EMBEDDING COMMANDS*. "Embedding" means filling a matrix that contains all responses to questions that the DOMODEL program generates in its repetitive use of the generic question with different elements from your set of elements.

1. **BO**--The BO ISM Command instructs the computer to apply the "transitive bordering method" as the algorithm for matrix filling. This BO ISM Command is the one that is most frequently chosen for the purpose.
2. **BOQ**--The BOQ ISM Command instructs the computer to carry out the same kind of activity as described for the BO ISM Command just described. However this command allows you to use "selected queries".

B. *DISPLAY COMMANDS*. This set of commands allows you to call up various displays of results.

1. **DI**--This command will display information concerning the *vertical layout* of a digraph that corresponds to the filled matrix. Level 1 will contain the top- level elements, Level 2 will contain the second-level elements, and so on. Information is given showing which elements at a certain level connect to elements at higher levels. Also the contents of the various cycles (if any) are identified. [The graphical convention used in identifying Levels is to place an element as close to the top of the digraph as possible consistent with keeping the Levels distinct.]
2. **DIS**--This command will display information concerning the *horizontal layout* of a digraph that corresponds to the filled matrix. Stage 1 will contain the left-most elements, Stage 2 will contain those just to the right of Stage 1, and so on. The graphical convention used in identifying Stages is to place each element as far to the left in the digraph as possible, consistent with keeping the Stages distinct.
3. **PRM**--This command requests the computer to put the reachability matrix on the screen for viewing.

C. *SUBSTANTIVE AMENDING COMMANDS*. These ISM Commands provide for a variety of amendment or editing functions.

1. **ADD**--   TEXT TO BE ADDED
2. **ELIM**-- TEXT TO BE ADDED
3. **AE**--   TEXT TO BE ADDED
4. **EE**--   TEXT TO BE ADDED

D. *FORMAT AMENDING COMMANDS*. These ISM Commands allows you to combine two elements from a digraph into a single element by the operations called "pooling" or "contracting".

1. **PO**--This ISM Command allows you to combine two elements that lie at the same level or in the same stage of a structure. The computer will ask you for a symbol to represent the pooled pair of elements.

2. **EC**--This ISM Command allows you to combine two related elements that lie on different levels or in different stages into a single element. The process is described as an "elementary contraction". The computer will ask you for a symbol to represent the two elements that have been combined in the elementary contraction.

E. TEXT EDITING COMMAND.

1. **ED**--This ISM Command allows you to edit an element or a relationship.

F. END STRUCTURING COMMAND.

1. **TE**--This ISM Command allows you to terminate a modeling session. It saves the structures and returns you to the command line. If you wish, you can then leave the ISM directory by typing C: followed by striking the Return or Enter key, which will return you to DOS.

A2.3   THE DOCLUS COMMAND. The description of the DOCLUS Command begins with assumptions.

Assumption 1	You have decided to use the DOCLUS Command.
Assumption 2	Your ISM Files Log does not contain any old files that you wish to use. If this assumption is correct, choose a name for your matrix file and a name for your text file and enter these names in your ISM Files Log, then proceed with the instructions below. Otherwise, go to A2.3.2.

■   NOW TYPE IN MATERIAL SO THAT THE COMMAND READS :

C:\ISM>>DOCLUS **JUDGE**.MAT   **JUDGE**.TXT

where I have chosen the highlighted name JUDGE for the file as shown in this command, but you would use the file name that you have chosen instead, as entered previously in your ISM Log.

Now hit the Enter or Return key.

250

As a result of this step, you should now see a screen display like this:

```
C:\ISM>>echo off
1 File(s) copied
TEXT FILE EMPTY - PLEASE CREATE ONE!
BLANKING OUT NEW TEXT DATA FILE.
PLEASE WAIT.......

-------------------BEGINNING OPTIONS----------------------
1.  CREATE RELATIONAL STATEMENTS
2.  CREATE TEXT ELEMENTS
?
```

■   Now set the caps lock so that any letter that you type in response to computer questioning will be a capital letter.

You have reached this point by starting to use the DOCLUS command, and by indicating that you are going to create new files for use in this particular activity.

The screen display gives you two options:

1. Create relational statements
2. Create text elements

You must do both of these because you have begun with a blank text file.

> **Assumption 1**   You have already constructed a generic question and are ready to fit it into the format that is required in this case. (The format is seen by pursuing option 1 above.)

If you have not constructed such a question, you will need to do so before continuing. Then select option 1. You will note that this option requires that you enter three distinct parts of your generic question in a required format.

At this point, an example is introduced that will take you through the DOCLUS Command in detail.

A2.3.1 Illustrating the use of ISM Through an Example (The DOCLUS command). The following example illustrates the use of the DOCLUS command.

1. *Goal.* I want to structure the following element set:

{1. Gone With the Wind, 2. The Bijou, 3. Bus, 4. General Cinema, 5. Bicycle, 6. The Maltese Falcon, 7. Snow White and the Seven Dwarfs, 8. Loews, 9. Early Show, 10. Midnight Show, 11. Taxicab, 12. Matinee, 13. Casablanca}

using the following generic question:

Is
Element A
in the same category as
Element B
?

2. *Flow of Activity Style.* I will write this example in the flow of activity style, i.e., I will present each step in the sequence that I do the step on the computer.

3. *Starting Conditions.* My ISM Files Log is empty. I have no prior matrix file and no prior text file. The ISM software is installed in my PC, which has the required math coprocessor.

Also I have decided to use the DOCLUS program because the nature of the generic question is such that all the elements in my set to be structured will end up being part of a symmetric relation, so that my outcome will be one or more cycles and no hierarchical component.

4. *Start the ISM Files Log (optional).* I will use my word processor to start my ISM Files Log. The entry I will make is as follows:

ISM Files Log

ISM MATRIX FILE
Entry #3.

File Designation:	HAROLD.MAT
Pertains to ISM Project:	creating an example to illustrate the use of the ISM PC Software
Involves the Application Structural Type:	None
Involves the Graphics Structural Type:	Cycle or set of Cycles

Involves the following elements: {Gone With the Wind, The Bijou, Bus, General Cinema, Bicycle, The Maltese Falcon, Snow White and the Seven Dwarfs, Loews, Early Show, Midnight Show, Taxicab, Matinee, Casablanca}

Involves the generic question: Is Element A in the same category as Element B?
Information prepared by: John N. Warfield
Date of Entry: February 16, 1991

ISM TEXT FILE

Entry #3.
File Designation: HAROLD.TXT

5. *Entering the ISM Directory.* I turn on my computer and enter the ISM Directory.

6. *Entering the DOCLUS command.* I create this screen display (entering the DOCLUS command)

C:\ISM>>DOCLUS HAROLD.MAT HAROLD.TXT

and then hit the Enter key.

7. *Choosing an Option from a Menu.* The machine asks me which of two options to choose, and I choose the option 1--"Create relational statements".

When it asks for R1, I enter   IS
When it asks for R2, I enter   IN THE SAME CATEGORY AS
When it asks for R3, I enter   ?

> **NOTE :** While entering this information, the screen asks me whether I want more lines, and whether I want to keep the displayed entry. The user should appreciate that the ISM program is written in such a way that when the user is asked to type in text information, the user should type only one line, and wait until the program asks you if you need more lines. Then you should type in the next line, and so on. If you don't fill up the line that's okay. The machine will later put all your lines together into an integrated text presentation. When the machine asks if you want to keep the entry you have just finished, it is giving you the opportunity to edit it further immediately before putting it in the text file.
>
> Also note that unless you use only capital letters in response to queries, the machine will ignore your responses. So use the Caps Lock before continuing.

8. *Limited Set Size*. As many as 150 elements can be used in the set to be structured with the DOCLUS Command. Note that other structuring modes do not allow this many elements. (The program has automatically put me in the position of starting to carry out the second option (see 7 above)).

9. *Responding to Queries*. Several questions appear in sequence on the screen and I respond Y to each of them and hit the Enter or Return key.

10. *Typing in the First Element*. The machine now asks for element #1. I type

GONE WITH THE WIND

11. *More of those Thrilling Queries*. Once again the machine asks if I need more lines and I reply NO, then it asks if I want to keep the element I entered and I reply YES, and then it asks if I want to continue with another element, and I reply YES. [I reply by typing Y or N as prompted by the screen.]

12. *Recycling*. I then recycle steps 10 and 11, entering a new element each time, until I have entered the whole element set that I began with as given in Item 1 above. After I have entered element #13, and the machine asks if I want to enter another element, I type in NO.

13. *Entering file reference Information*. The screen now asks me to type in file information. I then enter the following:

ISM FILES LOG ENTRY #3 DATED FEBRUARY 16, 1991

14. *Main Editor Options.* Next the screen shows me the Main Editor Options. The list is as follows:

```
--------------------- MAIN EDITOR OPTIONSᵉ ---------------------------
0 - EXIT THE EDITOR
3 - EDIT AN ELEMENT
4 - EDIT A RELATIONAL STATEMENT
5 - ADD AN ELEMENT
6 - LIST TEXT ELEMENTS IN THE FILE
7 - EDIT AN ELEMENT LABEL
8 - DELETE THE CONTENT OF AN ELEMENT
9 - MODIFY THE FILE INFORMATIONAL STATEMENT
```

15. *Review or Exit the Editor ?* If I have done everything correctly to this point, I don't need to do any editing, so I will press 0 to Exit the Editor. However if I did need to review, I would choose Option 6 followed by Sub Option 2 in order to change any element statements. If I needed to revise the generic question, I would choose Option 4 followed by the appropriate sub-option chosen from those shown on the screen following my choice of option 4.

16. *Exit Editor.* Next I would exit the Editor by pressing 0.

17. *Entering an ISM command.* The screen then shows me the following:

>>>> TYPE AN I S M COMMAND (OR "HELP")

If you type "HELP", the screen will display the ISM Commands.

ᵉ The word "label" normally refers to the number assigned to an element. The word "content" refers to the written statement of the element. A generic question typically is formed from three statements. The term "relational statement" is a misnomer, but that is what the programmer chose to use. The symbols chosen for the three statements are R1 R2 and R3 respectively.

> **NOTE :** The ISM Commands are not the same for the DOCLUS Command as for the DOMODEL or DOPRIOR Command. In this case, we have six possible commands. In this example, only the following three will be used:
>
> CL -- for clustering
> DI -- for displaying clusters
> TE -- for terminating the program

18. *Cluster.* I now choose the command CL to initate the ISM structuring activity.

19. *Responses the Machine Accepts.* The machine tells me I must choose one of the four responses to each displayed question:

> Y   yes, the relationship is true
> N   no, the relationship is false[f]
> AB, abort
> ED, suspend comparisons to edit and then continue

20. *Element Numbers to Start Structuring.* Now the screen asks for element numbers. First I type 1 and hit the Return key. Then I type 2 and hit the return key.

21. *Question Sequence.*[g] The following is the sequence of steps that represent the questions, answers, and new element entries:

---

[f] In the above the correct statement should read as follows:
No, the relationship is false OR I don't know enough to believe that the relationship is true.

[g] I will now use the shorthand symbol "R" to represent the relationship "is in the same category as".

IS 2R1?	N	IS 7R1?	Y	IS 10R9?	Y
IS 3R1?	N	IS 8R1?	N	IS 11R1?	N
IS 3R2?	N	IS 8R2?	Y	IS 11R2?	N
IS 4R1?	N	IS 9R1?	N	IS 11R3?	Y
IS 4R2?	Y	IS 9R2?	N	IS 12R1?	N
IS 5R1?	N	IS 9R3?	N	IS 12R2?	N
IS 5R2?	N	IS 10R1?	N	IS 12R3?	N
IS 5R3?	Y	IS 10R2?	N	IS 12R9?	Y
IS 6R1?	Y	IS 10R3?	N	IS 13R1?	Y

22. *Request for Next Command.* The machine now asks for an ISM Command.

23. *Display.* I type DI and hit return to ask for a display of the structural information. This is what the display shows me:

```
Cluster No. 1      1,6,7,13
Cluster No. 2      2,4,8
Cluster No. 3      3,5,11
Cluster No. 4      9,10,12

TYPE AN ISM COMMAND (OR "HELP")
```

This is how the structure that is defined by the screen display just given would be presented:

MOVIE	THEATER	SHOW TIME	TRANSPORTATION
■ Gone With the Wind	■ The Bijou	■ Early Show	■ Bus
■ The Maltese Falcon	■ General Cinema	■ Midnight Show	■ Bicycle
■ Snow White & the Seven Dwarfs	■ Loews	■ Matinee	■ Taxicab
■ Casablanca			

TIE LINE

24. *Interpretation.* The program has created the following cycles: {Gone With the Wind, The Maltese Falcon, Snow White and the Seven Dwarfs, Casablanca} [We can now name this cycle the "Movie Cycle"][3]

{The Bijou, General Cinema, Loews} [We can now name this cycle the "Theater Cycle"]

{Bus, Bicycle, Taxicab} [We can now name this cycle the "Transportation Cycle"]

{Early Show, Midnight Show, Matinee} [We can now name this cycle the "Show-time Cycle"]

25. *Terminating the Session.* Having completed the development of the structure, I type the command TE to terminate the session. The machine then transfers back to the screen entry C:\ISM>>.

A2.3.2 Using the DOCLUS Program with a Set of Old Files. As with the DOMODEL Program, there are many cases in which it is important to start using the DOCLUS Program with a set of already existing files; for those cases, assuming that you are ready to start using the software, the associated assumptions and steps are the following:

> **Assumption 1**   Your ISM Files Log contains old files that you wish to use. If this assumption is correct, identify the names of the files and write them down to be used in carrying out the steps below. Otherwise, go to A2.3

■   NOW TYPE IN MATERIAL SO THAT THE COMMAND READS AS FOLLOWS:

C:\ISM>>DOCLUS WWW.MAT ZZZ.TXT

except that instead of WWW you enter the name of the old matrix file that you are going to be using and instead of ZZZ you enter the name of the old text file that you are going to be using.

Now hit the Enter or Return key to activate the command.

As a result of this step you may now see a screen display like this, beginning with the command entered above:

```
C:\ISM>>DOCLUS  WWW.MAT  ZZZ.TXT
C:\ISM>>echo off
1 File(s) copied
NEW STRUCTURE (Y/N)?
```

■   Answer the query NEW STRUCTURE (Y/N)?

a) If you plan to create a new structure using the elements contained in the text file given in the above command, type Y and press the Enter or Return key.
b) If you are not planning to create a new structure using the old file material, type N and press Enter or Return.

You will see the following screen display:

>>>>Type an ISM COMMAND (OR "HELP")
?

■   In this case, you have two options :
a. If you are familiar with the ISM commands, enter one and continue; otherwise go to Step b.
b. Type HELP after the question mark, creating the following screen display:

?HELP

and press Return or Enter. You will then see the following screen display of the commands for use with the DOCLUS comand.

```
-------------------LIST OF CLUSTERING COMMANDS -------------
CL - FOR CLUSTERING
DI - FOR DISPLAYING CLUSTERS
ER - FOR ERASING AN ELEMENT FROM THE STRUCTURE
ED - FOR CREATING OR EDITING THE TEXT FILE
TE - FOR TERMINATING THE PROGRAM
HE - FOR REPRINTING THE ABOVE LIST
```

Enter the appropriate command and continue.

A2.4 THE DOPRIOR COMMAND

The description of the DOPRIOR Command begins with assumptions.

Assumption 1	You have decided to use the DOPRIOR Command.
Assumption 2	Your ISM Files Log does not contain any old files that you wish to use. If this assumption is correct, choose a name for your matrix file and a name for your text file and enter these names in your ISM Files Log, then proceed with the instructions below. Otherwise, go to A2.4.2.

■   NOW TYPE IN MATERIAL SO THAT THE COMMAND READS :

C:\ISM>>DOPRIOR   DAVID.MAT   DAVID.TXT

where I have chosen the highlighted names for the files as shown in this command, but you would use the file names that you have chosen instead, these being entered previously in your ISM Log.

Now hit the Enter or Return key. As a result of this step, you should now see a screen display like this:

```
C:\ISM>>echo off
1 File(s) copied
TEXT FILE EMPTY - PLEASE CREATE ONE!
BLANKING OUT NEW TEXT DATA FILE.
PLEASE WAIT.......
--------------------BEGINNING OPTIONS------------------------
1.  CREATE RELATIONAL STATEMENTS
2.  CREATE TEXT ELEMENTS
?
```

■   Now set the caps lock so that any letter that you type in response to computer questioning will be a capital letter.

You have reached this point by starting to use the DOPRIOR command, and by indicating that you are going to create new files for use in this particular activity.

The screen display gives you two options:

1. Create relational statements
2. Create text elements

You must do both of these because you have begun with a blank text file.

Assumption 1	You have already constructed a generic question and are ready to convert it into the format that is required in this case. The format is seen by pursuing option 1 above. If you have not constructed such a question, you will need to do so before continuing. Then select option 1. You will note that this option requires that you use two related generic questions, each of which involves three parts. The kind of relationship used for priority structuring is analogous to the "less than or equal" relationship in arithmetic. The program requires that you split this into two parts, one of which is analogous to exploring the "less than" and the other "equal to". You will learn more about the nature of the split when you work through the example provided now.

At this point, an example is introduced that will take you through the DOPRIOR command in detail.

A2.4.1 Illustrating the use of ISM Through an Example (The DOPRIOR command). The following example illustrates the use of the DOPRIOR command.

1. *Goal.* Page 352 of Volume II of the 1990 edition of A SCIENCE OF GENERIC DESIGN contains a priority structure developed by the Creek Indian Nation (East of the Mississippi). I will take part of that structure and use it as an example of structuring the following element set. Note that I have altered the numbers shown on page 352, but have kept the element wordings unchanged, so that a comparison can be made with the structure shown in Figure 10.15. I want to structure the following element set:

{1. Lack of adequate and reliable community communication, 2. Motivation and consistency of employees, 3. Maintenance of self-worth of the members, 4. Revival of lost tribal culture and traditions, 5. Pride of tribal participation, 6. Fast growth of the tribe, 7. Work load increase without additional personnel, 8. Lack of dedication of our younger generation, 9. Survival for the tribe, 10. Lack of recreation facilities }

using the following generic question:

Is
Element A
of equal or higher priority in organizing our discussion agenda than
Element B
?

2. *Flow of Activity Style.* I will write this example in the flow of activity style, i.e., I will present each step in the sequence that I do the step on the computer.

3. *Starting Conditions.* My ISM Files Log is empty. I have no prior matrix file and no prior text file. The ISM software is installed in my PC, which has the required math coprocessor. Also I have decided to use the DOPRIOR program because I am looking for a priority structure to govern the topical flow for discussion of the items to be structured. We will end up discussing the highest priority items first, and the lowest last, and this assures that if we run out of time we will have discussed those that are of highest priority in our thinking.

4. *Start the ISM Files Log.* I will use my word processor to start my ISM Files Log. The entry I will make is as follows:

ISM Files Log

ISM MATRIX FILE
Entry #2.

File Designation:	INDIAN.MAT
Pertains to ISM Project:	creating an example to illustrate the use of the ISM PC Software
Involves the Application Structural Type:	Priority Structure
Involves the Graphics Structural Type:	Hybrid Structure
Involves the following elements:	{Lack of adequate and reliable community communications, Motivation and consistency of employees, Maintenance of self-worth of the members, Revival of our tribal culture and traditions, Pride of tribal participation, Fast growth of the tribe, Work load increase without additional personnel, Lack of dedication of our younger generation, Survival for the tribe, Lack of recreation facilities}
Information prepared by:	John N. Warfield
Date of Entry:	February 16, 1991

ISM TEXT FILE
Entry #2.
File Designation: INDIAN.TXT
Other entries are the same as for Matrix File INDIAN.MAT

5. *Entering the ISM Directory.* I turn on my computer and enter the ISM Directory.

6. *Entering the DOPRIOR Command.* I create this screen display (entering the DOPRIOR command).

C:\ISM>>DOPRIOR INDIAN.MAT INDIAN.TXT

and then hit the Enter key.

7. *Choosing an Option from a Menu.* The machine asks me which of two options to choose, and I choose the option 1--"Create relational statements". In this instance, the machine tells me in effect that I have to create two generic questions. One of them will be looking for a distinct difference in priority, while the other will be looking for roughly equal priority. Accordingly, in developing the first generic question:

When it asks for R1, I enter IS
When it asks for R2, I enter OF DISTINCTLY HIGHER PRIORITY THAN
When it asks for R3, I enter   ?

> *NOTE :*   While entering this information, the screen asks me whether I want more lines, and whether I want to keep the displayed entry. The user should appreciate that the ISM program is written in such a way that when the user is asked to type in text information, the user should type only one line, and wait until the program asks you if you need more lines. Then you should type in the next line, and so on. If you don't fill up the line that's okay. The machine will later put all your lines together into an integrated text presentation. When the machine asks if you want to keep the entry you have just finished, it is giving you the opportunity to edit it further immediately before putting it in the text file.
>
> *Also note that unless you use only capital letters in response to queries, the machine will ignore your responses. So use the Caps Lock before continuing.*

When the machine asks me for information on the second generic question, it asks if

263

the first and third entries will be the same as for the question that I just formulated, and I answer Y. It is only in the R2 part that I make a change, and I enter:

OF ROUGHLY EQUAL PRIORITY WITH

Then I answer the remaining routine questions in order to proceed.

8. *Limited Set Size.* The screen then reveals that I am allowed up to 85 elements in the element file. (The program has automatically put me in the position of starting to carry out the second option (see 7 above).

9. *Responding to Queries.* Several questions appear in sequence on the screen and I respond Y to each of them and hit the Enter or Return key.

10. *Typing in the First Element.* The machine now asks for element #1. I type

LACK OF ADEQUATE AND RELIABLE COMMUNITY COMMUNICATION

11. *More of those Thrilling Queries.* Once again the machine asks if I need more lines and I reply NO, then it asks if I want to keep the element I entered and I reply YES, and then it asks if I want to continue with another element, and I reply YES. [I reply by typing Y or N as prompted by the screen.]

12. *Recycling.* I then recycle steps 10 and 11, entering a new element each time, until I have entered the whole element set that I began with as given in Item 1 above. After I have entered element #10, and the machine asks if I want to enter another element, I type in NO.

13. *Entering File Reference Information.* The screen now asks me to type in file information. I then enter the following:

ISM FILES LOG ENTRY #2 dated Feb. 16, 1991.

14. *Main Editor Options.* Next the screen shows me the Main Editor Options. The list is as follows:

```
┌─────────────────────────────────────────────────────┐
│ ------------ MAIN EDITOR OPTIONSʰ ------------        │
│ 0 - EXIT THE EDITOR                                   │
│ 3 - EDIT AN ELEMENT                                   │
│ 4 - EDIT A RELATIONAL STATEMENT                       │
│ 5 - ADD AN ELEMENT                                    │
│ 6 - LIST TEXT ELEMENTS IN THE FILE                    │
│ 7 - EDIT AN ELEMENT LABEL                             │
│ 8 - DELETE THE CONTENT OF AN ELEMENT                  │
│ 9 - MODIFY THE FILE INFORMATIONAL STATEMENT           │
└─────────────────────────────────────────────────────┘
```

15. *Review or Exit Editor ?* If I have done everything correctly to this point, I don't need to do any editing, so I will press 0 to Exit the Editor. However if I did need to review, I would choose Option 6 followed by Sub Option 2 in order to change any element statements. If I needed to revise the generic question, I would choose Option 4 followed by the appropriate sub-option chosen from those shown on the screen following my choice of option 4.

16. *Exit Editor.* Next I would exit the Editor by pressing 0.

17. *Entering an ISM Command.* The screen then shows me the following:

>>>> TYPE AN I S M COMMAND (OR "HELP")

If you type "HELP", the screen will display the ISM Commands.

Note that the ISM Command list is different for the DOPRIOR command than for the DOMODEL Command. We will only use commands from the following subset:

PR - Prioritize
DIS - Display results in stages
PRM - Print the reachability matrix, and
TE - Terminate the ISM activity

18. *Prioritize.* I now choose the command PR to initate the ISM structuring activity.

ʰ The word "label" normally refers to the number assigned to an element. The word "content" refers to the written statement of the element. A generic question typically is formed from three statements. The term "relational statement" is a misnomer, but that is what the programmer chose to use. The symbols chosen for the three statements are R1 R2 and R3 respectively.

265

19. *Responses the Machine Accepts.* The machine tells me I must choose one of the four responses to each displayed question:

> Y   yes, the relationship is true
> N   no, the relationship is false[i]
> AB, abort
> ED, suspend comparisons to edit and then continue

20. *Element Numbers to Start Structuring.* Now the screen asks for element numbers. First I type 1 and hit the Return key. Then I type 2 and hit the return key.

21. *Question Sequence[j].* The following is the sequence of steps that represent the questions, answers, and new element entries:

Is 1>>2?	N		Is 6>>3?	N		Is 3>>9?	Y
Is 1=2?	Y		Is 6=3?	N		Is 6>>9?	Y
Is 1>>3?	Y		Is 5>>6?	Y		Is 8>>9?	N
Is 4>>1?	N		Is 3>>7?	Y		Is 8=9?	Y
Is 4=1?	N		Is 6>>7?	Y		Is 3>>10?	Y
Is 3>>4?	N		Is 3>>8?	Y		Is 7>>10?	Y
Is 3=4?	Y		Is 6>>8?	Y		Is 8>>10?	Y
Is 3>>5?	Y		Is 7>>8?	Y			

---

[i] In the above the correct statement should read as follows:
No, the relationship is false OR I don't know enough to believe that the relationship is true.

[j] I will now use the shorthand symbol >> to represent "of definitely higher priority than" and the shorthand notation = to represent "of roughly equal priority".

22. *Request for Next Command.* The machine now asks for an ISM Command.

23. *Display.* I type DIS and hit return to ask for a display of the structural information. This command will display the structure in a staged format, which is useful for showing priority.

24. *Output.* The screen display gives the information in tabular form that is needed to draw the structure. The structure is drawn from this tabular information:

```
Cycle on 1,2
Cycle on 3,4
Cycle on 8,9
Stage 1              1 ==>>  3
Stage 2              3 ==>>  5
Stage 3              5 ==>>  6
Stage 4              6 ==>>  7
Stage 5              7 ==>>  8
Stage 6              8 ==>> 10
Stage 7                     10
```

When we draw the structure that is indicated by the above information, we can use at first only the stage information, and then we can add on the known cycle components to complete the drawing, as shown in the following figure:

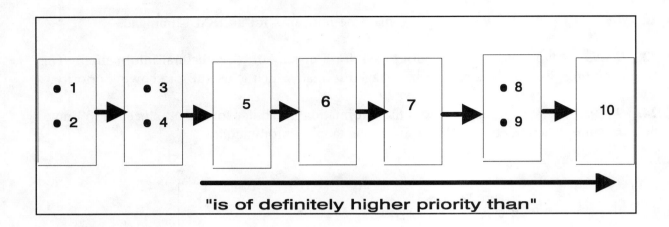

"is of definitely higher priority than"

25. *Terminating the Session.* Having completed the development of the structure, I type the command TE to terminate the session. The machine then transfers back to the screen entry C:\ISM>>.

This example illustrates the use of the DOPRIOR command.

After you have worked through the example, you should be in a position to do a more complex example using your own information. Alternatively, if you have available the book A SCIENCE OF GENERIC DESIGN: MANAGING COMPLEXITY THROUGH SYSTEMS DESIGN, you might choose one of the structures in Chapter 10 and reconstruct it using the DOPRIOR command to get practice in using this command.

A2.4.2 Using the DOPRIOR Program With a Set of Old Files. As with the other programs, this last section of the DOPRIOR deals with the case in which the program is going to be used with a set of already existing files; for those cases, assuming that you are ready to start using the software, the associate asuumption and steps are the following:

Assumption 1	Your ISM Files Log contains old files that you wish to use. If this assumption is correct, identify the names of the files and write them down to be used in carrying out the steps below. Otherwise, go to A2.4

■ NOW TYPE IN MATERIAL SO THAT THE COMMAND READS AS FOLLOWS:

C:\ISM>>DOPRIOR   FFF.MAT   GGG.TXT

except that instead of FFF you enter the name of the old matrix file that you are going to be using and instead of GGG you enter the name of the old text file that you will use.

Now hit the Enter or Return key to activate the command.

As a result of this step you may now see a screen display like this, beginning with the command entered above:

```
C:\ISM>>DOPRIOR   FFF.MAT   GGG.TXT
C:\ISM>>echo off
1 File(s) copied
NEW STRUCTURE (Y/N)?
```

■   Answer the query NEW STRUCTURE (Y/N)?

a) If you plan to create a new structure using the elements contained in the text file given in the above command, type Y and press the Enter or Return key.
b) If you are not planning to create a new structure using the old file material, type N and press Enter or Return.

You will see the following screen display:

>>>>Type an ISM COMMAND (OR "HELP")
?

■   In this case you have two options:
a. If you are familiar with the ISM commands, enter one and continue; otherwise go to Step b.
b. Type HELP after the question mark, creating the following screen display:
?HELP
and press Return or Enter. You will then see the following screen display of the commands for use with the DOPRIOR commands:

```
-------------- PRIORITY STRUCTURING COMMANDS ---------------------

===   EMBEDDING ELEMENTS
PR - PRIORITY STRUCTURING
PRQ - PRIORITY STRUCTURING WITH SELECTABLE QUERIES
=== DISPLAYING STRUCTURES
DI - DISPLAY MINIMUM EDGE DIGRAPH IN A LEVELS FORMAT
DIS - DISPLAY MINIMUM EDGE DIGRAPH IN A STAGE FORMAT
PRM - PRINT THE REACHABILITY MATRIX
===   SUBSTANTIVE AMENDING
ADD - ADD ELEMENTS
ELIM - ELIMINATE ELEMENTS
AE - ADD EDGES (RELATIONSHIPS BETWEEN ELEMENTS ON THE
MINIMUM EDGE DIGRAPH)
EE - ERASE EDGES (ON THE MINIMUM EDGE DIGRAPH)
===   FORMAT AMENDING
PO - POOL ELEMENTS
EC - ELEMENTARY CONTRACTION
===   TEXT EDITING
ED - EDIT AN ELEMENT OR A RELATIONSHIP
===   END STRUCTURING
TE - TERMINATE

N O T E:   ENTER   <<RETURN>> TO CONTINUE
```

Enter the appropriate command and continue.

A2.5 PROBLEM/SOLUTION (RESOLUTION STRUCTURE) ISM SOFTWARE.

The GMU PC Software described above offers the possibility of developing a problematique using a given element set and a relation such as "aggravates"--to be followed by continued structuring. This possibility was mentioned earlier in Sec. A2.2, Item 21, "Problem-Options Structure". (The GMU PC Software uses the language "problem/solution" structure. Chapter 6 uses the language "Resolution Structure", which is the preferred name for such a structure. The Resolution Structure is described in Sec. 6.11. The reader who wishes to develop a Resolution Structure should read Sec. 6.11, before proceeding to the outline of the description of how to use the GMU PC software for this purpose, which begins in the next paragraph.) The continued structuring allows for a second element set comprised of potential conditions that could alleviate one or more problems contained in the problematique. In this section, an explanation is given of how this feature can be used. An artificial example will be used to illustrate the feature.

A2.5.1 Example. Enter the ISM directory with the command ChDir ISM. Now enter the command DOMODEL Horse.Mat Horse.Txt. Then hit the carriage return. This command prepares the two empty files needed for this example. We will start developing a Resolution Structure, by first developing a problematique. It will be created using the element set: {1. poverty, 2. homelessness, 3. hunger, 4. illness, 5. a headache}, and using the relationship "aggravates".

1. ***Entering the Generic Question and the Element Set.*** Choose option 1 from the menu, i.e., "create relational statements". When the machine asks for R1, enter "Does". When it asks for R2, enter "Aggravate". When it asks for R3, enter a question mark. After each of these entries, a carriage return is needed. Use only capital letters to respond to queries. Answer "N" to the question that asks if you want more lines. When you are finished with the relational statements, go to menu option 2, and enter the element set given above. After you have finished supplying the five elements, you may enter any file reference information you wish to enter. If you are satisfied with your results, type 0 (zero) to Exit the Editor.

2. ***Preparing to Develop the Resolution Structure.*** Now the machine asks for an ISM Command. Type BO and hit return. Hit return a second time. Now the computer asks if you are using a subordination relation. Enter N and hit the return key. The machine then asks if you are constructing a problem/solution structural model, and you answer Y. The machine then asks you to tell how many problem statements will be used and you respond with number 5 (the number of elements given in the element set above).

3. ***Developing the Problematique.*** Next the machine asks you for an element number. Type in 1 and return. Type in 2 and return. Now the querying begins automatically, and you can respond to the queries until you have exhausted the possible questions. At this point, you have completed the problematique.

If you follow the sequence shown below, you can develop the problematique step by step.
1A2? Y,   2A1? Y,   1A3? Y,   3A1? Y,   1A4? Y,   4A1? Y,   1A5? N,
5A1? N.
You can now use PRM to see the matrix on the screen. It will appear as follows:

```
                    11110
                    11110
                    11110
                    11110
                    00001
```

You can use the DI command to see the structural information, which is:

```
Cycle on 1,2,3,4

Level #1
1
5
```

4. *Modifying the Relationship.* Now use the ISM Command ED to return to the Main Editor. In preparation for completion of the Resolution Structure, use Command 4 from the Main Editor, to edit the relationship. In the menu that appears, enter C to prepare to enter a new relationship. The new relationship can be formed from a generic question like: "Will X help resolve Y"?

5. *Entering the Remedial Elements.* After you have completed the creation of the new generic question, return to the Main Editor. Now select Command 5, to add elements to the list beginning with number 6 and extending through number 8. The remedial elements to be added in our example will be: {6. wealth, 7. friends in high places, 8. analgesic}. When you have added these elements, then choose Command 0 to exit the editor.

6. *Completing the Resolution Structure.* Next you present again the command BO, and the machine will now ask you questions about how members of the second set relate to members of the problematique. When the question set is exhausted, you can use the command PRM to see the binary matrix on the screen, or you can use the command DI to display the structure containing all 8 elements. Note that in this instance, the arrows from the remedial set to the problem set represent the relationship "helps resolve", while the arrows within the problem set represent the relationship "aggragavates".

If you answer the queries according to the following, you can check results with our results:

6R1? Y, 6R5? N, 7R1? Y, 7R5? N, 8R1? N, 8R5? Y.

The information presented in response to the DI command is:

272

```
Cycle on 1,2,3,4
Level 1
1
5
Level 2
6  ==>> 1
7  ==>> 1
8  ==>> 5
```

The completed structure now shows how the remedial elements act to alleviate the problems shown in the problematique.

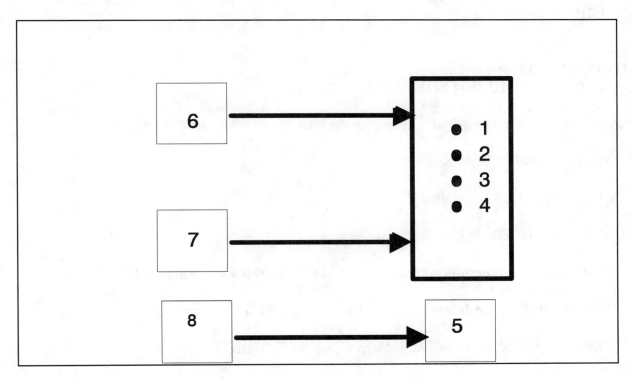

A2.5.2 Another Possibility. While the foregoing description has emphasized the problematique development, it is equally possible to develop an enhancement structure instead of a problematique. The procedural changes would only involve using an element set and a relationship that are characteristic of the enhancement structure (Sec. 6.3).

NOTES

1. The following reference defines "priority structure" in great detail: John N. Warfield, "Priority Structures", <u>IEEE Transactions on Systems, Man, and Cybernetics</u>, SMC-10, October, 1980, 642-645.

2. Alternatively, if you have available the book <u>A SCIENCE OF GENERIC DESIGN: MANAGING COMPLEXITY THROUGH SYSTEMS DESIGN</u>, you might choose one of the structures given in Chapter 10 and reconstruct it using the DOMODEL command to get practice in using this command.

3. Note that this example is discussed (with more elements) in the book <u>A SCIENCE OF GENERIC DESIGN</u>, starting on page 245..

STUDY QUESTIONS
APPENDIX 2. GMU ISM SOFTWARE

1. What are the three principal software commands in the GMU ISM Software?

2. When is DOMODEL to be used?

3. When is DOCLUS to be used?

4. When is DOPRIOR to be used?

5. What example can be followed to learn to use the DOMODEL command?

6. What example can be followed to learn to use the DOCLUS command?

7. What example can be followed to learn to use the DOPRIOR command?

8. What example can be followed to learn to use the software to construct a Resolution Structure?

APPENDIX 3

GROUP FACILITATION

A considerable amount of discussion has been devoted in this book to the various roles involved in Interactive Management. Among the roles discussed is that of the IM Facilitator. Because this is probably the most demanding single role in the entire cast, this appendix has been included to discuss group facilitation. In order to put this discussion in perspective, four cases will be considered, as indicated in Table A3.1. *The primary purpose of this consideration is to distinguish Case D from the other three cases.* This may assist the reader to think about the particular situation under review, for purposes of making a judgment about whether it is appropriate to apply IM to that situation. It may also help those who are accustomed to working with simple situations to understand that there are situations that do not meet that description, which may require IM instead of traditional practice.

TABLE A3.1
FOUR CASE TYPES FOR GROUP FACILITATION

	Simple Situation	*Complex Situation*
UNENHANCED FACILITATION	CASE A	CASE B
IM FACILITATION	CASE C	CASE D

Case A. Simple Situation, Unenhanced Facilitation. Case A refers to a simple problem situation that provides the stated rationale for holding a meeting, where the facilitator carries out the duties of the role without any enhancement. Imagine that there is a group of people and a facilitator to work with them. Suppose that the work environment is a typical conference room in which the seats may be uncomfortable, there is little display space (there may be a small blackboard or a flip chart, and possibly a projector, but these are now so commonplace that normally one would not describe their presence as "enhancement" for the facilitator, even though they do provide the possibility of enhancing the facilitator role). This Case reflects millions of meetings that are held every year, in which the facilitator typically is called a "manager" or a "discussion leader". In many of the instances of this Case, the facilitator has already determined a desired outcome from the meeting, including the key decisions, but may hold the meeting to gain acquiescence from the participants, to verify any information about which the facilitator is uncertain, or simply to reveal to the participants what has happened or what will happen. *This Chapter is not intended to provide guidance with respect to Case A.*

Case B. Complex Situation, Unenhanced Facilitation.   Case B refers to a complex problem situation that provides the stated rationale for holding one or a series of meetings, where the facilitator carries out the duties of the role without any enhancement. This Case also may be typical of millions of meetings that are held every year. This Chapter is not intended to be prescriptive with regard to how Case B is managed. **Tthis chapter is only intended to lay out in Section A3.1 the nature of the difficulties that are present (whether the facilitator understands them or not), and to suggest that Case B should ultimately be eliminated from human activity.**

Case C. Simple Situation, IM Facilitation. Case C refers to a simple problem situation that provides the stated rationale for holding a meeting, where the meeting uses Interactive Management as the basis for the meeting, thereby providing a significant number of enhancements that make the resolution of the problem situation much more likely, and which relieves the facilitator of many burdens. *This Chapter is intended to suggest that the use of Interactive Management is inappropriate for such meetings*. For these problem situations, Case A is the preferred arrangement.

Case D. Complex Situation, IM Facilitation.   Case D refers to a complex problem situation that provides the stated rationale for holding a meeting (or normally, a series of meetings). *This Chapter is intended to show initially the nature and types of difficulties facing the facilitator, and to show how IM is designed to eliminate or minimize most of these difficulties.* With enhancement provided through IM, the facilitator's duties involve a combination of operations (a) that follow specifically the IM Workshop Plan, and which place relatively little burden on the facilitator (compared to what would be present without the enhancement), and (b) that require on-the-spot creative activity by the facilitator in response to a spontaneous difficulty that arises.

A3.1 THE NATURE OF GROUP ACTIVITY INVOLVING COMPLEX ISSUES

Group activity involving complex issues is the primary context to which this discussion of group facilitation is directed. Such activity involves the following difficulties (the numbers preceding the statements are for ease of reference only, and do not indicate any priority):

1. The difficulty <u>inherent in the issue</u> to be discussed.
2. The difficulty (escalation) that is added to the inherent difficulty <u>when a group tries to work together</u>.
3. The difficulty brought about by the <u>unsuitability of the working environment</u> that is typically used for carrying out group work (e.g., the **presence** of factors in the environment that inhibit effective activity such as uncomfortable seating, external noise that makes it difficult to hear what is being said, and bad illumination that makes it hard to see what may be displayed)(e.g., the **absence** of factors in the environment that enhance group work such as large wall spaces for displaying relevant information, properly-functioning visual aid equipment

that does not interfere with other display requirements, a good sound system, computer assistance in organizing information for understanding and display, and facilitators who are both educated and experienced in assisting groups to work effectively on complex issues).

4. The difficulty of <u>maximizing the benefit of the presence of informed participants</u> for what is always a limited period of time (i.e., capitalizing on a scarce resource).

5. The difficulties stemming from <u>variations among participants</u> such as (a) some participants have much greater power than others (and may be supervisors of other participants in their organizations), (b) some participants have much more knowledge about the issue than others, (c) some participants are habitually inclined to talk much more than others, and (d) some participants may be there because they were ordered to be there, and do not really want to be present.

6. The difficulty stemming from <u>incorrect presuppositions</u> brought to the work by individual actors.

7. The difficulty in <u>role maintenance to avoid conflict of interest</u>; e.g., when persons who are supposed to be facilitating the group activity play the role of issue specialist, and try to press their own views on the group, or to construct solutions to the issue that reflect only their own perceptions of the issue.

8. The difficulty that is known as <u>"groupthink"</u> among scholars and <u>"the Abilene Paradox"</u> in some consulting activity, in which people fail to act in ways that reflect their own potential contributions to consideration of the issue.

9. The difficulty of <u>managing short-term incompatibility</u>, e.g., that can arise when the short-term interests of one participant appear to be incompatible with the goal of group productivity.

10. The difficulty of <u>coping with hidden agendas</u>.

11. The difficulty of <u>avoiding fatigue resolution</u> of issues.

12. The difficulty of <u>avoiding underperformance that occurs when pressure is brought to force-fit activity within a preconceived and inadequate period of time</u>.

13. The difficulty of <u>organizing and displaying intermediate group products</u> to the group, in the face of large amounts of generated information having variable and (at least initially) uncertain utility.

14. The difficulty of <u>sequencing group activity</u> involving complex issues.

15. The difficulty faced by participants <u>to articulate very well aspects of issues that they do not understand comprehensively</u>.

16. The difficulty brought about because participants <u>have not had an effective systems education and, consequently, lack a related functional language</u> for discussing complex issues.

Given all of these difficulties, it is not surprising that almost all meetings aimed at resolving complex issues fail to resolve them. *What is somewhat surprising is that people continue to conduct meetings that are unresponsive to all of these difficulties, in spite of the extensive experience showing that failure is the normal outcome of such meetings.*

A3.2 THE POTENTIAL ROLE OF SCIENCE IN RESOLVING COMPLEX ISSUES

Science has a role to play in resolving complex issues. One challenge that must be met is to create a science that is not only responsive to *each* of the individual difficulties mentioned in Sec. A3.2 but which is responsive to *the integrated system of difficulties.* (There is a law from systems science that corresponds to what has just been said: the Law of Requisite Variety. Basically it says that a scheme for resolving a system of difficulties must be precisely as expansive as the expansiveness of the system of difficulties which the resolution is intended to overcome.)

The reader can see that what has been said so far in this Appendix incorporates a significant challenge, all by itself. And this is without taking into account any difficulties that arise before and after group activity involving facilitation.

While all of the difficulties mentioned accrue to Workshop activity, and while all are difficulties that a group facilitator is potentially likely to encounter, *it does not follow that all of these difficulties must be resolved by the facilitator.* If that were the case, woe be unto the unfortunate soul who (a) is aware of all of these difficulties and (b) who tries to resolve them without any assistance!

Once the difficulties can be identified, the following strategy springs into view. A goal of science should be to discover *how to relieve the facilitator of all of those difficulties that can be overcome*, leaving to the facilitator only those that cannot be handled otherwise; and, even for the latter, to weaken the power of those difficulties to overwhelm the facilitator.

Several ways come to mind whereby scientific studies can contribute to this goal. First, the time before the workshop is held offers the possibility of carrying out a variety of activities to eliminate or relieve many of the difficulties. Second, it may be that the processes available for use (and often promoted for use) in conducting a workshop can vary tremendously in terms of their relative capacities to eliminate or weaken many of the difficulties given in Sec. A3.1. *If scientific study can identify criteria for selecting among the vast array of potential processes only those that, collectively, are responsive to the difficulties, the chosen processes can be learned and managed by the facilitator.* Moreover, assistants to the facilitator can take on process roles that diminish the amount of the effort which the facilitator must provide from personal energy and resource. Also in aspects that involve recording, organizing, and displaying large amounts of information, the modern computer can be expected to play a significant role.

Illumination and resolution of many of these issues is an appropriate role for scientific study. Is there any other clear avenue to improvement?

A3.3 HOW INTERACTIVE MANAGEMENT RELATES TO THE DIFFICULTIES

Table A3.2 shows each of the difficulties identified in Sec. A3.1 and how Interactive Management is responsive to that difficulty. Following the discussion of the contents of the Table, it will be possible to see what difficulties (challenges) remain for the facilitator to deal with during an IM Workshop after all of the remedies that IM provides have been exhausted.

TABLE A3.2
DIFFICULTIES AND MEANS OF RESOLVING THEM

Item No.	Short Description of the Difficulty	IM Means of Resolving the Difficulty
1	Inherent in the Issue	Workshop Plan; White Paper; IM Workshops
2	Group Working Together	Workshop Plan; Workshop Staff Training; IM Broker Activity
3	Unsuitability of Working Environment	Specially designed and equipped working environment
4	Maximizing Benefit of Presence of Informed Participants	Facilitator has complete control of the Workshop processes and process sequences, which are designed in the Workshop Plan
5	Variations Among Participants	All processes that facilitator uses are designed to develop and maintain participant symmetry within the group
6	Incorrect Presuppositions	Processes bring out ideas which are then clarified, edited, and tested in terms of relationships to other ideas; processes strongly encourage dialog for purposes of correcting misperceptions; processes develop products that illuminate perceptions
7	Role Maintenance	Roles are carefully defined, and actors' performances are evaluated in terms of their adherence to role definitions; actors are informed ahead of time of the nature of the roles they are expected to play
8	Groupthink	Processes and facilitator actions preclude the possibility of groupthink; experience in many workshops shows this to be true

9	Managing Short-Term Incompatibility	The facilitator must deal with this personally, but the task of doing so is greatly eased because of removal of so many other burdens that otherwise would have to be dealt with by the facilitator
10	Coping With Hidden Agendas	The processes are so thorough and the products so revealing that it is impossible to interject hidden agendas in any significant way
11	Avoiding Fatigue Resolution	The facilitator must take the responsibility for assuring that this does not happen (either because the participants or the facilitator are fatigued); this difficulty is greatly eased by the design of a facility that eliminates the most common sources of fatigue in group work
12	Avoiding Time-Pressure Impact on Performance	The Workshop Plan must incorporate contingencies related to time uncertainty; the facilitator must not violate the processes to save time; the sponsor must have adequate advance knowledge of the reasons for the time uncertainty
13	Organizing and Displaying Information	The processes are designed to take maximum advantage of the computer in organizing the information and printing out directions for the appropriate displays; the products of group work are designed to present patterns that reveal the hitherto unknown structures of the key information components of the issues; processes can be stopped and restarted at known points because of computer storage of results of each small step

14	Sequencing Group Activity	Each process is designed to provide automatic sequencing of group activity; in the structuring work, the computer optimizes the question sequences with an algorithm to provide highly efficient question sequencing; the facilitator does not have to make short-term decisions concerning next steps; where significant changes in direction are made, they are either anticipated in the Workshop Plan, or are worked out outside the group activity by an executive group consisting of the IM Broker, the IM Facilitator and, perhaps, the IM Workshop Planner; groups are never asked or allowed to try to decide on activity sequences during a workshop; their knowledge is used in developing the Workshop Plan
15	Lack of articulation capability	The processes (a) provide for asking many questionsof the participants, each question being highly-focused; (b) provide staff help in editing statements, to bring out author's intended meaning; (c) provide for designing questions carefully, and testing them before a Workshop is held. Also it is desirable to provide multilingual workshop staff when appropriate.

16	Lack of systems education	It is feasible to put all of the mathematics in the computer programs, to preclude any requirement on participants to know the mathematical process details; to design and use only processes that do not demand process knowledge, but only demand some knowledge of the issue; and to strive to influence educational institutions to develop systems programs in their institutions

To facilitate the discussion of the rather extensive content of Table A3.2, the means of resolving the various difficulties can be sorted out as a set, and a matrix can be constructed to indicate the application of them to the various types of difficulty. Table A3.3 provides this information.

TABLE A3.3
MEANS OF RESOLVING RELATED TO ITEMS OF DIFFICULTY

Means of Resolving	Item Number of Difficulty															
	1	2	3	4	5	6	7	8	9	10	11	12	13	14	15	16
Workshop Plan	X	X	X	X			X					X		X		
White Paper	X	X		X		X		X							X	
IM Workshop	X	X	X	X		X	X	X		X			X	X	X	
Workshop Staff Training		X	X	X			X						X			X
DEMOSOPHIA Environment		X	X	X			X	X	X	X	X		X	X	X	X
Workshop Processes	X	X		X	X	X	X	X					X	X	X	X
Workshop Process Sequence	X	X		X	X	X	X	X		X	X	X	X	X		
Workshop Products	X	X		X		X		X		X					X	X
Role Definition and Acceptance by Actors		X		X	X		X	X	X	X	X	X	X	X	X	X
IM Broker Activity		X	X	X	X	X	X	X	X	X	X	X		X	X	X
Client and Sponsor Awareness of IM		X	X	X			X	X		X	X	X				

Careful consideration of the contents of these Tables A3.2 and A3.3, in the light of the design science and the learning that has come from many applications, leads to the conclusion that the IM facilitator can be said to have two kinds of responsibilities in the Workshop. The <u>first type</u> involves pre-Workshop preparation, to take maximum advantage of the benefits provided by the various means that IM offers for resolving the difficulties. The <u>second type</u> involves becoming mentally prepared to deal on the spot with Items 9, 11, 12, and 14. These four items are, respectively, Managing Short-Term Incompatibility, Avoiding Fatigue Resolution, Avoiding Time-Pressure Impact on Performance, and Sequencing Group Activity (only in those instances where, for reasons that become clear as the Workshop evolves, the sequence of activities needs to be redesigned in order to complete the Workshop most effectively). In coping with Item 14, which may only arise in a small percentage of Workshops, the IM Facilitator relies on assistance from the IM Broker, but not on the group of participants, who are not expected to provide process guidance. The IM Facilitator may also anticipate some staff help (if requested) in dealing with Fatigue Resolution and Time-Pressure Impact on Performance. The IM Broker may also assist in sensing or planning with respect to these items while the Workshop is in progress. The IM Broker should generally remind the IM Facilitator that a break in group activity should be called for whenever it appears that these difficulties are beginning to arise.

A3.4 PROTOTYPES OF BAD FACILITATION

Observation of various facilitators and groups over a period of many years enables the identification of what might be called "prototypes of bad facilitation". Possibly no one who fits one of these prototypical styles would remain in a facilitating role for very long. Yet some facilitators will approach the descriptions given.

■ **Type 1: The Pure Tekkie.** The Pure Tekkie (the word "tekkie" has come into usage to represent someone who is heavily oriented to technology exclusively as the means of solving all problems; but it may also be used just to identify someone who has a technical education), who has eyes only for technology, sees facilitation as follows. Every participant is given a computer and printer, and a set of buttons to push to reflect various contingencies that may arise in a meeting or workshop. For the Pure Tekkie, none of the difficulties given in Table A3.1 is very significant, as long as the technology is provided.

The Pure Tekkie believes that people fall into two classes: (a) those that share the Pure Tekkie's love of technology, and thereby communicate with the same language as the Pure Tekkie and (b) those that don't. Only people in class A are worth spending time with.

The Pure Tekkie believes that the kind of graphics typically generated or used by other tekkies really communicates, at least to everyone in class A, and that those in class B should not attempt to read the graphics. Also the Pure Tekkie thinks that it is antisocial to question any graphics products.

If someone's house is on fire, and the Pure Tekkie is called on to fight the fire, only to find that the house that is on fire is outside the range of the fire equipment; the Pure Tekkie will nevertheless activate all the technology and start to pump water onto a house near the fire hydrant, although it is not on fire and not threatened by the fire at the other person's house.

■ **Type 2. The Pure Behaviorist.** The Pure Behaviorist (a person whose whole focus in life is on human feelings, knows nothing of languages other than prose and "body language", knows nothing about graphical communication, hates all technology except possibly that which is essential to that individual's life style, and who doesn't think computers have any sensible role in life) believes that any issue, simple or complex, can be dealt with in a group facilitated by the Pure Behaviorist. Also this individual tends to believe that none of the

284

participants are capable of resolving the issue, because they lack appropriate understanding of the human aspects of the situation. However the Pure Behaviorist thinks that in the process of facilitating it will be possible to conceive a resolution that can be passed on to the participants, and which will involve their own thoughts, appropriately organized to reflect the human aspects of the situation.

■ **Type 3. The Pure Systems Thinker.** The Pure Systems Thinker does not see the real issue as one of resolving a complex issue brought by the participants. Rather the real issue is to enhance the sensitivity of the group to systems concepts, and to make them aware that they are never going to resolve the problem until they also become Pure Systems Thinkers. Facilitation is an exposure to a personal philosophy constructed by the Pure Systems Thinker, and a mode of abstract communication that involves Venn Diagrams with many overlaps and very high-level concepts attached to the components of the Venn Diagrams. Success is measured by the depth of deferential adulation that is produced by the activity.

■ **Type 4. The Action-Oriented Manager.** The Action-Oriented Manager understands that the world continues only if decisions flow rapidly. All situations, no matter what their nature, should be resolvable by a meeting that lasts no longer than one hour. Moreover, the resolution should not require more than one page to express. It should be possible to make one phone call to the right person and get the action taken that is needed to resolve the situation.

■ **Type 5. The Improviser.** The Improviser draws great personal satisfaction from inventing on the spot. The Improviser typically provides lip service at best to the Planning Phase. If the Improviser is involved in a Planning Phase, the outcomes of the work will be treated with minimal interest. This type of facilitator does not think about much other people's needs and concerns. The staff of a workshop that is run by the Improviser will find it very difficult to provide the services needed from them, because they are constantly being surprised by the twists and turns introduced by the Improviser. The Improviser is also insensitive to the behavioral aspects of process designs, and is unaware of violations of behavioral concepts that are designed into the processes. The Improviser's insensitivity to the importance of the Planning Phase may be more than matched by insensitivity to the Followup Phase. The idea that the products of a workshop could be systematically used to bring about change in a Followup Phase may not be nearly as interesting to the Improviser as the idea that another workshop should be held, to provide more opportunities for improvising.

The Improviser is highly vulnerable to severe reactions in some workshops. This is because the Improviser may get a false sense of security by running some successful workshops where the improvisation was at a minimum. In the early days of working with IM, the Improviser may have had experienced people assisting in the planning and conduct of the workshop activity, and they may have helped the Improviser significantly to avoid pitfalls by detecting them when they begin to arise.

Later on, when the Improviser lacks such support, it is almost a certainty that situations will be encountered where the Improviser encounters significant opposition if not revolution, and this is almost totally predictable from a knowledge that the Improviser will violate behavioral process designs, without knowing that it is happening; whereupon all of the foresight and experience that went into creating such designs (partly to protect the facilitator from such events) are unknowingly dispensed with.

Facilitators and Prototypes. Facilitators may have some of the attributes of these five prototypes. To the extent that they approach any one of them in a Case D situation, they are likely to generate activity that is counterproductive and based on inadequate thought which may be widely disseminated.

The well-prepared IM Facilitator will differ substantially from all five prototypes. The IM Facilitator will incorporate a mix of technology application, humanistic concerns, and systems orientation. The urge to be inventive and creative (just for the sake of drawing personal satisfaction) will be suppressed in deference to adherence to theory and experience; and an interest in an ultimate action based on effective, efficient exploration will always be in the mind of this individual.

A3.5 BECOMING AN IM FACILITATOR

How does a person become an effective IM Facilitator? One of the reasons for introducing the five bad prototypes in the previous section is this: each of the five prototypes suggests a different challenge in terms of becoming an effective IM Facilitator. So by choosing each of the bad prototypes as a starting point for discussion, it becomes possible to describe how to become an IM Facilitator from five different points of view. The alternative of treating the question of how to become an effective IM Facilitator as a general abstract question, without reference to the initial condition of the person, seems much less attractive. Since people vary tremendously in their attributes, educational backgrounds, attitudes, prejudices, etc., it appears that a discussion centered around each of the bad prototypes will provide the reader with both the incentive to make an assessment of the person in question, and to envisage a set of options from which a composite educational and/or training program might be constructed that would be tailored to a particular person.

A3.5.1 Changing the Pure Tekkie. The primary components of the process of changing the Pure Tekkie are these: (a) sensitizing the individual to human beings, (b) developing the skill of thinking about how to serve needs of other human beings, (c) helping the individual learn the importance of articulating assumptions, and exposing those

assumptions to review and criticism as a learning experience, (d) developing a willingness to identify, learn and understand high-quality products of social science research, (e) gaining an in-depth insight into the vagaries of language and the need to distinguish between uncommunicative jargon and carefully constructed concepts, (f) developing an understanding of the severe shortcomings of long-standing modes of technical graphical communication, (g) developing a skill in adapting vocabulary selections to fit particular audiences, (h) gaining the capacity to exercise personal mastery skills in a conscious way, with due regard for those people with whom the individual interacts, and (i) gaining an appreciation for the essential aspects of scientific development in general, as opposed to ad hoc literature that has not been subjected to careful scientific scrutiny.

For the Pure Tekkie, works such as those in References 1-5 inclusive are seen as required reading. When the Pure Tekkie has gained enough behavioral sensitivity to try facilitating an IM Workshop, it will be very desirable to videotape the proceedings. Later on, a very valuable exercise in developing the individual will involve going back over the videotape and calling attention to various behaviors of the individual and the consequences in terms of group activity. The combination of reading and practice followed by critique may go a long way toward developing the Pure Tekkie into a different kind of person, capable of being an effective IM Facilitator.

A3.5.2 Changing the Pure Behaviorist. The Pure Tekkie tends to concentrate on production of results without regard to the human aspects, and certainly without any sense of how important the human aspects are in terms of attaining a high-quality product. The Pure Behaviorist, on the other hand, does not incorporate the quality of a tangible product as a primary factor in measuring success. The Pure Behaviorist is often uninformed about key findings in the social sciences. Instead, this individual may know many, many findings of social science which are disorganized and do not provide any basis for choosing among courses of action. The Pure Behaviorist may be concealing a strong inferiority complex about social science in general, and using a very other-oriented approach and style partly to hide this perceived shortcoming in the social sciences. The Pure Behaviorist will almost always lack knowledge in analytic philosophy, while sometimes having a background in statistical data analysis.

The Pure Behaviorist will need sooner or later to comprehend that while much of what passes for social science is not science and not social, nonetheless there are key findings from social science that are absolutely critical to effective group work on complex issues. By learning what these key findings are, and understanding their pivotal role in group productivity, as well as their pivotal role in producing deep satisfaction with achievement, the Pure Behaviorist can gradually lose any sense of deficiency stemming from perceived poor outcomes from social science. Among the key concepts from social science is that of *role and actor filling a role.* In the personal role as an individual, the social scientist must learn personal mastery. This means that it is necessary to be consciously aware of how to self-restrict behavior to playing a particular role and, in addition, to know when it may be appropriate to leave that role for another in the light of a well-founded rationale.

The Pure Behaviorist will also need to learn the fundamentals of formal logic, and comprehend how the computer makes it possible to assist human beings in arriving at well-structured, novel information patterns that reveal new kinds of understandings, including understandings of social issues. [A possible long-term, side effect of such learning is that the Pure Behaviorist might become active in reforming the organization of poorly structured social sciences such as economics, e.g., along lines suggested in Reference 6.]

With a new or renewed sense of the importance of certain social science findings, and with an understanding of how logic complements intuition (such as could be partly developed, e.g., by reading Reference 7), the Pure Behaviorist can begin to practice IM Facilitation. As in the instance of the Pure Tekkie, videotaping followed by appropriate critique will help develop personal ability to be effective as an IM Facilitator.

A3.5.3 Changing the Pure Systems Thinker.

All five of the prototype roles described offer severe challenges in terms of changing into effective IM Facilitators. Each challenge is different. The Pure Systems Thinker has to be willing to learn how to move into a completely different frame of thought where such things as detailed tasks and success measures enter the dialog in an operational way. In other words, specific performance must be addressed. Unlike the Pure Behaviorist, the Pure Systems Thinker is almost totally convinced that his or her field possesses the key to all knowledge, and if that key were only accepted, all the details would surface in shining form. While the Pure Behaviorist may not have confidence in any school of thought from the social sciences, the Pure Systems Thinker will have great confidence in just one school of thought from the systems sciences. Both share the same deficiency, in that they are both myopic; however from a behavioral point of view the Pure Behaviorist needs to be shored up, and the Pure Systems Thinker needs to be decimated (with the minimum possible pain but with some pain, nonetheless).

If the Pure Systems Thinker can begin to see that the systems field is organized into disconnected global models that (a) don't connect very well with each other and (b) don't connect well at all with any kind of practice, the natural motivation of the Pure Systems Thinker to appreciate high-level abstractions may possibly be tapped at a level of integration that had previously only been vaguely imagined. Among other things, it may be found possible to integrate the abstract with the specific, to integrate the cosmos with the behavior of individual human beings.

Old philosophical arguments tend to force systems thinkers into particular thought patterns. For example, the long-discussed distinctions between realism and nominalism seem to be very counterproductive when individuals insist on one extreme position or the other. It may be possible to strip away the sometimes damaging classical argument between realists and nominalists which are (even today) found highly-entrenched in different branches of the so-called "systems community", in light of the fact that unprovable arguments repeated for the millionth time merely absorb intellectual resources that might be honed to become contributory to improving the human condition.

For the Pure Systems Thinker, it may be best simply to move the individual directly into an IM Facilitator role, videotaping all the while, and then subject the individual to a very thorough and carefully conceived criticism that not only reveals the defects in the individual performance, but ties them to components of unproductive parts of systems thinking. In this way the Pure Systems Thinker meets the real world on its own terms. The outcome of such an event, repeated several times, is not predictable at the individual level; but the possible outcomes seem to be twofold: (a) either the individual will withdraw and revert to the more comfortable original state or (b) the individual will be reborn, and will begin to see ways to use the long-possessed ideas in constructive applications; in which case the whole effort will have been well-worth the energy that went into it.

A3.5.4 Changing the Action-Oriented Manager. Some prescriptions are necessarily speculative. While all of the prototypes offer special challenges, none of which are easy to carry out, the Action-Oriented Manager poses a particularly difficult challenge: that of gaining access to that individual long enough to start any change process. The Action-Oriented Manager, in some respects, is a combination of the Pure Behaviorist and the Pure Tekkie. This person believes that things can be done rapidly, and that management can cause the appropriate behavior to take place quickly. This person also believes that technology is the resource cord through which ties are made to other actors whose response can be programmed.

From the cognitive point of view, this individual should be required to study case after case of failure in projects, many of which can be unambiguously traced to behavior of the type this person exhibits. Case stories in the press, especially in the financial press, coming from large corporations and large government attest time after time to the futility of this kind of individual behavior. They also attest to its prevalence, and to the ability of this type of individual to survive repeated mistakes having major deleterious consequences.

The challenge seems to be to make this individual aware of the pervasiveness of bad consequences of this type of behavior. If this particular hurdle can be navigated, the high-energy level of this kind of individual may be redirected to a new kind of pacing. The goal would seem to be to slow this individual down until the point is reached where high-quality action plans are available, whereupon the particular talents of this personality may be more effective at producing those results than persons who attained the facilitation capability beginning from one of the other prototypical types.

Once this person has become convinced of the bad effects of the management style on complex issues, and seen and understood many high-cost consequences of such behavior (of which Reference 8 indicates a few), it may be possible to move this individual into a performance mode directing IM Workshops, again with videotaping followed by critique.

A3.5.5 Changing the Improviser. It may be true that not all personalities can be changed. The Improvisers of the world provide many valuable aspects to human activity. Whether they should ever become IM Facilitators is an open question. In any event, the most basic idea concerning the Improviser is to protect that person and all those who become engaged with that person from the thoughtless acts that precipitate bad outcomes. The Improviser is in the best position to allow this to happen. Rather than try to solve some deep-seated psychological issues that bring out the behavior exhibited, it may be best if the Improviser will simply:

(a) acknowledge openly the pathology that is exhibited
(b) vow to refrain from IM facilitation unless an appropriate Workshop Plan
    has been prepared and approved by the Improviser
(c) give up all rights to change direction during an IM Workshop, assigning these
    rights to another individual who is available at all times to provide
    necessary decision-making
(d) vow to construct a workshop followup plan before ever starting a workshop,
    so that those who are motivated to provide assistance to the Improviser
    will not be deprived of their desire to see change take place

The possible benefits of viewing videotapes of performance have not been investigated significantly for the Improviser. If opportunities to do so appear, it should be interesting to see what might be accomplished.

A3.6 CONCLUSION.

This Appendix has described an interacting collection of difficulties associated with the achievement of high-quality results by groups working on complex issues under the guidance of a facilitator. The contributions that Interactive Management can make to resolving these difficulties have been set forth. The vast majority of the difficulties are responsive to the Interactive Management system. All of them rely on a well-prepared IM Facilitator, but the bulk of what the IM Facilitator needs to do can become relatively standard, though not entirely routine. Only a few of the difficulties require specific invention on the spot by the IM Facilitator, in contrast to the situation that would hold without IM.

Because few people are presently prepared to serve as IM Facilitators, this Appendix has also discussed ways to prepare people to fill that kind of role. The strategy used to carry out this discussion was to describe five (non-existent, but indicative) extreme kinds of person, having particular deficiencies in their persons which have to be modified before they could be effective IM Facilitator. It was suggested that people who actually wish to become IM Facilitators share some of the deficiences of these bad prototypes. Therefore a suggested approach to changing each of the bad prototypes individually might provide useful information to use in planning a development program for any particular individual who could relate in some way to the prototypes.

Suggestions were offered for programs to make the necessary changes. The avenues of change are (a) reading, (b) talking to people who are able to diagnose difficulties, (c) carrying out IM Facilitation in particular trial cases, using videotape to provide a record for later review, and (d) developing sufficient personal mastery to allow the individual to develop better self-understanding and use this newly-developed insight to practice behaving in new ways that develop the talent of the individual to function as an effective IM Facilitator.

REFERENCES

1. B. J. Broome and M. Chen, "Guidelines for Computer-Assisted Group Problem Solving: Meeting the Challenges of Complex Issues", <u>Small Group Research</u> 23(2), 1992.

2. B. J. Broome, "Building Shared Meaning: Implications of a Relational Approach to Empathy for Teaching Intercultural Communication", <u>Communication Education</u> 40(3), 1991, 235-249.

3. B. J. Broome and I. L. Cromer, "Strategic Planning for Tribal Economic Development: A Culturally Appropriate Model for Consensus Building", <u>International Journal of Conflict Management</u> 2(3), 1991, 217-233.

4. B. J. Broome and D. H. Keever, "Next-Generation Group Facilitation: Proposed Principles", <u>Management Communication Quarterly</u> 3(1), 1989, 107-127.

5. B. J. Broome and A. N. Christakis, "A Culturally-Sensitive Approach to Tribal Governance Issue Management", <u>International Journal of Intercultural Relations</u> 12, 1988, 107-123.

6. J. N. Warfield, "Economics and Systems Science", <u>Journal of Management Science and Applied Cybernetics (SCIMA</u>, New Delhi) 19(3), 1990, 65-61.

7. J. Salk, <u>Anatomy of Reality: Merging of Intuition and Reason</u>, New York: Praeger, 1985 (originally published by Columbia University Press).

8. J. N. Warfield, "What Disciplines Large-Scale System Design?", <u>Proceedings of the 1987 Conference on Planning and Design in the Management of Business and Organizations</u> (P.C. Nutt, Editor), New York: American Society of Mechanical Engineers, 1987, 1-8.

STUDY QUESTIONS
APPENDIX 3. GROUP FACILITATION.

1. What five case types are used to distinguish IM Facilitation from ordinary facilitation?

2. When is IM Facilitation needed?

3. How many factors make group activity involving complex issues difficult?

4. What is done in ordinary meetings to deal with the factors of difficulty?

5. What should be expected from a science aimed at overcoming the difficulties involved in group activity?

6. Should the IM Facilitator be expected to resolve all of the difficulties associated with group activity?

7. How many means of resolving the factors of difficulty have been identified?

8. Describe the "pure tekkie".

9. Describe the "pure behaviorist".

10. Describe the "pure systems thinker".

11. Describe the "action-oriented manager".

12. Describe the "improviser".

13. How should the IM Facilitator relate to the five prototypes of bad facilitation?

14. How can the five prototypes be changed?

15. Which of the factors of difficulty require specific invention on the spot by the IM Facilitator?

16. What four avenues of change can be included in programs of IM Facilitator training?

APPENDIX 4

CASE STUDY: DEFINITION OF ANALYTICAL POWERTRAIN

This case study of an IM application is intended to illustrate the use of a problematique in interpreting a complex situation. It is intended also to illustrate how the interpretation of the problematique relates to other information produced during an IM Workshop.

A4.1 GENERATING AND CLARIFYING THE PROBLEM STATEMENTS.

During a workshop aimed at defining what is meant by "analytical powertrain", an NGT session was held to develop a list of problems in response to this triggering question:

"What problems (technical and/or cultural) should be anticipated in developing and implementing Analytical Powertrain?"

In response to this question, the participant group generated and clarified 127 problem statements, reflecting their views of problems that should be anticipated.

A4.2 PLACING THE PROBLEM STATEMENTS IN CATEGORIES.

Following the clarification of these problems, an ISM session was held to categorize these problems, in response to a generic question like the following:

"Does Problem A have significant attributes in common with Problem B?"

If the answer to this question is "yes", the two problems are placed in the same (initial) category. If the answer is "no", the problems are presumed to reside in different (initial) categories. When a sufficient number of sets has been generated, the participant group is asked to assign temporary names to the various sets. These tentative names of categories are used to refine the assignments to categories. During this refinement, the names of the categories may be changed. After all of the problems have been placed in named categories, the computer is asked to print out the Problem Field.

Table A4.1, Problem Field for Analytical Powertrain, shows the fourteen category names selected by the participant group. Under each category name is listed the problems that the participant group decided properly belonged in that category.

A) Cultural Barriers

- Resistance in manufacturing and material handling engineering to learn and use 3D CAD/CAE tools. (34)
- Unwillingness of some users to share data. (39)
- Hostility toward databases. (45)
- Loss of Ford expertise due to fear of transition to AP. (67)
- Unwillingness to give up current tools and practices. (73)
- Fear of black boxes. (76)
- Resistance to concurrent engineering. (78)
- *Resistance of Ford's culture to change to AP methodology.* (88)
- *Inability to resist temptation to roll it out too early.* (92)
- Unwillingness to use AP products because "not invented here." (99)
- Resistance to redefinition of jobs or roles by designers, design engineers and analysts. (118)
- Failure to accept computer simulation (CAE) in place of hardware tests for certification due to legal barriers. (124)
- Resistance to give up a known solution for a new or different one. (128)

B) Lack of Readiness of Technology

- *Shortfall of 3-D solid modeling systems that can meet the needs of all the different engineering environments.* (1)
- *Lack of a complete set of analysis methods.* (3)
- *Lack of readiness of some core technologies for implementation.* (4)
- *Inability of some technologies selected and initially implemented to survive as viable products.* (15)
- Shortage of proven knowledge-based engineering techniques. (18)
- Shortage of manufacturing process development and analysis tools. (20)
- Lack of standards/methods to interface different databases together. (23)
- Lack of clear definitions of design and manufacturing features. (55)
- Inability to create an always accurate analysis system. (57)
- Potential failure of automeshing to be ready on time. (65)
- Lack of strategic control of third party software vendors product or product direction. (70)
- Lack of stable industry standards. (72)
- Inadequate capacity to contain database content. (105)
- Lack of technology to reduce CAD solid to CAE model. (115)
- Lack of technology to supplement CAD model for CAE analysis. (116)
- Inability of technology to handle the volume of data required. (120)
- Immature Object Oriented Database (OODB) Technology. (122)
- Lack of computer models capable of correlating to physical testing. (123)

> Items that are highlighted in *italics* were selected by participants as being of "higher relative importance" and appear on the Problematique displayed in Figures A4.1 and A4.2.

Table A4.1 Problem Field for Analytical Powertrain

C) Misperceptions About Technology

- *Overanticipation by management that AP will solve more problems than it really will.* (22)
- *Failure to recognize that solid modeling and materials data represent only a small fraction of CAE needs.* (33)
- *Misperception by management that CAD solid provides adequate model for CAE.* (43)
- Inability of analysis of results to always converge to an answer. (87)
- Conflict between vision and reality. (109)
- Unreasonable expectation of management that AP be usable by totally CAE unskilled workforce. (111)
- Misperception that technology will last forever. (117)
- Misperceptions about CAE technology - Engineers will not accept computer simulation, even when past results have been well correlated. (125)

D) Incomplete Scoping/Planning

- *Scope of Analytical Powertrain undefined* (2)
- *Lack of clearly defined vision process for end user* (6)
- Analytical Powertrain too ambitious–doubt a sufficient technically skilled workforce will be put in place to implement and support. (11)
- Lack of accurate assessment of technologies defined for AP. (17)
- Lack of a complete definition of analysis tools required. (25)
- Unclear definition of AP scope related to manufacturing. (28)
- *Lack of clear role definitions among design engineer, designers and analysts.* (38)
- Conflict between priority of future AP implementation vs. solving engineers current problems/wants. (63)
- *Failure of AP team to include in its design the needs of all users.* (64)
- Failure to include suppliers as AP participants. (75)
- *Lack of definition of domain and scope of database contents.* (82)
- Unclear where AP fits with other corporate CAD/CAM/CAE strategies. (83)
- Inappropriate bench marking criteria for selecting technologies due to undefined scope of AP. (91)
- Failure to acknowledge or support existing minor CAE tools used by engineers. (101)
- Lack of a guiding corporate CAD/CAM/CAE strategy. (112)
- *Difficult to limit the domain and scope of AP application into S/T & L/T plans.* (114)
- Inability to plan effectively due to lack of technical dictionary. (127)

Table A4.1 Problem Field for Analytical Powertrain

E) Implementation Risks

- Lack of time required for training of users may jeopardize implementation plan. (24)

- Loss of momentum due to slow start. (58)

- Unwillingness to admit some decisions were wrong and restart. (86)

- Unacceptable responsiveness caused by system complexity. (90)

- Lost of product advantage through data theft. (108)

- Inability of some technology suppliers to survive. (119)

F) Lack of Implementation Tool Standards

- Inability to coordinate software development across activities. (47)

- *Failure to communicate precisely due to lack of technical dictionary (49).*

- Dilemma of having to deal with multiple solid modelers. (60)

- Lack of component and equipment supplier compatibility with Ford computer systems and software. (74)

- Lack of PTO standard tools/methods for developing system user's interfaces. (77)

- Difficulty in defining Ford standards for GUI (graphics user interface) ("What is easy to use?") (100)

- Difficulty in integrating applications from vendors with proprietary information. (106)

- Lack of corporate guidelines for solid modeling. (113)

G) Ineffective Management Participation

- *Resistance to change by management. (7)*

- *Lack of "effective" consensus among middle management on who does what. (30)*

- Failure of the organization to stick to an established plan. (32)

- Resistance of engineering managers to allow their engineers to design on CAD. (35)

- Resistance to remove organizational barriers. (69)

- Failure to maintain AP vision if top management changes. (96)

- Failure of management to commit to fully implement/utilize AP. (97)

- Interference from management during development process and component design. (102)

- Failure of management to allow AP to evolve beyond initial implementation. (103)

Table A4.1 Problem Field for Analytical Powertrain

H) Current Operational Constraints

- ***Demands by Ford culture for product hardware. (16)***

- Work load priorities may not support concurrent engineering. (26)

- Ford has budgeting barriers for procurement of software. (48)

- Demand for too many changes/scheduled inventions on new powertrain programs. (52)

- Work environment at Ford - too many meetings, too much mail, too little workspace, too much task interference and others. (54)

- Resistance to paying a supplier prior to issuing a PO hinders a supplier from being part of concurrent engineering. (56)

- Reluctance of Software vendors to accept Ford's standard terms and conditions. (68)

- Inadequate manpower resource allocation-priority given to current program versus future need, e.g., AP. (85)

- Resistance of management to allow sufficient time for their people to be trained. (121)

I) Lack of Skills/Training

- ***Inadequate skill level for using the specialized CAD/CAM/CAE techniques. (5)***

- ***Inadequate knowledge of Object Oriented Databases (OODB). (12)***

- Lack of skilled CAE computer system support personnel. (37)

- Shortage of skilled software development/management employees to achieve implementation. (40)

- Insufficient training/experience with CAE tools to allow acceptance of simulation results in place of physical testing. (126)

- Lack of user training to benefits and needs of database. (130)

J) Missing Application Knowledge

- Lack of a bookshelf methodology for manufacturing processes and product design. (9)

- Lack of definition criteria to enter bookshelf such as BIC (Best in Class). (31)

- Lack of a record of basic engineering elements/processes that are executed to manufacture a product. (44)

- Lack of agreed upon bookshelf content and DB structure. (89)

- Lack of complete documentation of current design and development knowledge. (98)

- Lack of bookshelf of product designs and manufacturing processes. (129)

Table A4.1 Problem Field for Analytical Powertrain

K) Maintenance Concerns

- Conflicts between versions of third party codes and operating system release versions. (27)
- Lack of adherence to standards caused by local support staffs. (62)
- Lack of computer systems are not 100% reliable. (81)
- Lack of reliability of local area network.(LAN) (93)
- Lack of resources to support software as it is introduced. (94)
- Lack of responsive computer system support. (104)
- Lack of resource allocation for proper maintenance of AP application. (110)

L) Development Resource Concerns

- Inadequate development resources. (10)
- *Limited financial resources. (14)*
- Conflict between development or purchase of software. (29)
- Inadequate present computer hardware to implement AP (workstations, data storage, graphics, speed) (36)
- Demand for a stable resource level for life of AP development. (61)
- Lack of resources to start prototyping of implementation options and ideas. (84)
- Reluctance to commit adequate dedicated resources to the task. (107)

M) User Participation Concerns

- ***Failure to get buy in from all powertrain offices. (21)***
- Inability to obtain complete buy-in by AP users prior to implementation. (50)
- Unwillingness of users to invest in understanding implementation details as stakeholders. (51)
- Conflict between user wants and AP wants. (53)
- Loss of a continuing focus on the user during the development period. (80)

Table A4.1 Problem Field for Analytical Powertrain

N) Software Development Concerns

- ***Difficulty in developing software to encapsulate AP tools to control information flow. (8)***

- Evolution of the AP may not keep pace with engineering needs. (13)

- ***Difficulty of dispersing CAE functions to multi-user environment. (19)***

- Failure to integrate existing/new systems to AP. (42)

- ***Inability to acquire the volume of data required. (46)***

- Conflict between a need for commonality and users desire for personalization. (59)

- Lack of knowledge of technical issues for integration. (71)

Table A4.1 Problem Field for Analytical Powertrain

A4.3 STRUCTURING A SUBSET OF THE PROBLEMS.

As explained elsewhere, as part of the NGT process, each participant is asked to vote privately on which five of the total set of problems is deemed by that participant to be the most important five in the total set. Moreover, having selected the "top five", each participant is asked to rank order them according to relative importance.

When the participating voting records are available, it becomes possible to split the total set of problems into two parts. Part 1 consists of those problems that received at least one vote from at least one participant as being in the top five in terms of importance (the "selected problems"). Part 2 consists of those problems that received no votes from any participant as being in the top five in terms of importance. In this case study, 35 of the 127 problems became selected problems.

A4.3.1 Composite Problem Ranking. It is possible to form an initial composite ranking of problems, based on the participant votes. In forming this composite, one may assign a weight of 5 to a top ranking, a weight of 4 to a ranking of second, a weight of 3 to a ranking of third, a weight of 2 to a ranking of fourth, and a weight of 1 to a ranking of fifth. Following this procedure, total scores may be obtained for each member of the Part 1 subset.

A4.3.2 Composite Category Ranking. Once scores are available for each of those selected problems, a composite score can be obtained for the problem categories by simply adding the scores for each of the problems in the category. Table A4.2 shows, for each problem category, the title of the category, the number of selected problems lying in that category, the weighted importance score for the category, and the rank of the category.

Table A4.2 does not show all 35 of the selected problems, because time did not permit the structuring of all 35. The number of problems actually structured in the Problematique was time-limited to 26. These 26 were among those receiving the highest scores in the composite ranking of problems.

The 26 selected problems that appear in the Problematique came from eleven of the fourteen categories, as Table A4.2 shows. Three of the fourteen categories are not represented in the Problematique.

The numbers shown in parentheses in the first column represent the number of problems represented in that category. Table A4.1 showed that there were 14 problem categories. Of these only 11 received a weighted score different from 0. As Table A4.2 indicates, three of the categories stand out from the rest. These three categories are: i) INCOMPLETE SCOPING/PLANNING, ii) LACK OF READINESS FOR TECHNOLOGY and iii) INEFFECTIVE MANAGEMENT PARTICIPATION.

As we will see, after discussing the problematique, the priorities on categories that Table A4.2 suggest are not readily sustained as additional learning takes place.

TABLE A4.2
VOTING ON PROBLEM IMPORTANCE

PROBLEM CATEGORY	WEIGHTED IMPORTANCE SCORE	RANK
D. INCOMPLETE SCOPING/PLANNING *(Six)*	50	1
B. LACK OF READINESS FOR TECHNOLOGY *(Four)*	22	2
G. INEFFECTIVE MANAGEMENT PARTICIPATION *(Two)*	19	3
C. MISPERCEPTIONS ABOUT TECHNOLOGY *(Three)*	9	4
N. SOFTWARE DEVELOP-MENT CONCERNS *(Three)*	8	5
H. CURRENT OPERATIONAL CONSTRAINTS *(One)*	7	6
L. DEVELOPMENT RE-SOURCES CONCERNS *(One)*	6	7 (tie)
M. USER PARTICIPATION CONCERNS *(One)*	6	7 (tie)
A. CULTURAL BARRIERS *(Two)*	6	7 (tie)
F. LACK OF IMPLEMEN-TATION TOOLS STANDARDS *(One)*	5	10 (tie)
I. LACK OF SKILLS/TRAINING *(Two)*	5	10 (tie)
E. IMPLEMENTATION RISKS; J. MISSING APPLICATION KNOWLEDGE; K. MAINTENANCE CONCERNS *(All, Zero)*	0	lowest

A4.3.3 Structuring the Problematique. The 26 problems that were structured were inputs for the ISM session. The generic question used in that session was:

"Does Problem A aggravate (make more difficult) Problem B?"

In clarifying this question, the participant group was told that they should suppose that problems A and B (which they had identified previously) are both troublesome. Now suppose that problem B happens to be a fire. If someone throws gasoline on the fire, this aggravates the fire, causing it to become more troublesome in a variety of ways. It is in this sense that the group is asked to decide whether a certain problem aggravates another problem.

As a result of the facilitated, computer-assisted, ISM process, the group was able to develop a Problematique for the Analytical Powertrain, which is shown in Figure A4.1.

A.4.3.4 Overlaying the Problematique With Problem Categories. Figure A4.2 shows the Problematique a second time. In constructing Figure A4.2, additions have been made to the drawing that appeared in Figure A4.1. Specifically, beside each problem in the problematique there has been added a capital letter showing the problem category to which that problem belongs.

This change has been made in anticipation that, while the Problematique can be used to see how an individual problem aggravates other problems or is aggravated by other problems, or both, it is also possible to make such an interpretation in terms of the problem categories.

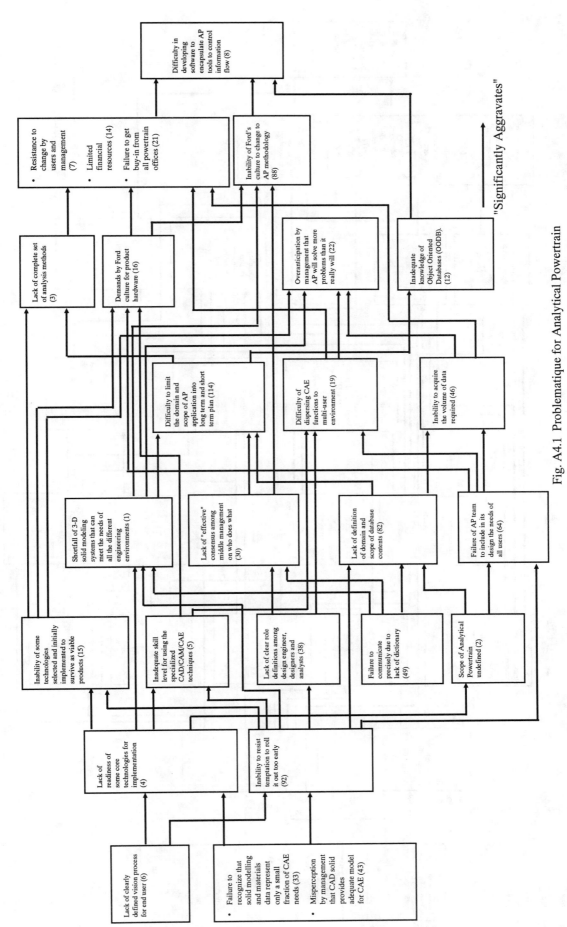

Fig. A4.1 Problematique for Analytical Powertrain

"Significantly Aggravates"

305

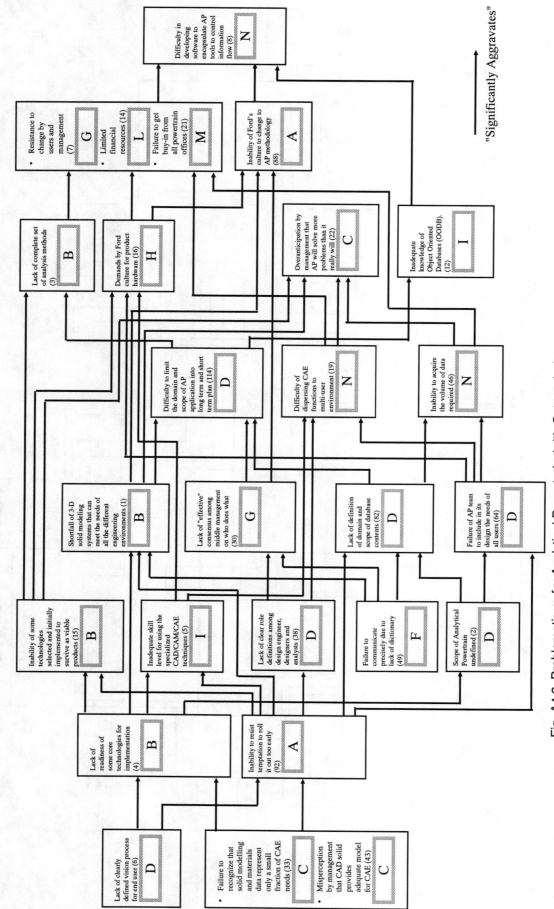

Fig. A4.2 Problematique for Analytical Powertrain (with Categories)

"Significantly Aggravates"

A4.4 INTERPRETATION OF THE PROBLEMATIQUE.

The Problematique is the most relevant source of interpretation of the results of the case study. Here are the reasons. First, *it is the only product that shows how the problems are interrelated.* Second, because of this, *it is the primary basis for understanding how the effects of work done to diminish problems propagates into the total program.* If, for example, someone diminishes a certain problem, but does nothing to diminish those other problems that have been aggravating it, it is very likely that the problem that was diminished will make a strong comeback, and nothing useful will have been accomplished; while time will have been lost. The interpretation of the Problematique is intended to overcome that possibility. Table A4.3 shows the composite results of structural analysis of the Problematique. We will now discuss how this analysis was carried out, and how the data in Table A4.3 can be interpreted.

A4.4.1 Position Score for Problems and Problem Categories.

The Problematique places problems in stages. A problem lying in the first (leftmost) stage has the potential to aggravate all of the problems lying to the right to which it connects. *It is strategically positioned to aggravate.* On the other hand, a problem lying in the last (rightmost) stage has no such power. *It is vulnerable to significant aggravation from the left.*

For these reasons, position is a factor in assessing relative significance of particular problems, and in deciding with what priorities to approach the total problem set.

Each problem can be assigned a "position score". Problems in the leftmost stage are assigned the highest score, and those in the rightmost stage are assigned the lowest score. In the Ford AP Problematique, problems at the left receive position scores of 8, and the single problem at the right receives a position score of 1. Intermediate problems lying in one of the eight stages receives an appropriate position score.

Once the position score for the problems has been set, position scores for categories can be found by simply adding position scores of those problems contained in the separate categories. This is how the position scores shown in Column 1 of Table A4.3 are found.

A4.4.2 Antecedent and Succedent Scores for Problems and Problem Categories.

Position scores are quite rough measures. More detailed measures can be found by assigning "antecedent scores" and "succedent scores" to problems. For a given problem, the antecedent score is simply the number of problems lying to the left of that problem which (according to the structure of the Problematique) aggravate that problem. Likewise, the succedent score is the number of the problems lying to the right of a given problem which it aggravates.

Handbook of Interactive Management

TABLE A4.3
STRUCTURAL SCORING ANALYSIS OF PROBLEMATIQUE

CATEGORY	POSITION SCORE	ANTE-CEDENT SCORE	SUCCE-DENT SCORE	ACTIVITY SCORE	NET A/S SCORE	NET SCORE
D. INCOMPLETE SCOPING/PLANNING (6)	34	32	71	103	39	73
C. MISPERCEPTIONS ABOUT TECHNOLOGY (3)	11	17	46	63	29	40
B. LACK OF READINESS FOR TECHNOLOGY (4)	21	27	39	66	12	33
F. LACK OF IMPLEMENTATION TOOLS STANDARDS (1)	6	0	13	13	13	19
A. CULTURAL BARRIERS (2)	9	17	20	37	3	12
I. LACK OF SKILLS/TRAINING (2)	9	17	9	26	-8	1
E. IMPLEMENTATION RISKS (0)	0	0	0	0	0	0
J. MISSING APPLICATION KNOWLEDGE (0)	0	0	0	0	0	0
K. MAINTENANCE CONCERNS (0)	0	0	0	0	0	0
H. CURRENT OPERATIONAL CONSTRAINTS (1)	3	9	5	14	-4	-1
G. INEFFECTIVE MANAGEMENT PARTICIPATION (2)	7	27	11	38	-16	-11
L. DEVELOPMENT RE-SOURCES CONCERNS (1)	2	21	3	24	-18	-16
M. USER PARTICIPATION CONCERNS (1)	2	21	3	24	-18	-16
N. SOFTWARE DEVELOP-MENT CONCERNS (3)	9	42	10	52	-32	-23

(**NOTE**: The numbers in parentheses in the Category column show how many problems that received votes are represented in that Category.)

Once these scores are determined by inspecting the Problematique, these scores can be given over to the Problem Categories by simply assigning to each category the antecedent scores and succedent scores of those problems lying in the category. In this way, the second and third columns were filled in Table A4.3.

A4.4.3 Activity Score for a Category. The activity score for a given problem or Problem Category is simply the sum of the antecedent score and the succedent score. The data in column 4 show the scores found by adding scores in data columns 2 and 3.

A4.4.4 Net Antecedent/Succedent Score. The Net Antecedent/Succedent Score is found by subtracting the antecedent score from the succedent score for a given problem or category. Thus data in column 5 of Table A4.3 reflects a subtraction of the entry in column 2 from the entry in column 3.

If the net A/S score is positive, it means that the problem or category *is a net source of aggravation.* If the net A/S score is negative, it means that the problem or category *is a net receiver of aggravation.*

A4.4.5 Net Score. The net score for a problem or problem category is found by adding the position score to the net A/S score. This addition gives some weight only to position and some weight to the specifics of antecedents and succedents. Thus the net score in data column 6 of Table A4.3 is the sum of the entries in columns 1 and 5.

A4.4.6 Using Two Scores for Interpretation. Note that Category I in Table A4.3 has a net score of 1, while it has an activity score of 26. This example illustrates the reason for having several measures. A net score of 1 indicates that Category I is almost equally balanced as a source and receiver of aggravation. Yet the activity score of 26 tells us that it is quite active in receiving and dispensing aggravation. We need to think about both of these in order to get a balanced picture. Categories E, J, and K, by contrast, have almost the same net score as Category I, namely a score of 0, but in contrast they also have an activity score of 0, because none of the problems placed in the Problematique come from these categories.

A4.5 SPECIFIC INTERPRETATIONS FROM TABLE A4.3.

A4.5.1 D. Incomplete Scoping/Planning. This factor has by far the highest activity score, net A/S score, and net score. **We conclude that it is the most significant of all of the problem categories in terms of making progress on AP.**

A4.5.2 C. Misperceptions About Technology. This factor has the third highest activity score, the second highest net A/S score, and the second highest net score. **We conclude that it is the second most significant of all of the problem categories in terms of AP progress.**

A4.5.3 B. Lack of Readiness for Technology. This factor has the second highest activity score, the fourth highest net A/S score, and the third highest net score. **We conclude that it is the third most significant of all of the problem categories in terms of making progress on AP.**

A4.5.4 Other Interpretations. We see that Category F, Lack of Implementation Tools Standards, has made a major leap upwards, when compared with where it stood in the NGT voting, illustrated in Table A4.2. We see also that Category G, Ineffective Management Participation, has moved downward to 11th rank, as compared with third rank in the NGT voting, as illustrated in Table A4.2. In looking at this Category G, we see that it has a high activity score, but its net A/S score is negative, showing that it is predominantly aggravated by other problem categories. *More specifically, management's participation cannot be highly effective if there are major problems in Categories B, C, and D that have not been resolved to the point where good management decisionmaking that requires knowledge about these categories is feasible.* Similar remarks apply in interpreting Categories M and N. Category N, for example, shows a very high activity score, and a high net A/S score, but the negative signs on the scores for Category N tell us that this category is heavily aggravated by other categories. This means that a frontal attack on software development concerns that does not deal with Categories B, C, and D, is not likely to be very fruitful. The reader can explore categories such as A, I, H, and L, in the light of these interpretations.

APPENDIX 5

QUALIFIED IM PRACTITIONERS [1]

Surinder K. Batra (5)
Centre for Interactive Management, India
5/11, West Patel Nagar
New Delhi - 110 008
INDIA

Phones: 574-5174 and 575-8942
Fax: 91-11-312-515

Dr. Benjamin Broome (9)
Professor of Communications
George Mason University
Department of Communication
Fairfax, Virginia 22030-4444

Phone: 703-993-1092
Fax: 703-993-1096
Bitnet: BBROOME@GMUVAX
Internet: BBROOME@GMUVAX.
  GMU.EDU

CWA, Ltd.
Christakis, Whitehouse and Associates
1004 Signal Hill Lane
Berwyn, PA 19312-2023
• **Dr. Alexander N. Christakis (20)**
• **Dr. Ali Geranmaye (1)**
• **Dr. John Pourdehnad (1)**
• **Robert J. Whitehouse (2)**

Phone: 610-651-0414
Fax: 610-651-2717

Defense Systems Management College
Fort Belvoir, Virginia 22060-2456
• **Professor Henry Alberts (5)**
• **Professor Stan Crognale (3)**
• **Professor John Snoderly (2)**

Phone: 703-805-3464
Phone: 703-805-3442
Phone: 703-805-3697

R. Keith Ellis (4)
Director of Research
School of Computing and Information Systems
University of Humberside
Cottingham Road
Hull HU6 7RT, United Kingdom

Phone: 44-482-440-550

---

[1] The number in parentheses after the name of the practitioner tells the approximate number of years since the individual started to practice Interactive Management up to and including the year 1994.

311

Ford Motor Company,
Ford Research Laboratory
P. O. Box 2053/MD 2122-SRL
Dearborn, MI 48121-2053
United States of America
• **Scott M. Staley, Ph. D., P. E. (3)**   Phone: 313-845-4119, Fax: 313-248-4602
• **Daniel J. Fagan (1)**   Phone: 313-845-5162, Fax: 313-248-4602

Ken Hammer (5)   Phone: 44-71-477-8373
Department of Systems Science   Fax: 44-71-477-8579
City University
Northampton Square
London EC1V OHB
England

Instituto Tecnológico y de Estudios Superiores
de Monterrey (ITESM)   Phone: 52-83-582-000, X5440
Sucursal de Correos 'J'   Fax: 52-83-588-931
C. P., 64 849
Monterrey, N. L., Mexico
Monterrey Campus:
• **A. Roxana Cárdenas (5)** E-mail: acardena@campus.mty.itesm.mx
• **Andres Sotomayor (5)**
• **Carlos Villanueva (5)**
• **Carmen A. Moreno (5)**
• **Hector Moreira (5)**
• **Hector Rincon (5)**
• **Mary del Carmen Temblador (5)**
• **Alvaro Rico (3)**
• **Francisco Colorado (3)**
• **Sandra Garzon (3)**
• **Sofia Frech (2)**
Chihuahua Campus:
• **Ana Carvajal (2)**
• **Leonel Guerra (2)**
Guadalajara Campus
• **Alfredo Molina (5)**

ITESM (continued)
<u>Leon Campus:</u>   Phone: 52-47-18-44-00, X187
- **Alberto Lenz (2)**   Fax: 52-47-17-79-32
- **Carlos Flores (2)**
- **Eduardo Sojo (2)**
- **Reynaldo Treviño (2)**
- **Rosa Elena Moreno (2)**
<u>Mazatlan Campus:</u>
- **Alejandro Cristerna (3)**

Dr. Ross Janes (13)   Phone: 44-71-477-8373
Senior Lecturer   Fax: 44-71-477-8579
Department of Systems Science
City University
Northampton Square
London EC1V OHB
England

The Jeffrey Group (4)   Phone and Fax: 703-590-8109
Carol Jeffrey
3962 Stirrup Court
Woodbridge, VA 22192

Dr. Kazuhiko Kawamura (19)   Phone: 615-322-2771 or
Professor   615-322-2735
Department of Electrical Engineering   Fax: 615-343-6702
and Program in Management of Technology
P. O. Box 1674, Sta. B
Vanderbilt University
Nashville, TN 37235

Dr. David Keever (13)   Phone: 703-749-8778
Science Applications International Corp.   Fax: 703-821-1433
1710 Goodridge Drive
McLean, VA 22102

David Mackett (12)   Phone: 619-546-7069
National Marine Fisheries Service   Fax: 619-546-7003
Southwest Fisheries Science Center
P. O. Box 271
La Jolla, CA 92038

Robert McDonald (13)
Division of Forestry
3125 Connor Boulevard
Tallahassee, FL 32399-1650

Phone: 904-488-6591 or
904-877-3956
Fax: 904-488-0863

Mr. Kenneth McIlvoy (2)
Senior Director, Technical Support
National Railroad Passenger Corporation
400 N. Capital Street, Northwest
Washington, D. C. 20001

Phone: 202-906-4515

Dr. Carl Moore (20)
Center for Peaceful Change
Kent State University
Kent, OH 44242

Phone: 216-672-3143

Ing. Cristina Salas-Porras
Director
Interact--Planning and Management Consultants
P.O. Box 1472
El Paso, TX 79948

Phone and Fax:
915-532-7573

Dr. Robert J. Waller (20)
Professor
School of Business
University of Northern Iowa
Cedar Falls, IA 50614

Phone: 319-273-6241

Dr. James T. C. Wright (14)
Professor
Instituto de Administração
University of São Paulo
Av. Prof. Luciano Gualberto, 908
05508 São Paulo, Brazil

Phone: 55-11-815-0291
Fax: 55-11-814-0439

Ms. N. S. Yamuna (5)
#D4 Alsa Manor
Gilchrist Avenue
Madras 600 031
India

Phone: (044) 86 4999

APPENDIX 6

THE IM WORKSHOP PLAN

Experience has shown that the conduct of workshops using Interactive Management (IM) can be very favorably influenced by preparing an IM Workshop Plan. The purpose of this Appendix is to provide additional insights into the preparation and content of such a plan. This material is intended to supplement the discussions in Chapters 10 and 11.

The following set of questions serves as a check list for developing the IM Workshop Plan. The section that follows this one will provide a prototype outline for the IM Workshop Plan.

A6.1 CHECK LIST FOR IM WORKSHOP PLAN

Context:

1. What is the situation that indicates a need for an IM Workshop?

2. What is the state of definition of the situation/issue?

3. What is the Scope Statement (**Chapter 10, IM Planning Phase, Phase 1**)?

4. What is the Context Statement (**Chapter 10, IM Planning Phase, Phase 1**)?

Content:

5. What is the principal (overview) issue that the IM Workshop will be considering?

6. What is the title of the proposed Workshop?

7. Which success level is sought (**Chapter 3, IM Success Levels**)?

8. Which outcome is sought (**Chapter 2, IM Outcomes**)?

9. What are the objectives of the proposed Workshop?

10. Is preparation of a White Paper possible (**Section 4.1, Phase 1**)? If so, who will write it, and when will it be distributed?

Roles:

11. Who is the Client (**Section 5.1.1, Client**)?

12. What actors will be involved in the planning activity (**Chapter 5, IM Roles**)?

13. Is the chosen IM Broker familiar with the role (**Chapter 5, Section 5.1.3, IM Broker**)?

14. What types of participants are needed (**Section 5.1.4, Participants**)?

15. What potential participants were identified, and on what basis was the selection made?

16. After discussions with the IM Broker, what participants were selected?

17. Who will be observers (if any) (**Section 5.1.5, Observers**)?

18. Who is the Sponsor (**Section 5.1.2, Sponsor**)?

19. Who will be involved in implementing IM Workshop results? (**Chapter 5, IM Roles**)?

Process:

20. What processes will be used (**Chapter 7, IM Processes**)?

21. What are the Triggering Questions that will be used to generate information?

22. What Application Structural Types will be sought (**Chapter 6, IM Products; Chapter 13, Evaluation Criteria for IM Applications**)?

23. What are the Generic Questions that will be used in structuring information?

Workshop organization:

24. What are the dates and schedules for the Workshop?

25. Where will the Workshop be held?

26. Has the Workshop schedule and the list of all the responsible parties for carrying out each detail been completed?

27. What is the Workshop Staff Plan?

28. Have appropriate flip charts been prepared for use in starting the IM Workshop?

29. If overheads are to be used in starting the IM Workshop, have they been selected, and are they ready for use?

30. What is the Budget?

31. What are the responsibilities of the IM Team?

32. What are the responsibilities of the Client?

33. Has an external reviewer examined the plan for readibility and consistency?

A6.2 OUTLINE OF IM WORKSHOP PLAN (See Chapter 10, for relevant definitions)

1. TITLE PAGE

2. AUTHOR

3. SCOPE STATEMENT

4. CONTEXT STATEMENT

5. MAJOR OUTCOME SOUGHT

6. PLANNED PROCESS SEQUENCE

7. TRIGGERING QUESTIONS

8. GENERIC QUESTIONS

9. WORKSHOP SITE INFORMATION

10. WORKSHOP ROLES AND ACTORS

11. OTHER ROLES

12. FACILITY PREPARATIONS

13. WORKSHOP FOLLOWUP PLANS

APPENDIX. PARTICIPANT LODGING, TRANSPORTATION, SERVICES.

INDEX TO TOPICS

INDEX TO ORGANIZATIONS

INDEX TO NAMES